Looking southwest across a furrow irrigated field of Black Mitcham peppermint in Central Oregon near Madras. The ice-capped volcanic peaks of the Cascade Range can be seen in the background.

AMERICAN ESSENCE

A History of the Peppermint and Spearmint
Industry in the United States

by
James E. Landing

Department of Geography
University of Illinois at Chicago Circle

Published as A Contribution of the
Kalamazoo Public Museum
315 South Rose Street
Kalamazoo, Michigan 49006

ACKNOWLEDGMENTS

A work on the history and geography of the American mint industry covers nearly 180 years of time. Such an effort could not have been accomplished without much outside assistance. For nearly seven years the writer has visited among mint growers in the United States and their kindness, assistance, and willingness to share their experiences and knowledge have been invaluable assets in adding numerous human touches, for, after all, the history of an industry is largely the story of the persons that have created it.

Without the insights provided by the major mint oil buyers and users in this country the story could have never been written. Without exception they have all cooperated in a manner far beyond any ordinary effort to be helpful. As a comprehensive history, the work necessitated journeys into the offices of an extraordinary number of local historical societies, libraries, and newspaper offices. Information was readily, often eagerly, furnished, and much of the present work is based on the material librarians were able to locate.

The foundations of the story lay in the author's early efforts to explain the mint industry in Indiana, begun during student days at Western Reserve University and the Pennsylvania State University. For early encouragement to delve more deeply into the historical roots of American mint production the writer is indebted to Mildred Walmsley and George F. Deasy. During portions of the work the writer was under stipend from the National Science Foundation and this assistance is gratefully acknowledged.

The writer has visited most of the staff members of the agricultural colleges involved in mint research projects and their donation of time and information has been significant. Special gratitude, however, is expressed to N. Kent Ellis, Purdue University, Lester N. Liebel, Washington State University, and C. E. Horner, Oregon State University, each of whom read and commented on various portions of the manuscript. If their suggestions have not been incorporated, the fault rests with the writer.

The entire manuscript was given a critical reading by Willis F. Dunbar, Professor of History at Western Michigan University, well

iii

known for his many works on Michigan history. His comments were of great assistance in aiding the writer to express what he wished to say.

The process of gathering illustrative material involved a search of numerous nooks and crannies, and credits for each of the figures are given in Appendix III. Valuable assistance in this regard was rendered to the writer by Mrs. Lothian Lynas of the New York Botanical Garden Library, G. H. M. Lawrence of the Hunt Botanical Library, Alexis Praus of the Kalamazoo Public Museum, and Leslie Guilford of Ashfield, Massachusetts.

Special assistance was given by Priscilla Howes of Ashfield, Massachusetts, and Linda Gaylord of Ontario, New York. Their interest in the history of the mint industry was a valuable asset for the writer.

Special appreciation is expressed to the A. M. Todd Company Foundation of Kalamazoo, Michigan. The generous financial assistance provided by the Foundation has made it possible for this work on the history of the American mint industry to be published.

For those interested in contemporary production figures for peppermint and spearmint oil in the United States, the information can be found in Tables 1 and 2 and in Appendix I. Since the counties of the various states involved in commercial mint production over the years are frequently mentioned throughout the text, a special set of state maps showing the county names and boundaries has been included in Appendix II to serve as reference.

The writer has lived for many years within view of some of the mint distilleries in northern Indiana. It has been a privilege to weave this small segment of the mint industry into a pattern which extends across nearly two centuries of time and countless miles of space. If the story finds welcome among its readers, the author will be more than gratified.

TABLE OF CONTENTS

Acknowledgements iii
List of Maps vii
List of Tables ix
List of Figures ix
Introduction xi

PART I: THE CLASSIC PERIOD: THE FIRST
        HUNDRED YEARS 1

Section A: The Mint Industry Becomes Established,
           1800-1838 3
  Ch. 1. The Origins of Peppermint and Spearmint
          Cultivation 3
  Ch. 2. The American Mint Industry Begins:
          Massachusetts 8
  Ch. 3. The Mint Industry Moves West: New
          York, Ohio, and Michigan 18

Section B: The Mint Industry Enters the World
           Market, 1839-1889 25
  Ch. 4. American Mint Becomes Big Business 25
  Ch. 5. The Great Rivalry: New York vs. Michigan . . . 35

Section C: On To New Horizons, 1890-1900 54
  Ch. 6. The Mint Industry Moves to the Mucklands 54
  Ch. 7. Perspective on A Century 66

PART II. THE GOLDEN PERIOD: TOWARD THE
         SECOND HUNDRED YEARS 69

Section A: Establishing A Stable Industry, 1901-1929 71
  Ch. 8. Toward A Domestic Market 71
  Ch. 9. The Great Price Rise 90
  Ch. 10. The Great Response 100

Section B: The Troubled Years, 1930-1946 123
  Ch. 11. The Mint Industry Faces the Depression 123
  Ch. 12. Peppermint and Spearmint Go to War 134

Section C: The Geographical and Technological
           Transformation, 1947-1969 149

Ch. 13. The Opening of the West 149
Ch. 14. Mint Industry Research and Service 177
Ch. 15. From Grower to Consumer 196
Ch. 16. Perspective On An Industry 207

Appendix   I. Peppermint and spearmint acreage in the
            U.S. in 1968 215

Appendix II. County reference maps of the major mint
            oil producing states 217

Appendix III. Figure Credits 228

Index 231

LIST OF MAPS

Map 1. Massachusetts, showing the villages associated with the early peppermint and spearmint oil industry between the 1790's and 1840. 10

Map 2. New York, showing the villages associated with the production of peppermint and spearmint during the 19th century. 19

Map 3. Ohio, showing the towns associated with the cultivation of peppermint during the 19th century. 20

Map 4. The lower peninsula of Michigan, showing the towns associated with the high ground cultivation of peppermint and spearmint between 1835 and 1885. 22

Map 5. Wayne County, New York, showing the villages associated with the commercial production of peppermint and spearmint during the 19th century. 31

Map 6. Townships of St. Joseph County, Michigan, showing the towns associated with the production of peppermint and spearmint oil since the first plantings on the White Pigeon Prairie in 1835. 48

Map 7. Counties of northern Indiana, showing the towns associated with muckland peppermint and spearmint oil production since 1846. 55

Map 8. Counties of southwestern Michigan, showing the towns associated with muckland cultivation of peppermint and spearmint since 1885. 58

Map 9. Ohio, showing the towns associated with peppermint and spearmint oil production since 1900. 80

Map 10. The Willamette River Valley of Oregon and the lower Columbia River Valley of Oregon and Washington, showing the towns associated with peppermint oil production since the beginning of commercial plantings near Albany, Oregon, in 1913. 82

Map 11. Counties of central Michigan, showing the towns associated with the production of peppermint and spearmint oil since the beginning of commercial plantings near St. Johns in 1913. . . . 86

Map 12. California, showing the towns associated with commercial mint oil production since 1925. 111

Map 13. Location of the major mint oil producing districts of Washington. Although the Puget Sound Lowland covers the largest area, the plantings were small and widely scattered and the district has been, historically, the least important. 115

Map 14. Location of the major mint oil producing districts of Oregon and western Idaho. 117

Map 15. The Lower Yakima Valley, Kennewick, and Columbia Basin districts of Washington and the Hermiston district of Oregon, showing the towns associated with commercial mint oil production since 1925. 144

Map 16. Field pattern of a 225 acre general farm, on which peppermint is grown, located in the Willamette Valley, Linn County, Oregon, just east of Corvallis. Water for overhead sprinkler irrigation is supplied from 4 thirty foot wells. (Modified from R. C. Brown, *The Agricultural Geography of Peppermint in the Pacific Northwest,* p. 37, M.S. thesis, Oregon State University, 1962.) 154

Map 17. Field pattern of a 160 acre specialized peppermint farm located just northwest of Madras, Oregon. The land has been levelled for gravity flow irrigation with water supplied from the Deschutes River. (Modified from R. C. Brown, *The Agricultural Geography of Peppermint in the Pacific Northwest,* p. 56, M.S. thesis, Oregon State University, 1962.) 157

Map 18. The spread of commercial peppermint oil production in Oregon, by counties, for selected years since 1913. Major producing counties are those in which 500 acres or more were reported under cultivation. 158

Map 19. Field pattern of a 280 acre specialized peppermint and spearmint farm located just west of Wapato, Washington, in the Lower Yakima Valley. Water for furrow irrigation is supplied through ditches from the Yakima River. (Modified from R. C. Brown, *The Agricultural Geography of Peppermint in the Pacific Northwest,* p. 48, M.S. thesis, Oregon State University, 1962.) ... 162

Map 20. The spread of commercial peppermint and spearmint oil production in Washington, by counties, for selected years

since 1917. Major producing counties are those in which 500 acres
or more of mint were reported under cultivation. 165

Map 21. Idaho, showing the towns associated with commercial
peppermint and spearmint oil production since 1905. 166

Map 22. Wisconsin, showing the towns associated with the
commercial production of peppermint and spearmint oil since 1945. 168

Map 23. The spread of commercial peppermint and spearmint
oil production in Wisconsin, by counties, for selected years since
1945. Major producing counties are those in which 500 acres or
more of mint were reported under cultivation. 169

Map 24. Field pattern of a 160 acre rotation muckland farm,
on which peppermint and spearmint are grown, typical of many
found in central and southwestern Michigan and northern Indiana. 170

Map 25. Counties of the thumb area of Michigan, showing the
towns associated with commercial peppermint and spearmint oil
production since 1936. 171

Map 26. The spread of commercial peppermint and spearmint
oil production in the lower peninsula of Michigan, by counties, for
selected years since 1847. In 1929, following the great price rise,
78 acres were cultivated in Schoolcraft County in the upper peninsula. Major producing counties are those in which 500 acres or
more of mint were reported under cultivation. 172

Map 27. The spread of commercial peppermint and spearmint
oil cultivation in Indiana, by counties, for selected years since 1846.
Major producing counties are those in which 500 acres or more of
mint were reported under cultivation. 173

LIST OF TABLES

Table   I. Spearmint Oil Production in the United States: 1967 . . 197
Table II. Peppermint Oil Production in the United States: 1967 . 198

LIST OF FIGURES

Figures   1-29 (Insert I) . . . . following 49
Figures 30-49 (Insert II) . . . . following 119
Figures 50-60 (Insert III) . . . . following 181

INTRODUCTION

Throughout all time there have been certain activities of mankind that have involved only a few persons, interested many, and benefitted all. Such has been the case with the cultivation and production of Peppermint (*Mentha piperita* L.) and Spearmint (*Mentha spicata* L. and *Mentha cardiaca* G.), among the more important flavoring, essence, drug, and aromatic plants raised in the world today.

Peppermint and spearmint are members of a complex botanical family referred to as *Labiatae*, meaning two-lipped, a reference to the distinctive arrangement of the flower petals. The Genus *Mentha*, which includes the true mints, is believed to have originated in the Mediterranean basin[1]* and spread to the rest of the world, by both natural and artificial means, from there. According to Greek legend, the first mint plant was the bodily transformation of the nymph Mintho who had angered Proserpine, wife of Pluto, by casting covetous eyes on the philandering god of the underworld. Proserpine gained her revenge by artfully turning Mintho into an herb where "as an humble mint plant, the nymph lost some of her beauty, yet continues to attract men by her freshness."[2]

It is doubtful that contemporary botanists place much credence in the Greek myth, yet the passage of time has clearly revealed that, of the some 200 genera and over 3,200 species in the family *Labiatae*,[3] peppermint and spearmint have emerged as two of the most important commercial representatives, a distinct honor since the family is represented in essential oil production by such well known and widely used plants as rosemary, lavender, basil, sage, salvia, pennyroyal, hyssop, and thyme.[4]

Although the mints had been recognized for centuries as plants with delightful aromas and tastes, it was not until the mid-eighteenth century when, in the drug gardens of England, peppermint and spearmint began to achieve commercial significance. Since that day both the herb and the oil of the two mint plants have been intimately associated with the daily activities of English life.

*Footnotes are compiled at the end of each section or chapter.

Commercial mint production soon spread from England onto the continent of Europe and, at a later date, found its way to the shores of North America. From a few plants in New England the commercial mint industry spread in the United States until, today, nearly 100,000. acres are devoted to the cultivation of peppermint and spearmint. Near Coburg, Oregon, contemporary Americans are taking up residence in a newly developed rural subdivision known as "Peppermint Acres." Each spring the graduating seniors at Bremen High School in Indiana find their portraits and exploits enshrined forever in the annual school year-book known as the "Sprig o' Mint." In southwestern Michigan residents of St. Joseph County decide important matters of local government at their meetings in the "Mintdale Community Center" near Nottawa. Across the entire breadth of the United States and across the wide expanse of the whole globe, millions of persons find temporary release from tension and fatigue by savoring the taste of mint flavored chewing gum, and millions more perform daily oral ablutions with mint flavored toothpaste. For many persons in the world the use of mint products has become a way of life.

The commercial mint industry has never been large when compared to such agricultural enterprises as the production of cereal grains, yet the growth of the enterprise, and the activities related to it, have become part and parcel of the history, lore, and legend of nearly every major agricultural region in the United States. In the late summer months the smoke begins to pour forth from countless steam boilers as the freshly cut mint hay is hauled in from the fields for processing. The major salable commodity is the peppermint and spearmint oil which is ob-tained from the plants by distillation. Practically all of the distilling in this country is done on the farm and the specialized stills, of countless shapes and designs, powered by the steam boilers, mark mint agriculture as distinct and unique.

Peppermint and spearmint oils belong to a chemical class of plant products variously referred to as essential, volatile, or ethereal, oils, terms which distinguish the group from the fixed oils, such as those of linseed and coconut, which contain quantities of fatty acids. Essential oils are quite volatile and are composed chemically almost entirely of various hydrocarbon compounds known as terpenes. The major terpene in peppermint oil is menthol, accounting for the cooling sensation, and that of spearmint oil is carvone. The dilution or elimination of certain terpenes is often necessary, as the various users of the oils all have differing requirements based on such properties as taste, aroma, and color.

This work is an effort to tell the story of the rise and development of the commercial peppermint and spearmint industry in the United States. It is the story of an industry which has suffered prosperity and depression; an industry which has seen more than its share. of promoters, speculators, and quick profit artists; an industry of highly localized production and highly specialized technology; an industry which, originally and firmly based on European standards and tastes, has become synonomous with the preferences and activities of the people of the United States. It is a story which, although placed in words by this writer, has actually been written by the countless Americans, known and unknown, who have contributed their time and energies, in some cases their lives and fortunes, to the development of one of the most distinct agricultural enterprises in the United States today.

The title of the work itself, *American Essence,* is intended to portray a double meaning. The early success of the commercial mint industry in western Massachusetts was centered around the sale of essence of peppermint and spearmint, a by-product of the distillation process through which the natural oil was obtained. As the industry developed and expanded, however, there came an increasing concern for standards, high quality, self-regulation, technical excellence, and honesty. As the mint growers over the years adjusted their practices to the American ecology an increasingly high degree of sophistication was necessitated to cultivate the product in such a way that the excellence in quality was maintained. Dealers and users now insist on the highest quality product at the lowest price consistant with these standards. In this view, *American Essence* is not only the history of two essential oils, but the history of the industry which demonstrates the essence of the finer attributes of the American free-enterprise system.

REFERENCES

[1]C. F. Millspaugh, *Medicinal Plants*: *An Illustrated and Descriptive Guide to Plants Indigenous to and Naturalized in the U.S. which are Used in Medicine,* vol. 2, p. 116-3, John C. Yorston and Co., Philadelphia, 1892.

[2]H. N. and A. L. Moldenke, *Plants of the Bible*, p. 140, Chronica Botanica, Waltham, Massachusetts, 1952.

[3]G. H. M. Lawrence, *Taxonomy of Vascular Plants*, p. 690, Macmillan Company, New York, 1951.

. [4]E. Guenther, *The Essential Oils*, vol. 3, D. Van Nostrand Co., Inc., New York, 1949.

PART I:

THE CLASSIC PERIOD: THE FIRST HUNDRED YEARS

Chapter 1.

The Origins of Peppermint and Spearmint Cultivation

The Ancient Period

On a hot summer day in ancient Egypt a Hebrew woman bent low over the tiny fire as she prepared her husband's supper. As she moved across the hardened dirt floor, strewn with fresh mint leaves, her heel ground the foliage and released the cooling fragrance which filled the home. Such a practice, a distant forerunner of the modern scenting industry, was in vogue in Egypt long before Moses led the Hebrews on their Exodus.

The major properties of the mints, a delightful aroma and a mildly stinging, pleasant taste have been recognized since the most ancient days. Mints are mentioned twice in the New Testament (Matthew 23:23 and Luke 11:42), and the distillation of mint oil appeared in the literature as early as 410 A.D. in an account written by Synesius of Alexandria, the Bishop of Ptolemais.[1] The herb and the oil of the mint plants found wide acceptance in the culinary and medicinal arts of the ancients and, in the 10th century A.D., a Japanese medical book described the utilization of mint oil in an eye wash preparation.[2]

The Medieval Period

As church life strengthened in early medieval Europe monasteries and convents abounded. On the grounds of these religious communities was generally found a small plot where the more common and useful herbs were planted and meticulously tended.[3] The monks and the nuns carefully and laboriously compounded from these herbs countless

3

prescriptions which became the medicines for the ailments of the day. Charlemagne, himself, recommended three mints for cultivation in his famous *Capitulare* of 812,[4] the Abbess Hildegard mentioned four mints in her *Subtilitatum* of 1160,[5] and five mints are discussed in the oldest German treatise on the subject of distillation, the *Liber de Arte Distillandi* of Hieronymus Brunschweig, published in 1500.[6]

The Modern Period

The plant which we know today as spearmint (named for its arrow-like flower spires) first appeared in the European "convent gardens" about the 9th century (Figure 1), but peppermint (named for its pepper-like taste) was not listed until 1696 when specimens, still preserved in the herbarium of the British Museum, were discovered near Hertfordshire, England, by a Dr. Eales and later in Essex by a Mr. Dale. They were described by John Ray (Joannis Raii),[7] the clergyman botanist (Figures 2 and 4).

The utility of the mints made the plants quite popular among the herbs and from the "convent gardens" they quickly found their way into the "kitchen gardens" and the daily lives of countless persons. An 1892 work stated that peppermint oil was

> considered specific in renal and vesical calculus, dyspepsia, and diarrhoea; being considered a stomachic, tonic, stimulant, antispasmodic, and carminative. It was found useful in bowel troubles, especially those associated with flatulency, colic, retching, vomiting, spasmodic actions, and hysteria. Its rubefacient action is intimately associated with what may be considered anodyne properties, when the trouble is neuralgic or rheumatoid, and the affected nerves or muscles are somewhat superficial. Facial and sciatic affections are greatly relieved by fomentations of the leaves, or rubbing the oil, or menthol, directly over the course of the nerve itself; the action is temporary, but decidedly happy.
>
> The principal use of the essence or oil is as a flavoring for confections, and a jucund ingredient of prescriptions containing nauseous, and especially griping drugs.[8]

Spearmint, which had been longer known and more widely used in Europe, received great tribute in 1640 when the English apothecary and botanist John Parkinson, the King's herbarist, extolled the "Vertues" of various mints.[9]

> *Dioscorides* saith it hath an heating, binding, and drying quality, and therefore the juyce taken with vinegar stayeth bleeding. It stirreth up venery or bodily lust, and as hee saith killeth the round wormes, which hath not usually beene knowne to take effect with any, two or three branches thereof taken with the juyce of sour Pomegranats staieth the hickok, vomitings, and alleieth choler, it dissolveth impostumes being layed to with barley meale: it

is good to represse the milke in womens breasts when they are swolne therewith, or otherwise, for such as have swollen, flagging, or great breas.s, applyed with salt, it helpeth the byting of a mad Dogge, with Meade or honied water it easeth the paines of the eares: applyed to the privie parts of a woman before the act of generation hindreth conception, which is con-tradicted as you may read a few lines below, and rubbed upon the tongue, taketh away the roughnesse thereof. It suffereth not milke to curdle in the stomack, if the leaves hereof be steeped or boyled in it before yee drinke it. Briefly, it is very profitable in the stomack, and in meates is much accepted. It is of especial use to stay the feminine courses when they come too fast, as also to stay the whites, for which purpose no other herbe is more safe and powerful, for by taking it often it hath cured many. Applyed to the forehead or the temples of the head it easeth the paines thereof. It is also good to wash the heads of young children therewith, against all man-ner of breaking out therein, whether sores or scabs; and healeth the chaps of the fundament. It is also profitable against the poison of venomous crea-tures. *Simeon Sethi* saith it helpeth a cold liver, and strengtheneth the stomack and belly, stayeth vomitings and the hickok, is good against the gnawings of the heart, and stirreth up the appetite, it taketh away the obstructions of the liver, and stirreth up bodily lust; but thereof too much must not be taken, because it maketh the blood thin and whayish, and turneth it into choler, yea, and causeth the blood which is of very thin parts, after it is separated, to become thick and melancholick; and therefore cholerick persons must abstaine from it . . . taken with wine it helpeth women in their hard and fore travels in child-bearing: it is also thought to be good for blear eyes applyed to them: and that the decoction of them being drunke, doth helpe the bleedings at the mouth speedily, or presently. It is good against the gravell and stone in the kidneys and strangury. It is also comfortable for the head and memory, not onely to be smelled unto, but chiefly to be applyed unto the head and temples, and easeth the head-ach: the decoction thereof cureth the gums and mouth that is sore, if it bee gargled therewith, and mendeth an ill-favoured breath, as also with Rue and Coriander, causeth the uvula or palate of the mouth that is downe, to returne to its place againe, the decoction thereof being gargled and held in the mouth. Aristotle and other in the ancient times forbade mints to be used of Souldiers in the time of warre, because they thought it did so much to incite to Venery, that it tooke away, or at least abated their ani-mosity or courage to fight. Divers have held for true, that Cheeses will not corrupt, if they be either rubbed over with the juyce or decoction of Mints, or they laid among them. . . The vertues of the wild Mints are more especially to dissolve winde in the stomack, to helpe the chollick and those that are short-winded, and are an especial remedy for those that have venerous dreames and pollutions in the night, used both inwardly, and the juyce being applyed outwardly to the testicles or cods; the juyce thereof dropped into the eares easeth the paines, and destroyeth the wormes that breed in them. . . *Pliny* saith, that in the time of the Great *Pompey*, it was found out by experience of one to cure the Lepry by eating the leaves, and applying some of them to his face, and to help the scurfe or dandruffe of the head used with vinegar.

A modern most likely pales at the thought of devouring several branches of spearmint with sour pomegranate juice to stay the hickok but, in the limited experience of that time, any herb which could alleviate the whites, reduce flagging breasts, heat a cold liver, act not only as a contraceptive but as a wondrous aphrodysiac, aid in child-birth, cure leprosy, scurvy, dog and snake bites, nocturnal pollutions, bad breath, colic, and dandruff, and act as a preservative for meat and cheese, was bound to become quite popular. Peppermint and spearmint, serving these purposes and more, became increasingly important garden plants in Europe.

By 1750 both peppermint and spearmint were being commercially cultivated in the medicinal herb gardens centered near Mitcham in County Surrey, England. By 1796 from 2,000 to 3,000 pounds of oil were being produced annually from 100 acres of mint at Mitcham but, no farm equipment having yet been developed, the mint hay was hauled to nearby London for distillation. Within a few years commercial peppermint culture had spread into Lincolnshire (Market Deeping), Hertfordshire (Hitchin), and Cambridgeshire. The English mint industry was never large and today the original planting area near Mitcham is only a memory as the farmlands have been swallowed by the urban sprawling of that section of London known as Merton. Although the British industry is no longer extensive the use of peppermint as a flavoring for tea and spearmint for sauce continues as part of the English custom and heritage.

Many Europeans simply used the fresh mint herb in making various preparations but when the commercial cultivation and distillation started it became possible to buy various "decoctions" in the apothecary stores. These were generally sealed in small vials or bottles of glass and consisted of several preparations. Most expensive, but most useful, was the natural oil itself, the chief product of the distilling. The waste water, being mildly tinctured with the oil, was sold as mint essence or mint spirits, or greatly diluted into a beverage and marketed as mint cordial. Small quantities of the oil were also made into mint syrups and mint emulsions to serve as cough and cold medicines and Peppermint Lozenges from Europe appeared in the United States early in the nineteenth century.[10]

Commercial peppermint production moved outward from England and was first reported from the European continent at Utrecht in the Netherlands in 1770[11] and soon spread into Germany and France where mint has been cultivated continuously since that time. The industry appeared in the United States before 1800. Theophrastus, Hippocrates, and Pliny, all of whom mentioned the mints in their writings,[12] would stand in wonder if they could gaze upon the well developed industry in the United States today.

None of the commercial mint plants was native to the United States. Like so many of the utilitarian herbs peppermint and spearmint apparently found their way to the shores of the United States in the belongings of the early American colonists. It seems almost as if Shakespeare was prophesying the rise of the American industry when he mentioned through the lines of Perdita in *The Winter's Tale,* ". . . Here's flowers for you; Hot lavender, mints, savory, marjoram; . . ." (Act IV, scene 3). The American colonists took peppermint (Figures 3 and 6) and spearmint (Figure 5), planted them in the new world, and found new uses to supplement those of their homeland. The rest of this work is devoted to the story of peppermint and spearmint as commercial crops in the United States.

REFERENCES

[1]N. K. Ellis and E. C. Stevenson, "Domestic Production of the Essential Oils of Peppermint and Spearmint," *Economic Botany,* vol. 4, p. 139, 1950.

[2]N. Inouye, "Japanese Peppermint," *Semi-annual Report,* Schimmel and Co., p. 199, Nov., 1908. Japanese mint (incorrectly called Japanese peppermint), however, is a species quite distinct from the English and American peppermint, and is used primarily in the manufacture of menthol.

[3]Because of the lack of specimens or drawings it is not really known if the mints of the medieval gardens were the modern spearmint or peppermint. Similarity of names may have been a coincidence.

[4]E. Gildemeister and F. Hoffman, *The Volatile Oils,* English translation by E. Kremers, vol. 1, pp. 190-191, John Wiley and Sons, Inc., New York, 1913.

[5]*Ibid.,* p. 191.

[6]*Ibid.*

[7]J. Raii, *Synopsis Methodica Stirpium Britannicarum,* 2nd edition, p. 124, S. Smith and B. Walford, London, 1696.

[8]C. F. Millspaugh,. *Medicinal Plants: An Illustrated and Descriptive Guide to Plants Indigenous to and Naturalized in the U.S. which are Used in Medicine,* vol. 2, p. 116-3, John C. Yorston and Co., Philadelphia, 1892.

[9]J. Parkinson, *Theatrum Botanicum: The Theater of Plants. Or, An Herbal of A Large Extent,* p. 35, Tho. Cotes, London, 1640.

[10]*The Story of An Unique Institution: Dodge & Olcott, Inc., 1798-1948,* p. 23, Dodge & Olcott, Inc., New York, 1948. The work shows an early nineteenth century drug price list on which peppermint oil, essence, and lozenges are itemized.

[11]E. Gildemeister and F. Hoffman, *op. cit.* p. 192.

[12]C. L. Porter, "History of *Mentha piperita* and Its Economic Importance in Indiana," *Proceedings of the Indiana Academy of Science: 1951,* vol. 61, p. 264, 1951.

Chapter 2.

The American Mint Industry Begins: Massachusetts

The Colonial Period

As the early Americans settled the lands along the Atlantic coast they uniquely blended their European heritage with that of their newly discovered Indian friends. In just a few years they had discovered many new medicinal plants with which they had been completely unfamiliar in their homeland. When illness struck, however, it was common practice to fall back upon the tried and true. When John Winthrop of the Massachusetts Bay Colony fell ill about 1635, his friend John Endecott, who had arrived in the colony in 1628, made a diligent search for remedies:[1]

> I have sent you of all I have or what I can get: viz. Syrup of violetts Sirrup of Roses: Spirit of Mints: Spirit of Annis as you may see written upon the several vialls.

John Winthrop survived his malady and the spirit of mints, a medicinal long used in England, and probably imported from there, may have aided in this end. Perhaps it was because the English colonists were so familiar with the culinary and medicinal uses of the mint plants that they seldom received attention in the early writings.

It probably will never be known who the colonist was that quietly secreted some mint roots in his sack of possessions and imported them into the new world. Peppermint and spearmint seldom set seeds but are easily propagated from rootstock. The original roots lay, at one time, on a sailing ship tossing back and forth as the vessel laboriously plied the

8

waters of the Atlantic. Because of the important uses of the mints the colonists probably imported both the oils and the plants at a very early date since "SpearMint" was first described in what is now the United States in 1672 in a work by John Josselyn who had made voyages to the United States in 1638 and 1663 (Figure 13).[2] Peppermint did not appear in the literature until much later which is understandable since the usage of peppermint did not become common until after its cultivation in the medicinal gardens of Mitcham, England, about 1750.

Cheshire, Massachusetts

Though peppermint and spearmint were not native to the United States both plants became quickly adapted to the shores of smaller streams and the swampy marsh bottoms and were soon spreading throughout New England. By the time the first American herbal was published, 1801, both peppermint and spearmint were recognized as garden plants and their uses described as follows:[3]

Peppermint
Mentha Peperita L.

It is raised in some of our gardens. It is a stimulant. It restores the functions of the stomach, promotes digestion, stops vomiting, cures the hiccups, flatulent colic, hysterical depressions, and other like complaints. It does not heat the constitution so much as might be expected.

Dose, Of the juice from an ounce to one and an half. The leaves when dry may be drunk as a tea.-Of the oil from one to two drops in sugar. Of the distilled water, from one to two ounces.

Spear Mint
Mentha Sativa
Mentha Viridis L.

Spear mint, garden mint, and green mint. It is stimulant, stomachic, carminative, and restringent. A strong infusion of the leaves is good for a weak stomach, loss of appetite, nausea, vomiting, gripes, colic pains, lientery, immoderate fluxes, hysterical affections, languors, and other debilities consequent upon delivery, and for a foremouth and throat if sweetened with honey. The leaves boiled in port wine and applied to the wrists and pit of the stomach, are said to stop vomiting. This plant retards the coagulation of milk.

Doses. Of the leaves an infusion one or two handfuls. Of the dry, half as much. Of the essential oil, from two to three drops in sugar. Of the distilled water, two ounces.

In the meantime developments were taking place in western Massachusetts that would make peppermint and spearmint the most important drug and flavoring crops in the United States.

Situated a few miles northeast of Pittsfield, the county seat of Berkshire County, Massachusetts, along the west bank of the Hoosic River,

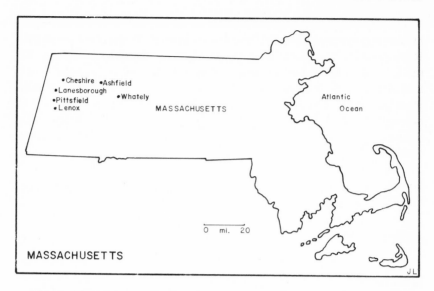

Map 1. Massachusetts, showing the villages associated with the early peppermint and spearmint oil industry between the 1790's and 1840.

lies the charming village of Cheshire (Map 1). Sometime in the 1790's some unknown parties there began the commercial cultivation of peppermint which was "grown quite extensively and the essence manufactured."[4] South of the village, on the road that leads southwest to Lanesborough were two peppermint distilleries, one close to Cheshire owned by Nathan Wood and one close to Lanesborough owned by John Hart. Had it not been for the enterprising Mr. Hart this notable aspect of American mint history might have been completely forgotten, but he diligently advertised his wares in *The Sun*, a newspaper published in Pittsfield, between December 1, 1800, and March 3, 1801.[5] The advertisement, the first mention of American peppermint oil in the new world literature (Figure 10), read as follows:

> Distillery and Brewery,
> One mile east of the meeting house in Lanesborough.
> Where may be had, Beer of the best quality by the hogshead, Barrel, or less quantity, as may suit the purchaser. Also, Essence of Pepper Mint, American and English, warranted genuine, in patent vials by the single, dozen, gross or thousand. Mint Cordial by the Gallon.
> Barley, Rye, Indian Corn, and Hops received in payment, and a generous price given. Malt constantly on hand to be exchanged for said articles—Hams are taken in and smoked in the best order, by the public's humble servant,
>
> John Hart
>
> N.B. Cash paid for Hops.
> Lanesborough, Dec. 9, 1800

The fact that peppermint cordial was offered by the gallon certainly indicated common usage and intimate knowledge by the local residents. It is regrettable that not more is known about the industry of that day in the Cheshire-Lanesborough area, but the commercial peppermint business did spread to nearby localities and, by 1829, cultivation of the plant for distillation of Essence of Peppermint was common in Lanesborough, Pittsfield, and Lenox.[6] Just what happened is unknown, but the industry disappeared as quietly as it had emerged, and the modern residents of the Hoosic and Housatonic valleys of western Massachusetts carry on their daily activities unaware that the grassy covered mud flats bordering their streams gave birth to the commercial mint industry in the United States.

Ashfield, Massachusetts

Thirty-five miles northeast of Pittsfield, nestled in the foothills of the beautiful Berkshires, is the village of Ashfield, a small New England town settled long before the American Revolution. The village rests on an elongated, narrow flat completely surrounded by the rolling, wooded hills of the Berkshire outliers, the whole capped by the magnificent Christopher Wren style steeple which sits proudly atop the Ashfield town hall. If this building could only speak it would have many tales to tell concerning mint for it was built in 1812, the same year that tradition says peppermint was first grown commercially in Ashfield. The industry brought to Ashfield its most prosperous years and, as has been the story in many specialized communities, was also responsible for its eventual decline.

In the early 1800's an old wagon trail led southward from Ashfield across the hills several miles through Tinkertown, where a number of tinsmiths and other metal workers had established flourishing businesses, then to the small settlement of South Ashfield. Numerous springs gushed forth along the wooded slopes and rivulets of fresh water seeped downward toward the creek and kept the hillsides moist and fresh. The old wagon trail has long since been replaced by Massachusetts highway 116 but the visitor can still follow by foot from the lovely Guilford home in Ashfield southward past the "Farragut Castle," once occupied by relatives of the Admiral, to South Ashfield. It was along this trail that the Ashfield peppermint story began.[7]

Thomas Ranney was a Scotsman who had settled in Chatham Town (township), Connecticut, the ancestor of a large family now spread across the entire United States. Some of his descendants began moving to Ashfield in the late 1700's, George in the spring of 1780 and Thomas in 1792. Both of these men had sons who figured prominently in the Ashfield peppermint enterprise. According to local historians it was Samuel Ranney, son of George, who began the raising of peppermint along the old trail in 1812,[8] apparently with plants he had found growing along the stream banks. The business proved to be a profitable one and, by 1817, three other Ashfield farmers, Cyrus Alden, Samuel Bement, and Joseph Ranney, had joined Samuel in the raising of peppermint and had constructed stills to extract the oil.[9] According to local records, the two Ranneys had their stills housed in some sort of shelter.[10] Apparently, the other two stills were in the open.

Distilling the Mint Oil

There is little specific information on just how the peppermint oil was distilled at Ashfield, but it was probably done in one of two ways. In the beginning the freshly cut herb was simply placed in large wash tubs or kettles, immersed in water, and boiled over a large fire. As the oil was released from the plants, being of lighter specific gravity, it would float to the top where it could be skimmed off. As the distilling techniques became more sophisticated copper kettles with tight lids were used and a metal worm or condenser pipe would conduct the vapor from the kettle to a metal receiving can where the oil could be continuously drawn off (Figure 8). When the water in the copper kettle was exhausted a fresh supply of herb was inserted and the process repeated. These men were real chemical pioneers, since the home distillation of mint oils on the farm property had not yet even been developed in England, although there is evidence that farm distillation had been practiced in Europe for many years (Figure 15).

By 1821 there were five peppermint distilleries operating along the old trail and, in 1830, nine.[11] The peppermint business proved profitable enough that, by 1830, spearmint, hemlock, spruce, tansy, wintergreen, and other oils were also being distilled.[12] Although the Cheshire area preceded that of Ashfield in the production of peppermint oil, the first commercial raising and distilling of spearmint oil seems to have been at Ashfield.

Peddling the Essences

As the production of oil plants increased in the community various essences, spirits, and cordials were processed and, along with the natural oils, began to be sold widely throughout New England. Ashfield became one of the great centers for the distribution of Yankee notions. Two brothers, Jasper and Joseph Bement, became especially renowned by establishing warehouses from which they supplied countless itinerant peddlers with a host of wares (Figure 14). The variety of notions handled by these peddlers was truly amazing. A partial listing of items sold by Jasper Bement to Thomas and Chapman Kelly on April 25, 1839, showed the following items:

1/2 dozen straps	@	$4.50	$2.25
2 gross stay lacings		1.25	2.50
1 dozen G.S. pencils			2.25
6 dozen hooks and eyes		.25	1.50
1 dozen shaving brushes			.67
1 gross hasps			1.25
3,000 needles		1.375	4.13
1,000 Victoria needles			2.00
1,000 Box needles			2.25
3 dozen Paysons Ink		1.50	4.50
72 rolls tape		.035	2.52
1 dozen spools thread			.30
1 package patent pins		.31	.62
2 dozen wood pencils			.13
6 rolls silk braid		.055	.33
6 gross bone shirt buttons		.16	.96
7 gross jewel buttons		.50	3.50
2 gross iron side combs		3.00	6.00
2 dozen fancy rings			.33
2 dozen dressing combs		.75	1.50
1/2 dozen breast pins		6.00	3.00
1 pound peppermint oil			4.25
3 bottles essence of peppermint			.44
1 gross assorted essences		.40 dozen	4.80

The entire purchase of the two peddlers amounted to nearly $75.[13]

Not only did Ashfield become a plant and oil producing center, but a number of citizens developed thriving businesses devoted to the promotion and selling of peppermint and other oils. Among the more prominent were Asher Belding[14] and Captain Roswell Ranney, son of Thomas.[15] Captain Ranney, twice representative in the Massachusetts legislature, twice captain of militia, and frequent moderator in town meetings, had been born in Chatham Town, Connecticut, in 1782, and moved with his family to Ashfield when he was ten years old. He was, for many years, a "farmer and speculator, dealing largely in peppermint and other essential oils,"[16] and owned one of the mint distilleries along the old trail.

Over $40,000 worth of peppermint oil was produced at Ashfield in 1824[17] and, by 1825, several hundred acres of peppermint were under cultivation and from 25 to 40 pounds of oil were being extracted from each acre of plants. The following winter, 1825-1826, however, was so severe that many of the fields were destroyed and several growers were forced to abandon cultivation.[18] Since closely associated with the thriving oil business was the supplying of peddlers, by 1838 "there was hardly a young man who did not set forth with his strap-neck yoke over his shoulder from which was suspended a basket of essences"[19] on one side and a "tin trunk of Yankee notions on the other"[20] (Figure 7). Many of the peddlers were satisfied with a single trip but some continued the business for years.

The peddlers did not want for customers. They fanned out from Ashfield in all directions, many to the newly opened lands of the west. The peddlers headed north along the Connecticut River Valley, then west following the Berkshire Trail to Albany, and moved by a succession of toll roads to Schenectady and Utica west into the Genesee and Niagara countries.[21] So many travellers were on the roads of that day that there were 52 taverns and inns within 50 miles of Albany, and it was not uncommon for 80 to 100 horses to be stabled at a single inn.[22] Although peddling was hard and tedious work, it was exciting and great adventure for young men, and many frontier families eagerly looked forward to the peddler's arrival. In the early 1800's eight peddlers set forth each year from Burlington, Vermont, forty each year from Meriden, Connecticut and, in 1829, more than sixty peddlers moved out from Hartford.[23] As many as seventy set forth each year from Ashfield which was only one of a host of cities supported by the business of supplying drugs, fancies, and notions to the frontier.

The Peppermint Market

The peppermint industry of Ashfield had wide repercussions. At the onset imported European mint oil was selling for about $16 a pound.[24] The Ranney enterprise soon brought the price to $12 a pound, then to $8 where it stayed fairly even for some years. By this time some of the Ashfield residents were engaging in speculation and promotion, the market became overstocked, and the price of peppermint oil, by 1829, plummeted to a meager 75 cents a pound. Prices rose in eight months to $8 a pound but dropped again to $3 by 1833. Despite the wide price fluctuation Ashfield growers were still able to make a handsome profit,[25] and the oil was being delivered over a wide area. "Almost every house had its still and a great many pretty properties were made there while the place enjoyed a monopoly of the business."[26] The prosperity of the Ashfield peppermint growers was chronicled in a nearby newspaper:[27]

> we could mention names of those who began with peddling essences, who are now thriving and wealthy merchants in the Atlantic Cities; men who after penetrating all the mysteries attending the manufacture of peppermint, spearmint, goldenrod, wintergreen, worm-wood, etc., now control the movements of commercial fleets, and decide the daily fate of stocks. The number is of course infinitely greater of those who have made this business an apprenticeship to regular country trading, and an avenue to moderate wealth.

The fact that some twenty different oils were being peddled,[28] many processed in the local distilleries, contributed immeasurably to this success.

Ashfield Declines

After a generation, however, the Ashfield mint industry began to wane. The American frontier had become extended to great distances in the west, many of the local residents, including the peddlers, moved from Ashfield, the price of peppermint and other oils had dropped quite low, newer and more productive areas for raising peppermint were discovered, and Ashfield farmers moved west to try the new lands. The Ashfield residents themselves introduced peppermint into northern New York. An enterprising individual was reported "making annually 1,500 pounds of high quality peppermint oil"[29] in the Cincinnati, Ohio, area, and peppermint oil was reported from New Jersey in 1834.[30]

By 1836 only four persons were engaged in peppermint and other oil production in Ashfield and the total value of essences had dwindled to a meager $9,500.[31] Local dealers were forced to order mint oil from the newly established New York growers to fill their orders. Although distilleries operated for some time at Ashfield and nearby Whately, the thriving peppermint industry of western Massachusetts soon faded into quiet oblivion and a romantic period in American agricultural and commercial history became a memory. As Ashfield and Cheshire passed from the mint oil scene, however, a newer and more promising area was developing in the emerging American west.

REFERENCES

[1]*Winthrop Papers*, vol. 3, p. 222, The Massachusetts Historical Society, Boston, 1943.

[2]J. Josselyn, *New-Englands Rarities Discovered*, p. 89, G. Widdowes, London, 1672.

³S. Stearns, *The American Herbal*, pp. 227-228, Thomas and Thomas, 1801.

⁴E. M. Raynor and E. L. Petitclerc, *History of the Town of Cheshire, Berkshire County, Massachusetts*, p. 75, C. W. Bryan and Co., Holyoke, Massachusetts, 1885.

⁵*The Sun*, Pittsfield, Massachusetts, December 9, 1800, and March 3, 1801. The advertisement also appeared in several issues between these two dates.

⁶D. D. Field (ed.), *History of the County of Berkshire, Massachusetts*, pp. 86-87, Pittsfield, Massachusetts, 1829.

⁷The most complete accounts of the Ashfield peppermint oil industry are the following: F. G. Howes, *History of the Town of Ashfield, Massachusetts, from Its Settlement in 1742 to 1910*, pp. 103-105, 126, published by the town of Ashfield, c. 1912; D. J. Malcolm, "America's Least Remembered Industry," *Yankee*, pp. 34-37, July, 1957; I. Zieget, "Where Mint Was Once a Major Industry," *The Herbarist*, vol. 25, pp. 52-54, 1959; and, "Mint Made A Mint," *Food Marketing in New England*, p. 4, summer, 1965. Ashfield, at the time, was in Berkshire County, but became part of Franklin County when the latter was established in 1825.

⁸Most of the accounts mention 1812 as the year but 1814 is listed by E. R. Ellis, *Biographical Sketches of Richard Ellis, the First Settler of Ashfield, Massachusetts, and His Descendants*, p. 356, Wm. Graham Printing Co., Detroit, 1888. Two writers place the first successful plantings of peppermint in western Connecticut: J. K. Reeve, "Peppermint Culture," *American Agriculturist*, vol. 53, no. 8, p. 432, August, 1894; and, L. H. Bailey, "Mentha," *The Standard Cyclopedia of Horticulture*, vol. 2, The Macmillan Co., New York, 1943. The origin of these accounts is unknown, but they may have been references to the Ranney family. If the Ranneys had cultivated peppermint in Connecticut it hardly seems likely they would have waited 32 years before attempting it in Ashfield. As of this time there has appeared no extant material which relates in any way to the commercial production of mint in Connecticut.

⁹*Town Valuation: 1817*, Town of Ashfield, records preserved in the town hall.

¹⁰*Ibid*. The records were listed as "still" and "still and still house."

¹¹*Grand Valuation for 1821*, Town of Ashfield, "distill houses" were assessed for Cyrus Alden, Roger Brownson, Wm. Flower, Roswell Ranney, and Samuel Ranney; *The Valuation for 1823,* Town of Ashfield, assessments for Arthur Belding (1 distill house), Wm. Ranney (1 still), Jonathan Richmond (1 still), Joseph Ranney (1 still and still house), Samuel Ranney (1 still and still house), and Israel Williams (1 still and still house). Howes, *op. cit.*, mentions 10 distilleries in operation in 1830, but a search of the assessment records revealed only nine: *Town Valuation for 1830*, Town of Ashfield, assessments for Samuel Ranney (1 still and still house), Joseph Paine (1 still and house), Salmon Miller (2 stills and house), Silas Blake (1 still and house), Cyrus Alden (1 still and still house), Israel Williams (2 stills), and Jasper Bement (1 still and still house). All records preserved in the town hall of Ashfield. Apparently no assessments were made of distilleries after 1830. Among other family names associated with mint at Ashfield were Burnet, Ellis, and Phillips (F. G. Howes, *op. cit.*, pp. 104-105).

¹²F. G. Howes, *op. cit.*, p. 104. No specific dates for spearmint growing in Ashfield have been obtained, but commercial spearmint production probably originated in Ashfield before 1830. There is no mention of spearmint in the Cheshire-Lanesborough area.

¹³Information from the ledger of Jasper Bement preserved in the Ashfield Museum.

¹⁴E. R. Ellis, *op cit.*, pp. 117-118.

¹⁵*Ibid.*, p. 389.

¹⁶*Ibid.*

¹⁷F. G. Howes, *op. cit.*, p. 126.

[18]"Peppermint," *Hampshire Gazette*, Nov. 16, 1825. The same article also appeared in the *New England Farmer*, vol. 4, p. 141, Nov. 25, 1825. See also, "Peppermint," *Hampshire Gazette*, p. 3, June 6, 1827.

[19]I. Zieget, *op cit.*, p. 53.

[20]F. G. Howes, *op. cit.*, p. 104.

[21]J. R. Dolan, *The Yankee Peddlers of Early America*, p. 69, C. N. Potter, Inc., New York, 1964.

[22]*Ibid.*

[23]*Ibid.*, pp. 72-73.

[24]"Essence Peddling," from the *Greenfield* (Franklin) *Mercury* in the *New England Farmer and Horticultural Journal*, vol. 12, no. 23, p. 181, Dec. 18, 1833. The article in *Food Marketing in New England, op. cit.*, is partially based on this account.

[25]"Essence Peddling," *op. cit.* Some representative prices, taken from the Bement ledger, were as follows: 1839, $4.25 per lb. of peppermint oil, bottles of essence of peppermint at $1.75 per dozen, peppermint oil at $0.28 per ounce, $5.00 for 6 dozen 4 ounce containers of peppermint oil; 1841, $3.00 per lb. of peppermint oil; 1842, peppermint oil at $0.125 per vial.

[26]"Essence Peddling," *op. cit.*

[27]*Ibid.*

[28]Some of the oils listed in the Bement ledger included; peppermint, spearmint. lemon, spruce, antiseptic, balsam, cloves, castor, red cedar, cedar, macassar, wintergreen, sweet, cinnamon, rose, British, antique, hemlock, bean, and buffalo.

[29]F. P. Weisenburger, *The Passing of the Frontier*, vol. 3 of *The History of the State of Ohio*, C. Wittke (ed.), p. 83, Ohio State Archaeological and Historical Society, Columbus, 1941.

[30]*The Dispensatory of the United States of America*, 2nd edition, p. 429, Lippincott, Grambo and Co., Philadelphia, 1834.

[31]From a letter by L. H. Bronson on file in the Ashfield Museum covering the year ending April 1, 1837. Three of the four persons still distilling were Anson Bement, Isaac Taylor, and Childs Sanderson. Bronson mentions the fact that J. H. Maltby (1829-1918) was the last of the Ashfield essence manufacturers but gives no dates. It is in Bronson's letter that the village of Whately is listed as having a distillery.

Chapter 3.

The Mint Industry Moves West: New York, Ohio, and Michigan

New York

In the early 1800's the southern shore of Lake Ontario was becoming home to thousands of settlers. The Yankee peddlers from New England diligently followed these pioneers into the new lands with their notions and essences and many, finding the frontier to their liking, stayed. In 1810 two Ashfield peddlers, Archibald Burnett and George Cobb, set forth on a selling trip to the "far West."[1] Upon arriving in New York they settled temporarily among the drumlin covered hills of the Finger Lakes region near the village of Vienna (also known as Phelps, officially since 1855) along the Lake Canandaigua Outlet in Ontario County (Map 2). Archibald obtained summer employment on a farm owned by Henry VanDemark and peddled notions during the winter months. In 1814 he married the farmer's daughter, named Experience, and rented a nearby farm.

About this time Archibald received a letter from his brother Nahum in Ashfield requesting him to return immediately as he had important news that he dared not trust even to the mail. Nahum had a few stony acres near Ashfield and, following the lead of Samuel Ranney, had experimented with peppermint growing and distilled the oil in a laundry tub. He had sold the oil at a handsome profit and desired his brother to return and engage in the business with him. When Archibald learned of his brother's plan, he was quite certain that peppermint could be grown more satisfactorily on the rich, alluvial flats of the Canandaigua Outlet than in Ashfield, so he returned carrying a bag of peppermint roots over

18

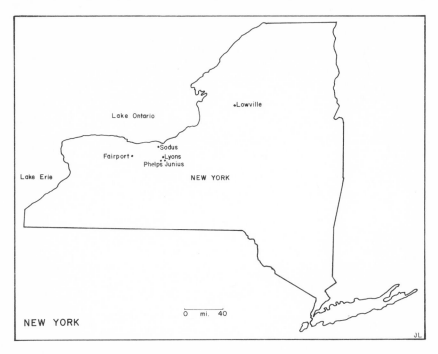

Map 2. New York, showing the villages associated with the production of peppermint and spearmint during the 19th century.

his shoulder and planted them on the terraces of the river bank in 1816 (Figure 12).

Nahum disposed of his farm in Ashfield and soon followed with his family and another brother, Andrew. Both Nahum and Archibald bought new farms, Archibald near Junius (Seneca County) and Nahum near Alloway (at that time in Ontario County, but now in Wayne County) just south of the village of Lyons. Both erected crude distilleries designed by Nahum and the peppermint industry of New York was established.

When it was discovered that the plants flourished along the Outlet, produced more oil, and required less cultivating than in Ashfield, the peppermint growers of Massachusetts began to move to the new locality. Many of the Beldings, Ellises, Ranneys, and Phillips joined the Burnetts in the Vienna area.[2] Samuel Ranney arrived in March, 1836, and Captain Roswell Ranney came in 1839.[3] The loss of so many prosperous families was a severe blow to Ashfield and the peppermint industry of Vienna thrived as the Massachusetts venture waned.

Unlike Massachusetts, Vienna did not develop a peddling industry

and the bulk of the local peppermint oil was either traded by the
farmers or sold over the counter by country store operators. The lack of
a well organized marketing procedure limited the development of the
industry for some time but did not deter new growers from setting out
roots and distilling the oil.

Ohio

By 1833 the cultivation of peppermint had been extended into the
Connecticut Western Reserve of northeastern Ohio.[4] It is quite likely

Map 3. Ohio, showing the towns associated with the cultivation of peppermint
during the 19th century.

that relatives of the Ashfield and Vienna families were responsible for this development for the land records of Ashtabula, Cuyahoga, Lake, Lorain, and Huron counties in Ohio (Map 3) contain numerous deeds between the years 1812 and 1835 for such Ashfield names as Ranney, Burnett, Ellis, and Phillips. As the Massachusetts and New York peppermint families migrated westward to new localities the mint industry migrated along with them.

Michigan

The westward movement of settlers continued right across northern Ohio into the Middlewest. Streams of New Yorkers rounded the shores of Lake Erie and sought out new lands in southern Michigan and northern Indiana. A great number of descendants of the peppermint families in New York and Ohio were among these early pioneers and the cultivation of peppermint soon developed in southwestern Michigan.

An 1858 writer stated that peppermint culture

> was first introduced into St. Joseph County in 1835, by Calvin Sawyer, who brought the roots from Ohio, and made the first plantation on White Pigeon Prairie, in the township of White Pigeon. In the spring of 1836, two farmers named White and Earl, procuring roots from Calvin Sawyer, made plantations on the same prairie, and in the same township.[5].

Sawyer disposed of his farm in 1836 but production on the White Pigeon Prairie was continued by White, Earl (Earle), and Glover, who had also obtained his peppermint roots from Sawyer.[6] Production on the prairies was not too successful because the level lands were excessively windblown and the roots were subjected to severe winterkilling.[7] In 1838 production was shifted northward to Florence Township near the present town of Constantine (Map 4) and the culture was attempted on burr oak soil by two brothers, Marshall and Orrin Craw, and by Lewis Ranney (Figure 11).[8] The area was gently undulating and covered with scattered groves of scrub, or burr, oak which caused the early settlers to refer to the land as "oak openings." The burr oak openings production was quite successful; the peppermint plants required less cultivation than on the prairies, and winterkilling was not as great a problem. In 1838 Reuben and Otis Matthews constructed the first permanent distillery in the township.[9] Peppermint cultivation had come to Michigan to stay.

Cultivation on the prairies was soon discontinued and, for some years, peppermint raising in Michigan was confined largely to the burr oak openings of Florence Township. As in New York, the mint farmers exchanged their oil with country store merchants who, in turn, traded

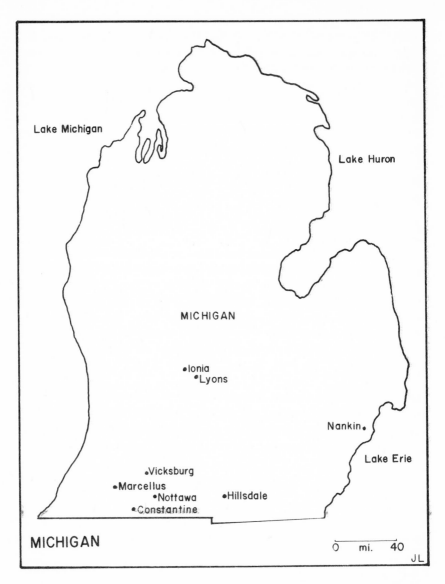

Map 4. **The lower peninsula of Michigan, showing the towns associated with** the high ground cultivation of peppermint and spearmint between 1835 and 1885.

the product in New York city for merchandise suitable to their needs. As oil production increased the country merchants acted as agents for eastern dealers who marketed and exported the commodity, Liverpool being the major export destination.

Although commercial mint production did not originate in Michigan until 1835 imported mints had reached the state much earlier. There is a note concerning the importation of "2 dozen peppermints"[10] about 1815 through the port of Detroit from Canada with a nominal value of $4.50. Apparently bottled essences were peddled quite widely, as two small, rectangular glass bottles with short necks and flaring lips (Figure 9) were discovered in an Indian grave near Galesburg, Michigan, and dated about 1820. One of the bottles, preserved in the Kalamazoo Public Museum, is inscribed, in raised letters, on one side "PepperMint" and "Kings Patent" on the other. This was a British oil manufactured by Robert Turlington,[11] and was an imported brand quite commonly peddled in the early days.

Conclusion

As the year 1838 drew to a close the commercial cultivation of peppermint and spearmint had been firmly established in the United States. From the early origins on the mudflats of the Hoosic River near Cheshire, Massachusetts, the industry had spread to the stony highlands of the Berkshire foothills at Ashfield, Massachusetts, where the peddling of essences had enabled many growers and dealers to compile fortunes. As the Ashfield families migrated westward the cultivation of the mints was introduced into New Jersey, the river terraces of the drumlin covered hills near Vienna, New York, and the glacial moraine country of southwestern Michigan. The cultivation of the plants and the distilling of the oil were specialized practices that farmers had developed to a considerable degree. It remained only for some enterprising individual to advertise the oil and market it on a wide scale. Such a development was soon forthcoming in New York State.

REFERENCES

[1]The Burnett peppermint story has been told in a great number of sources, always with minor variations. The account in this work is based primarily on an article which appeared in 1913 in the *Lyons* (New York) *Republican* written by the grand-daughter of Nahum Burnett, Mrs. Emma Burnett Harris of South Bend, Indiana. The article is in the files of Mrs. Mabel E. Oaks, the historian of Phelps.

The farm on which Archibald Burnett first planted peppermint in 1816 was known, in 1913, as the Lewis Holbrook farm. His later farm was located on the New Pre-emption Road near Junius in Seneca County, but also contained land in Ontario County. The numerous references referring to the establishment of the New York peppermint industry in Wayne County near Lyons are historically incorrect since Wayne County was not legally constituted until 1823.

[2]F. G. Howes, *History of the Town of Ashfield, Massachusetts from Its Settlement in 1742 to 1910*, pp. 104-105, published by the town of Ashfield, c. 1912.

[3]E. R. Ellis, *Biographical Sketches of Richard Ellis, the First Settler of Ashfield, Massachusetts, and His Descendants,* pp. 386, 389, Wm. Graham Printing Co., Detroit, 1888.

[4]F. Stearns, "The Peppermint Plantations of Michigan," *Proceedings of the American Pharmaceutical Association,* 7th annual meeting, p. 449, 1858. The article also appeared in the *American Journal of Pharmacy,* vol. 31, pp. 33-52, 1859. The reference to Ohio is on p. 33. A. Henkel, "Peppermint," *Miscellaneous Studies,* Bulletin 90, Bureau of Plant Industry, pp. 19-29, USDA, 1906; "Essence Peddling," *Greenfield* (Franklin) *Mercury* in the *New England Farmer and Horticultural Journal,* vol. 12, no. 23, p. 181, Dec. 18, 1833.

[5]F. Stearns, *op. cit.,* p. 33, 1859.

[6]*Ibid.*; H. G. Cutter, *History of St. Joseph County, Michigan,* vol. 1, pp. 5-6, Lewis Publishing Co., Chicago, 1911; *History of St. Joseph County, Michigan,* pp. 19-20, 131, L. H. Everts and Co., Philadelphia, 1877.

[7]F. Stearns, *op. cit.,* p. 34, 1859.

[8]*Ibid.,* p. 33; H. G. Cutter, *op. cit.,* p. 6.

[9]*History of St. Joseph County, Michigan, op. cit.,* p. 131, 1877.

[10]*Historical Collections,* vol. 16, p. 125, Michigan Pioneer and Historical Society, Robert Smith and Co., Lansing, 1890. The note was dated June 1, 1815, and the customs duty assessed at $1.35.

[11]G. I. Quimby, *Indian Culture and European Trade Goods,* p. 74, U. of Wisconsin Press, Madison, Wisconsin, 1966.

Chapter 4.

American Mint Becomes Big Business

Cultivation of Mint

As the mint industry was extended into newer areas the development of proper cultivation was largely a process of trial and error. It had been discovered that the rich bottom lands of the river terraces of northern New York and the burr oak openings of southwestern Michigan provided excellent locales for production and, within a short time, agricultural techniques became somewhat stabilized.

The, method of cultivation, as described in New York, was generally the same as that in other areas.

> The mode of propagation is by transplanting the roots, which may be done in Autumn or Spring, though generally the latter, and as the herb is perennial, it does not require replanting till the fourth year. To ensure a good crop and obviate the necessity of extra attendance the first · season, the ground intended for planting should be fallowed the preceding summer, though this is not necessary if the land is ordinarily clean. The ground should be prepared as for maize, as soon as possible in the spring, furrowed, and roots planted in drills, twenty inches apart, and covered with loose earth, two inches deep, the planter walking upon the drill and treading it firmly. The proper time to procure roots is when the herb is a year old, when from six to eight square rods of ordinary mint will yield a sufficient quantity of roots to plant an acre and the crop from which the roots are taken will not be deteriorated, but rather benefitted by their extraction. As soon as the herb makes its appearance it requires ʻa light dressing with the hoe, care being taken not to disturb the young shoots, many of which have scarcely made their appearance above the ground. In the course of a week or two the crop requires a more thorough dressing, and at this stage of growth the cultivator may be used with advantage, followed by the hoe, carefully eradicating weeds and grass from the drills, and giving the herb

a light dressing of earth. Another dressing a week or two later is all the crop requires.

The two following years no labor is bestowed upon the crop, though it is sometimes benefitted by ploughing over the whole surface, very shallow, in the autumn of the second year, and harrowing lightly the following spring, which frequently renews the vigor of the plant and increases the product..

The mint should be cut as soon as it is in full bloom, and the lower leaves become sere; the first crop will not be fit to cut as early as the two succeeding ones. It is then to be hayed and put in cock, and is then ready for distillation.[1]

The distilling technique was that of the copper kettle and condenser pipe which had been developed in the Ashfield days.[2] This was a slow and tedious method and only twelve to fifteen pounds of oil could be processed in a day.[3] Despite the prodigious amount of labor required in the fields and the distillation process new growers were not reluctant to enter the business and, by 1847, there were 210 peppermint growers in Ontario, Seneca, and Wayne counties, New York. Shortly after the introduction of peppermint into Michigan its cultivation was extended into the northern section of Indiana. The first account of production in Indiana was about 1846 when Hawley Peck journeyed to the Michigan mint area near Constantine and returned with a sack of roots, planting them in section 27, Clearspring Township, Lagrange County.[4] He was soon joined in this venture by Erastus Nelson and Charles Roy.

As the industry expanded and the technology improved marketing was still a problem. The American oil did not find ready acceptance in the export trade and the amount that could be consumed locally was limited. Frequently, supply exceeded demand, which made the price structure quite variable. When oil was scarce it could command $5.25 a pound, but frequently dipped to as low as $0.75.[5] About 1835 the price levelled off somewhat and for a number of years averaged nearly $2.50 a pound.[6] But the price structure was not entirely a natural process. As the industry grew larger it naturally attracted the interest of financiers who wished to promote the enterprise.

Hiram G. Hotchkiss

Leman Hotchkiss was a merchant who moved with his family to the village of Vienna (also known as Phelps, officially since 1855) in Ontario County, New York, in 1811. There, with his partner, David McNeil, he opened a mercantile store and a grist mill which became quite successful soon doing a gross business of over $100,000 per year.[7] In 1822 the partners opened a new store in Miller's Basin (now the village of Newark) in which they employed Hiram G. Hotchkiss (Figure 17), the twelve year old son of Leman, as a clerk. Six years later

Hiram entered into partnership with his brother, Leman B., and cousin, William T. Hotchkiss, and the three opened a general store in Vienna and also operated three flour mills, two in Vienna and one in Seneca Falls.[8]

Both the store and the mills were successful and the partners watched the wheat market quite diligently. It was customary for mint farmers to exchange their oil at country stores in order to obtain goods they desired. In 1837 Hiram began accepting local peppermint oil and stored the jugs in the store cellar. When nearly 1,200 pounds of oil had been accumulated Hiram took a supply to nearby Lyons and journeyed down the Erie Canal by barge, transferred the jugs of oil to a boat at Albany, and sailed to New York City to attempt to market the oil. The New York dealers rejected the peppermint supply and Hiram carted the entire lot back to Vienna and reported failure.

Hiram and his brother then bottled a quantity of oil and shipped it to dealers in Hamburg, Germany with a label reading "Peppermint Oil from Wayne County, U.S.A. Guaranteed Pure by H. G. Hotchkiss." After a considerable wait they were notified that the oil was acceptable, would be purchased for $1,000, and further supplies would be desired. In 1839 the first consignments of oil were shipped to London and Rotterdam.[9] After this small beginning Hiram devoted more and more time to the oil business and, in 1841, dissolved his partnership and moved to Lyons, on the Erie Canal, to establish a peppermint oil works (Figure 18).[10]

Hotchkiss in Lyons

From this point Hiram Hotchkiss devoted his entire attention to the peppermint business. He obtained land and entered the field as a grower, encouraged local farmers to produce more and better quality oil, and established the Hotchkiss Peppermint Planters Banking House to serve as a financial center for oil producers (Figure 22).[11] He experimented with mint cultivation on new types of soil, the sand and gravels of the uplands, and was one of the first to attempt to grow peppermint on drained marshland. On one of Hotchkiss' farms near Lyons he was cultivating 150 acres of drained marshland and could cover the shoots with six to ten inches of water during the winter to protect from freezing.[12] This was an interesting technique since any such attempt, today, would certainly result in the drowning of all the plants. The shores of Mud (Ganargwa) Creek near Lyons (after 1823 in Wayne County) became filled with peppermint plants as growers began entering the business and selling to Hotchkiss.

From the very first Hiram had emphasized the quality and purity of his product. He had discovered that much of the oil being disposed of through the New York market was being adulterated with undesirable substances. Using this fact as his keynote he first advertised his "Wayne and Ontario counties peppermint oil equal to the best English Oil" in the trade papers in New York in 1844.[13] The business prospered and soon canallers knew when they were approaching Lyons because the smell of peppermint oil could be detected for miles up and down the Erie Canal (Figure 21). For many years Hotchkiss marketed his oil primarily through the firm of Dows and Cary in New York.

With the success of the peppermint business Hotchkiss soon turned his attention to other oils. Spearmint was introduced into the Lyons area by George Hanson about 1846 and Hiram purchased 20 pounds 8 ounces for $20.50.[14] Eventually, wintergreen, sassafras, pennyroyal, tansy, and wormwood were added to the company's product list.

The Great Monopoly

Mint production in New York had expanded considerably. In 1845 the cultivation of peppermint was found in Wayne, Ontario, Seneca, Monroe, and Lewis counties. In 1846 nearly 40,000 pounds of oil was produced in the Lyons area (Wayne, Seneca, and Ontario counties) and 4,500 pounds in Lewis County where mint was being grown on "drained swamp" areas;[15] in addition, 10,000 pounds were produced in Hillsdale and St. Joseph Counties, Michigan; 3,000 pounds in northeastern Ohio, and about 700 pounds in northern Indiana.[16] This production offered lucrative possibilities for a dealer and, in the spring of 1847, Hiram G. Hotchkiss arrived at an agreement with the firm of E. C. Patterson and Company of New York to attempt to corner the oil market.

The plan was well devised. An agent was sent to Liverpool to ascertain the approximate demand for peppermint in the European market for the year, an amount estimated at about 12,000 pounds. New York growers greatly exceeded this amount in their production and the combined Ohio and Michigan supply was nearly equal to the European demand. As a result a meeting of mint growers was called by Hotchkiss in the village of Newark, New York, in March, 1847. Growers were propositioned to plow under their peppermint, growing only a supply to serve as seed stock, and guarantee not to extend plantings or sell roots for a period of two years. Hotchkiss had estimated that the proposition could be carried off for about $30,000, $20,000 in the Wayne County area and $5,000 in Lewis County, New York, with $5,000 elsewhere in the United States. His estimates proved to be quite high as, by May 17, he had successfully negotiated the proposition with 181 of the 210 growers in the Wayne County area involving nearly 1,000 acres for about $10,000.[17] This represented an average expenditure to the mint growers of $10 per acre. The contract read as follows:[18]

know all men by these presents that we the undersigned inhabitants of Wayne, Seneca and Ontario Counties in the State of New York each for ourselves, individually, hereby agree with E. C. Patterson Co. of the City of New York for and in consideration of the sum of money set opposite our respective names to sell to the said E. C. Patterson Co. the number of acres of peppermint below enumerated as growing in the county set opposite our respective names below which includes all the peppermint roots in which we each of us respectively are interested either directly or indirectly preserving only to each one of us not exceeding the quantity of peppermint specified opposite our respective names below and the right to set not exceeding the same quantity for seed roots for two years from the first day of March AD1847. And we each for ourselves respectively agree to sell the same for the sum and price set opposite our respective names at any time between this date and the fifteenth day of June next. And upon payment to us of said sums of money respectively we each for ourselves agree to plough up or otherwise wholly destroy the said peppermint excepting only the quantity reserved for seed roots on or before the fifteenth day of June next. And we each for ourselves respectively agree with the said E. C. Patterson Co. that upon payment of the said peppermint now growing we will thereafter wholly discontinue the production of peppermint or the oil of peppermint for two years from the first day of March 1847. And we further agree with the said E. C. Patterson Co. that we will not allow peppermint to grow upon lands owned or occupied by us excepting for seed roots as above reserved from which seed mint it is agreed that the oil shall not be extracted for two years from the date specified. And we each for ourselves respectively hereby agree with the said E. C. Patterson Co. that from and after the payment of the said sums of money we will wholly cease to be engaged or interested in either directly or indirectly in growing peppermint for two years from the first day of March 1847 and that we will neither directly or indirectly sell barter or give away or otherwise in any manner dispose of any peppermint roots for two years from the first day of March 1847. And we each for ourselves respectively further agree with the said E. C. Patterson Co. upon the payment of the said sums of money not to distil peppermint or manufacture peppermint oil for any person whatever (excepting only for such as shall have contracted to deliver their oil to the said E. C. Patterson Co. and shall exhibit their contract as evidence of this right to produce oil) for two years from this date, nor to rent, sell, or give away the use or right of use of each or any one or all of our distilleries for the purpose of manufacturing peppermint oil for two years from this date. And we further agree each for ourselves individually to pay all damages arising from any breach of this contract.
Witness our names hereto subscribed this 10th day of May 1847.

In the meantime the New York firm had sent agents into Michigan to contract the peppermint oil crop for two years guaranteeing a price of $2.50 per pound. This negotiation was successfully completed and the agents went on to Ohio where they attempted to persuade the farmers to contract their oil as was being done in Michigan. A letter from one of the agents in Ohio is a classic of humorous capitalism as well as being a fairly complete picture of the mint industry in that state in 1847. The letter read as follows:[19]

> Headquarters Contracting Department
> Painesville, O.
> June 15th, 1847, 9 P.M.

Dear Hotchkiss!

Since our last hurried dispatch of 6inst. from Elyria we have finished the war in this region, and we now proceed to give you a detailed account of it.

On arriving at Birmingham we found the enemy drawn up in three divisions as follows: His right near Birmingham and extending in a circular form about five miles in diameter. His left rested on this place and his center occupied the towns of Mentor, Kirtland, & Chardon whilst his rear was so exposed as to put us to great trouble in attacking him extending as it did for twenty miles in a southerly direction. On the first day of our arrival we made a vigorous attack on the whole of that division. By rapid marches we reached Mentor—six miles west of this on Monday last the 7th inst. where we attacked the center. It was at this point we found the most difficulty for the enemy's forces were so scattered that we were obliged to make no less than four engagements. On Monday the 7th we attacked Mentor and appointed the following day for a pow-wow which proving unprofitable said pow-wow was adjourned to the following Friday. We then pursued the enemy into Chardon and we appointed a pow-wow for Thursday which was also unsuccessful and adjourned until the following Saturday. We then made a retrograde movement on Mentor and met the enemy according to agreement on Friday when we captured the main body of his forces. By a rapid movement we regained Chardon met the enemy there on Saturday & captured his main body when the remaining forces of Mentor, Kirtland, Concord, & Chardon surrendered at discretion excepting a few who escaped and two or three who were allowed to go on parole. The whole district of country thus subdued extends sixty miles in length by thirty in width.

To drop the military and assume the mintiary style we would inform you that we have contracted for nearly the whole Ohio crop. The crop this year will be small, not half of that of last year. Many of the growers have gone out of the business and many more are sick of it. We could not get the whole for the growers are so scattered that they cannot be made to pull together. We leave from 500 to 800 lbs. uncontracted mostly old and harmless however. Some of them had got the news of the rise in New York and thus had contracted to the swindling shopkeepers. . .

In conclusion allow us to observe that we are much pleased with the result in our labors. This state contains much fine land but Ohio can---when we can live in the state of New York.

> Yours truly
> E. C. Patterson &
> (N. B.) Henry Dougherty not
> Dugerty (if you please)

Hiram Gilbert Hotchkiss Esq. Gen. in Chief
of Lyons, Wayne Co. State of New York
United States of America

With the negotiation completed, Hotchkiss then ordered brokers holding his oil in New York to remove all offer of sales for a period of four months, then market the oil at $4.00 a pound.[20] The attempt to corner the market and force a price rise was insured further success when the peppermint harvest in Michigan during 1847 and 1848 proved to be a poor one and the oil supply was less than expected.

The monopoly was a mixed success and had wide and far reaching repercussions: it firmly established Hotchkiss as the primary country dealer in mint oils; it gave the industry in Michigan great impetus; but it seriously retarded the industry in New York for a considerable period of time. For about $15,000 Hotchkiss and Patterson gained virtual control over the peppermint oil supply in the United States for a period of two years.

Hotchkiss Reigns Supreme

The monopoly contracts ran out in the spring of 1849 and the New York growers began again to enter the field. Production that year was limited by drought, but nearly 8,000 pounds of peppermint oil was produced in the Wayne County area which included the villages of Lyons, Newark, Palmyra, Rose, Huron, and Sodus in Wayne County (Map 5), Phelps in Ontario County, and Junius in Seneca County; 1,000

Map 5. Wayne County, New York, showing the villages associated with the commercial production of peppermint and spearmint during the 19th century.

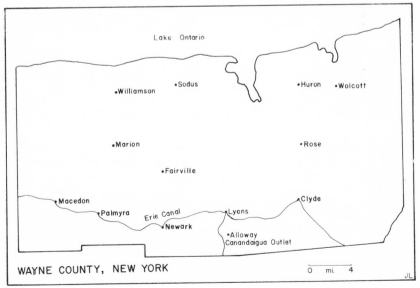

pounds in Lewis County, New York; in addition, 8,000 pounds were produced in Michigan; 1,000 pounds in Ohio; and 500 pounds in Indiana.[21]

Hotchkiss continued to cement his position as the leading buyer of oil, but not without difficulty. The idea of the monopoly was probably given great impetus in the spring of 1845 when a promoter named Ranney had attempted to buy up all the oil then stored in the warehouses of brokers in Boston and New York and capitalize on an impending price rise.[22] Such speculative activity was by no means uncommon in the early days.

Hotchkiss, apparently, had occasional difficulties with his brother Leman, who still resided in Vienna. "Working together, they might have cornered the world market for essential oils but, acting as actual competitors, they drove up prices on crude oils and allowed others a foothold."[23] One such was Alfred Hale who had settled near Alloway and, in 1832, began the raising of peppermint. An inventive and active man Hale devised numerous improved methods and machinery for cultivating and distilling mint. In 1862 Hale formed a partnership with a Mr. Parshall, bottled oil under the trademark "Hale and Parshall," and became a successful competitor of Hotchkiss (Figure 19).[24]

The Hotchkiss Company received new impetus in 1851 when Hiram and his brother exhibited oil of peppermint at an international exhibition in London and received a prize medal and certificate signed by Prince Albert, husband of Queen Victoria. The certificate read as follows:[25]

Exhibition of the Works of Industry
of all Nations   1851

I hereby certify that her Majesty's Commisioners upon the
award of jurors have presented a Prize Medal to
Messrs. H. G. and L. B. Hotchkiss for
oil of Peppermint shown
in the Exhibition.
Exhibition Hyde Park, London, 15th Oct. 1851
Albert
Pres. of the Royal Commission

A similar award was received at the Exhibition held in New York city in 1853. Upon the bestowing of such honors the company name was changed to The Hotchkiss International Prize Medal Essential Oil Company (Figure 18) and the peppermint oil was packaged in beautiful, deep blue 21 ounce bottles with a flared lip manufactured by the Ely

Glass Works of Clyde, New York, and sealed with labels representing facsimiles of the various awards (Figure 16). From this time Hotchkiss concentrated on producing and marketing only New York oils.

Conclusion

As the middle years of the nineteenth century passed Lyons, New York, was the undisputed mint oil capital of the United States, and Hiram G. Hotchkiss reigned as its leader. He had firmly established an export market for a high quality product, had been instrumental in promoting effective new means of cultivation and processing essential oil plants, had become internationally renowned through his prize exhibits, and had demonstrated great sagacity in understanding and, to a certain extent, controlling the source of oil supply. His intense desire, however, following the monopoly to market only pure peppermint oil grown and distilled in Wayne County and area meant that much of the oil produced in Ohio, Michigan, and Indiana had to be handled through other outlets. This concentration, this dedication by Hotchkiss to his local region enabled the growers in western states to structure their marketing around new personalities and new leaders. In very short time the states of New York and Michigan were engaged in a great rivalry for supremacy in the mint oil market.

REFERENCES

[1]D. C. VanSlyck, "Cultivation of Peppermint," *Report of the Commissioner of Patents for the Year 1849,* U.S. House of Representatives, Executive Document No. 20, pp. 388-389, Part II, Agriculture, 1850. The letter from VanSlyck was dated November 28th, 1849, from Alloway, Wayne Co., N.Y. (p. 387).

[2]*Ibid.,* p. 389.

[3]*Ibid.*

[4]*History of Northeast Indiana,* vol. 1, p. 169, Lewis Publishing Co., Chicago, 1920.

[5]D. C. VanSlyck, *op. cit.,* p. 388.

[6]*Ibid.*

[7]G. W. Cowles (ed.), *Landmarks of Wayne County, New York,* Part 2, p. 29, D. Mason and Co., Syracuse, New York, 1895.

[8]*Ibid.*

[9]L. O'Connor, "Peppermint King of the World," *Yankee,* p. 37, April, 1958. See also H. Kraemer, "Michigan—An Important Source of Raw Vegetable Products," *21st Annual Report of the Michigan Academy of Science: 1919,* pp. 175-178, 1920.

[10]W. H. McIntosh, *History of Wayne County, New York,* facing p. 103, Everts, Ensign and Everts, Philadelphia, 1877.

[11]A deposit slip from this bank dated November 26, 1853(?), was found in the collection of the Hiram G. Hotchkiss Papers on file in the Library of Regional History, Syracuse University, New York. See: *Third and Fourth Annual*

Reports of the Curator, 1946-1948, pp. 30-31, and *Fifth and Sixth Annual Reports of the Curator*, 1948-1950, p. 43, for brief descriptions of the collection.

[12]*Moores Rural New-Yorker*, vol. 8, p. 214, July 4, 1857.

[13]From the Hotchkiss Papers, a letter to Dows and Cary dated Nov. 15, 1844.

[14]From a bill of sale in the Hotchkiss Papers dated February 15, 1847. Other early Wayne County and area mint growers mentioned in the Papers were Robert Sutton, Eli Middaugh, Isaac Corwin, Blackmer, Miller, Moseby, Timothy Brink, Maltby Clark, I. C. Force, Robert Reinhard, A. F. Galushka, David VanAuken, Jeremiah Beal, Ira Fenney, Elias Fenney, Seth Godfrey, Joel Burnett, James Colborne, Richard Jones, William Mentz, Joshua Jennings, B. P. Beardsley, Anson F. Leusch and Benjamin Vandemark (Hotchkiss Papers, August 30, 1845 to October 16, 1847).

[15]D. C. VanSlyck, *op. cit.*, p. 387; J. Sullivan (ed.), *History of New York State, 1523-1927*, vol. 2, p. 515, Lewis Historical Publishing Co. Inc., New York, 1927. It is believed that the Lewis County production was near the town of Lowville.

[16]*Ibid*; the Hotchkiss Papers, May 17, 1847.

[17]Letter in Hotchkiss Papers dated March 26, 1847, and May 17, 1847. An article in the *Western Argus* dated Sept. 1, 1847, stating that $200,000 had been paid for the mint manufacturing establishment in Palmyra, New York, was undoubtedly in error.

[18]Hotchkiss Papers, May 10, 1847.

[19]A copy of the letter dated June 15, 1847, is in the Hotchkiss Papers.

[20]Letters in Hotchkiss Papers dated May 17, 1847, and June 10, 1847.

[21]D. C. VanSlyck, *op. cit.*, p. 388.

[22]Letters from the Hotchkiss Papers dated Sept. 15 and Sept. 17, 1845.

[23]M. E. Oaks, *Phelpstown Footprints*, pp. 54-55, Carpenter-He Prints, Geneva, New York, 1962.

[24]L. Gaylord, *A Survey of the Peppermint Industry of Wayne County*, historical term paper, p. 34, on file in the Wayne County Historical Museum, Lyons, New York, 1965. A very detailed account of the industry with an excellent bibliography.

[25]The original certificate hangs on the wall of the Hotchkiss Company office in Lyons, New York.

Chapter 5.

The Great Rivalry: New York vs. Michigan

Developments in Michigan

The Hotchkiss-Patterson monopoly had given great impetus to the mint industry in Michigan, that state being the only considerable source of supply during the monopoly years of 1847 and 1848. Several factors, however, limited the expansion of mint cultivation in Michigan to such a degree that the growers were not successful in ousting New York from the business.

One serious problem was a pesky weed known variously as mare's tail, fieldbroom, or fireweed. The fireweed spread its root network in such a way that it paralleled that of mint and cultivation necessitated considerable chopping with a resultant damage to the mint crop. Many growers simply let the weed grow, cut it with the mint, and distilled it. As a result the bulk of the Michigan product contained a large proportion of fireweed oil.[1] Certain unscrupulous growers frequently distilled the fireweed and used it along with turpentine, alcohol, and certain fixed oils "in adulterating their Mint oil."[2] This led very early to the general opinion that the "western" oils were inferior to those produced in New York, an opinion that was probably correct since Hotchkiss had always emphasized very clean cultivation to keep weeds out of the mint fields thus insuring the purity of the product. The New York mint oil, therefore, was preferred in the brokerage trade and, despite the monopoly, continued to be foremost in demand.

An additional disadvantage for Michigan growers was marketing. The bulk of the production moved through the city of New York into the foreign trade. The proximity of the Lyons area gave a decided advantage in shipment because of the Erie Canal. Even with the advent of the railroads the New York growers continued to enjoy this advantage.

Steam Distillation

Growers in both states continued to search for more efficient means of distilling the mint oil. There must have been a good deal of communication between the eastern and western growers because the application of steam to the distillation process was developed in both New York and Michigan about the same year, 1846.

> As the area under cultivation increased, the need for better appliances was felt, and Michigan's genius gave to the world the greatest invention of the century in the distillation of essential oil plants,—the Steam Distillery—by which the rate of distillation was increased from about fifteen pounds to over one hundred pounds of essential oil per day.[3]

The same development was described as follows in New York.[4]

> Several years since, the only method of extracting the oil then known was by distilling the herb in a copper kettle, or boiler, and condensing in the usual manner; a slow and tedious process, by which about 12 or 15 lbs. of oil could be separated in a day. But recently steam, that powerful agent, which has wrought such immense changes in our social and national economy, has been applied to this subject with its usual attendant success. The present method consists in the use of a common steamboiler, of the capacity of from 100 to 150 gallons, from which the steam is conveyed by conductors into large wooden air-tight tubs, of 200 gallons capacity, containing the dried herb; from which it is conveyed, charged with the volatile principle of the plant, into a water-vat, containing a condenser. The water collected at the extremity of the condenser, although it does not readily commingle with the oil, is highly tinctured with it, and is used to feed the boiler. Two tubs are necessary, in order that when the "charge" is being worked off in one, the other can be refilled. The oil is then to be filtered and is ready for market. The expense of a distillery is estimated at $150 which, with the labor of two men, and a cord of dry wood, will run 41 lbs. of oil per day. The usual price of distilling is twenty-five cents per pound.

The new process was further described in Michigan.[5]

> In the year 1846 a radical improvement in the form of distillery was effected in Michigan by substituting for the "Copper kettle still" large wooden vats with steam tight covers operating upon hinges, allowing them to be opened and closed at pleasure. A short distance above the solid bottom upon which the dried plants were closely packed after which the cover was closed down, distilling being effected by the ingress of steam under the perforated bottom by means of a pipe with valves connected with a steam generating boiler placed some distance away. Two of these vats were placed in each distillery. With this improvement it was possible to

keep continuous fires in the furnace, also to allow distillation to progress constantly, as one vat could be filled with plants and made ready for distillation while the other was being distilled and the change to fresh charge could be made instantly by means of the valves in the steam pipe. This system allows a more uniform distillation since the ingress of the steam could be regulated so that a temporary variation of the fire made little difference only in the speed of distillation. Under the new system economies resulted also in many other ways, and the yield of a single distillery increased from fifteen pounds to about fifty or seventy pounds of oil per day as well as producing a higher quality, since the danger of forming empyreumatic products by direct contact with the fire was eliminated.

The development of the steam distillery, one of the most significant technological advancements in the commercial mint industry, enabled acreage to be expanded considerably since growers now had the means to efficiently process large crops (Figure 30). The distillation of mint in Michigan in 1858 was described in great detail by Frederick Stearns, founder of the Stearns pharmaceutical company in Detroit.[6]

The apparatus used in distilling the oil is—
1st. A boiler with a flat bottom of boiler iron, and a circular top of sheet iron. The boiler is about nine feet in length, and thirty inches in diameter, with three flues six inches each in diameter. The boiler is set upon a brick arch, which receives the fuel.
2nd. A well and hand-pump to supply the boiler and other apparatus hereinafter described.
3rd. A round tub, made of pine or whitewood staves, hooped with iron bands; the staves from one and a half to two inches in diameter. The tub is set up from the ground and from three to six inches, on bricks or wooden blocks; one half or one third of the top, or head, is constructed with the tub—that is, it is set in a groove in the staves like a barrel head, leaving an aperture of half or two-thirds of the circumference of the top. To this apperture is fitted a movable lid, which shuts down tightly, and can be, when shut down, made steamtight by means of oakum stuffing.
4th. A cooler; being a large tub, set two feet from the ground, filled with water, and containing a worm of tinned-iron about one hundred feet along, the lower end of which projects through one side of the cooler, about three inches from the bottom; the upper end of the worm connects by a pipe of similar material, with the top of the first described tub, which tub is called "the steam tub," or "still."
5th. A receiver of tin, placed under the opening of the lower end of the worm. The receiver is eighteen inches deep, and ten inches in diameter; from the bottom of this there issues a discharging pipe at an angle of about 25 degrees, similar to the spout of the receiver. A tub or pipe extends from the top of the boiler to the bottom of the steam tub, or still.
The whole structure is generally covered with a temporary shed, for protection against the weather—this covering being open upon the sides. Underneath the covering is erected a plank floor, twelve or fifteen feet square, to receive the Mint. This floor stands at a level with the top of the steam tub, or still.
After the boiler has been supplied with water, the fire is started in the arch, the Mint has been drawn in from the cock, and deposited on the

plank floor, from whence it is pitched with a hay fork into the still, and packed down as it is thrown in, by one of the hands, who goes into the tub for this purpose, and packs it with his feet until the still can receive no more. This is called a "charge." The movable lid is then adjusted and the steam applied from the boiler. The essential oil of the Mint passes with the steam into the worm; is condensed with it,* (*By exhausting each charge as rapidly as possible, by using steam under as high a pressure as the strength of the boiler will warrant, it is found that though the yield of oil is lessened, it is nearly colorless and of a firm odor.) and passes into the receiver, where it rises to the top of the water. As the receiver gets filled, the water constantly escapes by the spout, while the oil is dipped off, and placed in cans ready to receive it. When the charge is exhausted, and yields no more oil, the steam is shut off; the lid of the steam tub, or still, thrown open, and the reeking contents removed with hay forks. This is called "Mint straw." Horned cattle and sheep are fond of it, and will subsist upon it through the winter. It is thrown into large piles about the Mint still, after being dried, or else drawn into barns, where it lies till fed to the cattle in the winter.

The oil cans are made of the best tinned-iron, after the model of the tin powder cans, and contain each twenty pounds of oil. In these cans the oil is shipped, the small aperture at the top being soldered. Three, four, or five cans are placed in a case, the tops of which are sloped like a house roof.

This description of the method of extracting the mint oil could be, with certain modern modifications, equally applicable in the twentieth century. The "house roof" cans, known as demi-johns, were commonly used on mint farms for nearly 100 years (Figure 31).

Mint Production Costs

As the possibility of handling larger acreages increased mint growers began paying more attention to their production costs, a necessity due to the wide variation of prices paid for the oil. The cost of growing an acre of mint for three years in the 1840's in New York was calculated as follows:[7]

First Year	
Rent of an acre of land for one year	$ 8
1 day plough and drag, 1 hand and team	2
½ " furrowing, digging roots, one hand and horse	1
3 days planting, at 75 cents	2.25
2 " dressing with hoe, at 75 cents	1.50
2 " with cultivator and hoe, 1.00	2
2 days with cultivator and hoe (3d dressing)	1.50
1½ " cutting new mint, at 75 cts.	1.50
Curing and drawing to distillery	1.50
Distilling 18 lbs. oil, at 25 cts.	4.50
Can for oil	.25
	$25.63

	Second Year	
Rent of one acre of land for one year		$ 8
Cutting one acre of old mint		.75
Curing and hauling to distillery		1.50
Distilling 14 lbs. oil, at 25 cts.		3.50
Can for oil		.25
		14.00

	Third Year	
Rent of an acre of land for one year		$ 8
Cutting, curing, &c.		2.25
Distilling 8 lbs. of oil, at 25 cts, and can		2.25
		12.50

Total expenses for three years	$52.13
Forty pounds of oil, at $1.37½ per lb.	55.00
Deduct expenses	52.13
Net profit	$ 2.87

The New York writer went on further to explain that:

in the above estimate I have omitted the expense of roots, for the reason that the crop will yield as many as are required for planting. The price of roots is about 50 cents per square rod, and if they are in demand, the profit of the crop will be greatly enhanced by selling them at that, or even a lower price.

It will be readily perceived that the culture of peppermint promises no great return of profit in sections of country where land is valuable, and where the expense of production is nearly double what it is in newly-settled districts. It is a fact that in Michigan, and other Western States, the actual expense of production is about one-half less than the above estimate, and the yield is a fourth greater.[8]

The New York writer's assessment of the "western" situation was slightly generous as the following description of production costs of mint in Michigan in 1858, given by Stearns, indicated.

There are now in this State about 2100 acres employed in producing the Mint plant, all of which, except about one hundred acres are in the county of St. Joseph. It produces in oil, per acre, as follows:

Maximum   20 lb. av.
Minimum   2   ″
Average   7   ″

In England, at Mitcham, where the Mint plant is raised in richly manured land, the average yield is stated to be 17½ lbs. to the acre. Upon the plantations of the Messrs. Hotchkiss in Western New York, the average yield is said to be 20 lbs.

The average product per annum in this State has been as follows, from the commencement to the present time:

Maximum   30,000 lbs.
Minimum   8,000   ″
Average   15,000   ″

The crops vary, for several reasons. That of 1855 was large, being 30,000 pounds; the dry season following, it was reduced one sixth, i.e., to 25,000 pounds; and the severe cold of the winter of '56 and '57, by killing the roots, reduced the crop to one half that of '55, being variously estimated from 12,000 to 15,000 pounds.

The prices obtained by producers of the oil have been as follows:

Highest price per lb. $4.00
Lowest price per lb.   1.25
Average price per lb.   2.37

There having been as much oil sold at $1.25 as at $4.00, the average is taken between $1.75 and $3.00, the usual prices. The prices ranged somewhat as following: 1844 to 1847, at $2.50; 1847 to 1852, at $1.50; 1853, at $2.00; 1854, at $4.00; 1855, at $3.50; 1856, at $2.50; 1857, the crop of which is yet partially unsold, from $2.00 to $2.50.

The land with its improvements, is valued from $30 to $35 per acre. The cost of cultivating a Mint field the first year is $22 per acre; and for the succeeding three years, $5 a year per acre.

The following statement will show an approximation to the amount of capital invested in this industry in our State, and its returns:

2100 acres of Land and Improvements are valued at	$75,000
Total average value of Oil to producers	37,500
Total cost of Production, including interest upon $75,000 at 7 per cent	24,000
Profit to producers	13,500

This profit is over one-third the receipts for the oil, and 18 per cent upon the capital employed. Assuming that there are 500 acres in Mint plant in Western New York, and 500 acres in Ohio, which, I presume, is nearly correct, at least a low estimate, and that the average product of the New York plantations be 12 lbs. of oil to the acre, while that of Ohio is reckoned at 8 lbs., the total annual product of these States will be 10,000 lbs., valued at $25,000—making the average value of the whole crop of oil of Peppermint produced annually in the United States to be over $63,000 to its producers.[9]

The figures presented for New York and Michigan partially account for the rise of Michigan to a position of importance in mint production despite the fact that there was a premium placed on the New York oil. In 1849 the New York grower could produce an acre of mint for three years at an expense of $52.13. Nearly ten years later, in 1858, a Michigan grower could produce mint for 3 years for only $32 per acre. With slightly higher yields, even at a price disadvantage, the Michigan grower could make more money than his counterpart in New York. As the inevitable realities of cost vs. profit became increasingly apparent New York growers slowly began to turn attention to more profitable products. The commercial mint industry had become part and parcel of the American capitalistic system.

Albert M. Todd

The problem of producing high quality mint oil continued to plague Michigan producers. Not only was there a problem with weeds, but oil dealers, once they had pure mint oil in their hands, commonly mixed it with other substances in order to increase their profit. Japanese mint oil became a major adulterant and a spurious brand of peppermint oil reported to be from Evart, Michigan, appeared on the market containing 50 percent turpentine.[10] The Michigan farmers were at the mercy of the dealers since no Hotchkiss had emerged in the new state to buy the oil, package it, and guarantee its purity. This situation was soon remedied.

Albert M. Todd was born on June 3, 1850, the last of ten children in the family of Alfred Todd (Figure 24). In 1838 the Todd family had moved from Marcellus, New York, to a 45 acre farm near the village of Nottawa in St. Joseph County, Michigan, where Alfred proceeded to support his large family near the peppermint district. Albert graduated from Sturgis High School and, for a short time, attended Northwestern University where he majored in chemistry. As a result of illness he was forced to drop out of college and, at the age of 17, made an extended trip throughout Europe.[11]

The following year, 1868, Albert returned home and, in a small way, entered into the growing of peppermint and distilling the oil with his older brother Oliver H. Todd. As a chemist Albert was seriously interested in the distillation process as well as the problem of detecting adulterated oils. Noting that the increased rapidity of distilling by steam was not followed by a corresponding advance in quality, Todd commented that

> no true system of tests was known by which the quality of the oil could be established, and weedy, resinous, or adulterated oil continued to be the rule. Seeing the need for an advancement of the standard, the present manufacturer, (who planted his first fields in the year 1868), commenced his labors for the accomplishment of this purpose; the result being that a system of tests was established, and a process of steam rectification, with elaborate appliances was perfected, for bringing the crude oil to a uniform state of purity and excellence.[12]

Todd claimed that the New York oils were bottled directly from the still and, therefore, could not be as pure as those processed by his rectification method which he described as follows:[13]

> for the purpose of rendering the oil of absolute purity, and the highest possible concentration, aroma, solubility, and therapeutic value, and freeing it from any foreign substances contained therein, it is placed in special

refining stills, (perfected and controlled by the manufacturer), by the means of which fresh steam is diffused through the oil in numerous jets, evaporating the most valuable and aromatic portions. This steam is generated at a distance from the refineries, so that no direct heat is used, and by this process the scorching of the oil or formation of any empyreumatic product is absolutely impossible. The supply of steam admitted and the consequent force of distillation is regulated by valves controlled by the operator. The first fraction is distilled very slowly, so that any foreign hydrocarbons present are eliminated. Afterward the pure aromatic essential oil is volatilized, the speed of distillation now being increased. After the aromatic oil has been recovered there remains an oleo-resin, (the bitter and insoluble principle), which is cast away. This in old and oxidized oil sometimes is found to the extent of over 25 per cent.

The refined essential oil thus obtained has the pure and sweet odor of its true plant in a high degree, is of the greatest strength, unusual solubility, brilliant and limpid, and is absolutely pure.

After several years Todd bought out the interests of his brother, established the "Steam Refined Essential Oil Works" at Nottawa and devoted his attention to processing peppermint, spearmint, and other essential oils. In 1875 he began marketing his oils under the name "Crystal White" produced by "Albert M. Todd, Distilling Chemist" (Figure 25). He also developed, from peppermint oil, crystals of menthol which he marketed under the trade name "Pip-Menthol." Although the product never successfully competed with Japanese produced menthol Todd converted a good deal of the 40,000 pounds of oil he purchased in 1886 into these menthol crystals.

Very active in the chemical and pharmaceutical associations, Todd traveled widely and contributed numerous papers and articles to professional journals.[14] In June, 1886, he distributed a brochure describing twelve different methods of testing peppermint oil for such qualities as odor and taste, specific gravity, solubility, presence of alcohol, turpentine, erigeron and other foreign contaminants, and adulteration with penny-royal and Japanese mint. His early emphasis was on research but, as his reputation became more widely known and the business expanded, increasing attention was paid to buying oil from other growers and marketing in New York. It was largely through the professional endeavors of Todd that one of the major problems of the Michigan mint industry, reservations concerning the purity and reliability of the oil, became resolved.

The Centennial Exposition

The Centennial Exposition of the United States, marking 100 years of national independence, was held in Philadelphia in 1876. Five samples of peppermint oil and three samples of spearmint oil were submitted for judging. Hiram G. Hotchkiss had offered samples of peppermint, spearmint, wintergreen, sassafras, wormwood, and tansy oils. In addition, there were two other submissions of peppermint oil from Wayne County, New York, Hale and Parshall, and L. B. Hotchkiss, Hiram's brother. A. M. Todd submitted a sample of "Crystal White Peppermint Oil" and a dish of special peppermint lozenges which he had developed. Other exhibitors from Michigan were J. H. Gardner and Wolf Brothers and Keech, both of Centreville, St. Joseph County.[15]

The judges of essential oils, a distinguished panel of foreign dignitaries,[16] granted five awards "For the Beauty and Purity of Their Products." The awards, including medals and certificates, were granted to Hotchkiss, Todd, Wolf Brothers and Keech, and the additional two Wayne County growers.[17] This recognition firmly established Michigan oil as being comparable in quality with the finest of that from New York.

Production Developments in Other Areas

As Albert M. Todd attempted to move Michigan mint oils into the same markets as those dominated by Hiram G. Hotchkiss, the industry expanded to some extent in new areas.

Following the monopoly the industry in northeastern Ohio continued to remain small. Production did, however, last for a time in Lorain County where "some" peppermint oil was produced in 1850,[18] and in Lake County which reported $1,000 to $2,000 worth in 1853.[19] A "little" was produced in Wood County near Bowling Green in 1850,[20] and "very little" in Ross County near Chillicothe in 1852.[21] Other than the references to 1,000 pounds produced in Ohio in 1849,[22] and an estimate of 500 acres in the state in 1858, producing 4,000 pounds of oil,[23] nothing further is known about mint production in Ohio during the nineteenth century.

By 1887 there had been a number of unsuccessful attempts to introduce peppermint cultivation into other states, including California, Texas, Kansas, Iowa, Illinois, and Minnesota.[24] In 1889 the Colorado Agricultural Experiment Station announced plans for experimentation on the culture and distillation of peppermint[25] but apparently the proposal, the first announcement of interest by an agricultural college, was never implemented.

Mint had been grown continuously in northern Indiana since 1846 but production must have remained very meager since the state is seldom mentioned in the literature of the period. There must have been some production in New Jersey since a researcher in 1922 obtained samples of oil reported to have been grown and distilled in that state in 1874.[26]

The most notable expansion of the peppermint industry during this period took place in Mississippi.[27] The obtaining of oil from mint plants in the southern states was mentioned as early as 1869 when it was noted that "the essence and mint water can be extracted in any quantity."[28] But the first successful commercial development came in Clay County, Mississippi, and had its origins in 1879. In the fall of that year M. B. Hillyard of Clay County had been invited to speak at a meeting of the agricultural society of St. Joseph County, Michigan. While there, Hillyard had been greatly impressed by the activities of the society president, D. D. Antes, a peppermint grower. Hillyard resolved to employ Antes in his work to "develop East Mississippi"[29] and returned with him over the Mobile and Ohio Railroad. When Antes noticed that peppermint, spearmint, tansy, hoarhound, and other herbs grew profusely in the wild in Clay County he concluded the area offered great possibilities for the development of peppermint culture.

A partnership was formed with three men in Aberdeen, Mississippi, and Antes returned to Michigan, bought a carload of roots, and had them sent south. The articulate Hillyard described the reaction of the Michigan growers as follows:

> the wiseacres said mint could not be raised in Mississippi; they had tried it in Kansas, California, and Texas, and said that it would not "oil." But Mr. Antes had faith, and in February, 1880, formed a partnership with G. V. and W. Young of Waverly, Miss., and sent down another carload of roots. The mint raisers in Michigan got alarmed, notwithstanding all their affected unfaith in the experiment, and organized to prevent any further deportation of roots.[30]

The roots were a long time on the way and the time for planting in Mississippi was inopportune so that the first oil was not produced until 1881. This success, which had been "derided" in Michigan, caused Hillyard to laud Antes in most eloquent terms.

> . . .mint culture in East Mississippi is a demonstrated success. Mr. Antes is the founder of a new industry here. His success is as certain to work a revolution in the place of mint raising, as the world is to endure long enough for the revolution to be wrought.[31]

The enterprising Antes planted peppermint on "the sandy loams of the Tombigbee Valley, the stiff prairies, sandy prairies, and mulberry hummocks."[32] He instructed Negro laborers in the techniques and organized some to raise it on shares. Antes discovered that, on certain lands, yields of 25 pounds to the acre could be taken from a second cutting of mint hay.

Hillyard had obviously taken a long look at the situation and "visited the most celebrated distillers and refiners in the world."[33] Noting that the world consumption of peppermint oil was about 100,000 pounds annually and brought prices averaging $2.50 to $3.00 per pound, he concluded that Mississippi growers could sell their oil for as little as $1.50 per pound and still make considerable profit. "Mississippi will soon raise so much that the price will fall so low that New York and Michigan will have to go out of the business."[34]

Unfortunately for the "development of East Mississippi" Hillyard proved to be a poor prophet and the revolution of Mr. Antes never took place. Just how long the cultivation went on in Clay County is not known but commercial peppermint production in Mississippi was never important. A sample of oil from the state, however, was reported in 1893[35], and a 1917 description of the American industry listed Mississippi as a producing region.[36]

Despite the prodigious efforts of Hillyard, Antes, and peppermint cultivators in other areas, the chief producing regions continued to be western New York and southwestern Michigan.

Production in New York and Michigan

During the latter half of the nineteenth century the peppermint and spearmint production lead see-sawed back and forth between New York and Michigan. The vagaries of the weather and marketplace caused growers to alternately increase and decrease acreage and the two states continued to vie for supremacy.

Mint production in Michigan continued to be restricted primarily to St. Joseph County. In 1850 a town in the county had gained some notoriety for having nearly 960 acres in cultivation from which was earned $16,775. There were more than 100 distilleries in 1858 and the county produced, in 1864, 10,782 barrels[37] and a local agricultural expert lamented that so much land was in peppermint culture that improvements in stock raising and other departments had been seriously retarded.[38] The same year growers in the Wayne County, New York, area had sold between 9,000 and 10,000 pounds of peppermint oil.[39]

The year of 1866 was an extremely bad season in Michigan due to excessive winterkilling, the crop was estimated at half off, and production dropped to 9,000 pounds.[40] A few years later, by 1870, production had been extended due to a price rise to Cass, Ionia, and Wayne counties, and there were 44 peppermint distilleries in the state, 39 of which were in St. Joseph County.[41] The production area continued to expand. In 1874 peppermint was also being grown in Hillsdale and

Berrien counties and shortly afterward in Kalamazoo County. The state had 1,969 acres under cultivation in 1883 and an Association of Peppermint Growers had been originated.[42]

Between 1870 and 1880 New York enjoyed a very clear production lead. According to Hotchkiss New York growers marketed 51,365 pounds of mint oil in 1871,[43] an enormous production for that day. Michigan growers had marketed nearly 24,000 pounds in 1870,[44] but were producing only one-fifth of the world's supply of 90,000 pounds in 1876.[45] New York, at this time, must have enjoyed a comfortable production margin.

This sudden spurt of production in New York was a vigorous response to high prices. In 1868 Wayne County oil was being bought for $4.75 per pound and many growers were holding out for $5.00; an account of that period made note of the high prices:[46]

> besides the Hotchkiss brothers, many local farmers grew and processed some mint. Theron vanAuken's account book (owned by Mrs. Willie Kregloh) tells his peppermint story. Theron's home is now that of Mrs. Roy Facer, Fort Hill Rd. In Sept. 1867 he received $440 for 88 pounds of oil—also paid $18.50 for distilling. Apparently it was not just then the custom to "toll" a crop—that is for the distiller to keep a set part of the oil as his payment. In 1868 Mr. vanAuken sold 140 pounds for $632. The following year he made $88 on sale of peppermint roots. By then he had his own still for which the old book records his purchases, from brass faucet to boiler. In the fall of 1870 Theron distilled for eighteen neighbors—for Ringer, Blount, Warner, Dimock, Gates, Griffith, Severance, Whitbeck, Crittenden, and others. 1878 found him still steeped in mint, his own and others'. Cooper, Crandall, Heater and Jameson were customers; John Cross, east of Oak Corners, drew his loads of mint hay up the west road to vanAuken's still.

As a result of Todd's efforts in Michigan, however, western oil became increasingly in demand, prices fell, and New York growers, by 1890, were again turning their interests to other crops.

Mint Cultivation

Much of the discussion so far has centered upon the American production of peppermint. The spearmint market was always quite limited but the crop was generally grown to some extent wherever peppermint was cultivated. Spearmint was being distilled at Ashfield, Massachusetts, by 1830[47] and was introduced into New York about 1846.[48] Its appearance in Michigan was first noted in 1876 when J. H. Gardner of St. Joseph County exhibited a sample at the Centennial Exposition in Philadelphia,[49] but it probably was grown long before that. One farmer, noting the cultivation of the two mints in Ontario

County, New York, in 1879, presented the interesting hypothesis that ". . .mint oil is an original ingredient in the soil"[50] which was removed with the first crop, and this explained why yields declined in succeeding years.

It is doubtful if many mint growers believed in this hypothesis but the fact that mint yields declined after the first year was true. In the early days it had been the custom to keep the fields in mint for about three years in New York and five years in Michigan, a practice still in use in 1866.[51] By 1887 the two or three year cycle had been generally adopted in Michigan where mint was rotated with clover, corn, wheat, and potatoes.[52] Yields in the state were from 10 to 35 pounds to the acre, averaging 15 to 25, comparable to those in New York about the same period.[53] In both states cultivation was generally found unprofitable after three years because of the weeding problem as well as decreased yields.

In 1860 Hotchkiss had over 100 acres of peppermint near Lyons, one-fifth of which was on upland soil,[54] and many growers in New York, by 1869, were rotating mint fields after only a single year's production.[55] The rotation procedure, necessary in both Michigan and New York, had acted since the earliest days to limit an individual grower's acreage since the amount of rotational land on the small Middlewest and eastern farms was not unlimited. In Michigan, although acreage varied considerably from farm to farm, from five to forty acres was the norm.[56]

The major production area in Michigan continued to be St. Joseph County and the industry had spread considerably since the early days. An English visitor to the area in 1848, unaware that a monopoly was then in existence and the Michigan fields were the only major ones in the country, described his visit.[57]

> There is considerable peppermint near Constantine. They get from four to six pounds of oil to the acre. The first year after the roots are set out the crop is small but the second and third it yields abundantly so that they mow it as we would clover. The mill used in its manufacture costs about one hundred dollars.

Production in the county spread outward from Florence Township and was soon found on the burr oak soils in most areas (Map 6). Peppermint was introduced into Sherman Township in 1846 by Eric Jones who built a distillery a year later;[58] into Lockport Township near Three Rivers in 1848 by D. Francisco;[59] and into Mendon Township in 1856 by S. D. Angevine.[60] In 1877 some of the largest mint growers in the county were listed in a local history as follows:[61]

Map 6. Townships of St. Joseph County, Michigan, showing the towns associated with the production of peppermint and spearmint oil since the first plantings on the White Pigeon Prairie in 1835.

Lockport Township, John F. and Daniel Wolf, George Keech, Jr.; Florence Township, William, George, and Frank Roys, William Hagerman; Colon Township, George Engle, George Teller, Lowder Brothers, Wagner, Bastian, Coney; Mendon Township, Aaron P. Emery (Figure 26); Sherman Township, Charles Jones; Nottawa Township, Robert Schermerhorn; Fabius Township, Charles Sholl. Other large growers of the time were Henry Hall of Three Rivers and Todd at Nottawa.

Todd did have considerable competition. H. D. Cushman of Three Rivers, George Keech of Centreville, and Aaron P. Emery of Mendon had all developed rather extensive mint oil buying operations and the latter was also a large grower. An account of Emery, who had started peppermint growing in 1867, listed his business accomplishments with the same relish as those of his physiognomy.[62]

He purchased and sold in 1878 and 1879, 15,000 pounds (peppermint oil), and the year following probably came up to the same figure. He also deals in other essential oils. His operations extend not only throughout the U.S., but to all parts of the world, London, and other principal cities of the Eastern Hemisphere. His long experience in the business has made him an expert, while his remarkable business talents attract more than passing attention. He is strong, physically, and has a large and active brain.

Keech, who with the Wolf Brothers, had exhibited a sample of peppermint oil at the U.S. Centennial Exposition, was described as a "large wholesale dealer and has been established since 1863. His business has steadily increased, and he is classed by the New York jobbers as one of the solid men of his section in that enterprise."[63]

Mint Technology

Improvements in mint technology continued (Figure 29). Henry Hall of St. Joseph County, Michigan, was among the first in the Middlewest to adopt the rectangular distilling condenser (Figure 32).[64] Instead of having the condenser coiled in a water tub he had the pipes arranged in longitudinal sections about 14 feet long, underneath one another, and tapering from about six inches in diameter at the top to two inches at the bottom. A large trough with a perforated bottom, filled with water, was placed above the condenser and the liquid allowed to continuously pour down across the pipes thus cooling the distillate.[65]

An interesting case of unfriendly competition involving the manufacture of distilling tubs developed in New York in 1869. J. R. VanMarter and M. S. Pomeroy of Lyons were engaged in the manufacture of essential oil distilleries. They had made improvements on a distilling tub patented by B. P. VanMarter in 1868 which development caused the latter VanMarter to warn all parties in a Lyons newspaper:[66]

Caution
My Patent gives to me the EXCLUSIVE RIGHT OF USING RUBBER in distilling essential oils. Parties using any other patent will do well to be secured, as I shall hold any one using it to answer in heavy damages before the United States Court.

Pomeroy, in the same paper, replied scornfully:[67]

B. P. VanMarter claims the "exclusive right" of using Rubber in distilling Essential Oils. It is one thing to claim and another thing to have. Here is just what the Patent Office gave him: The right of employment of a rubber ring secured within a groove in the underside of the cover, so that when pressure is applied upon the upper end of the staves a steam-tight joint is easily produced. Is there anything "exclusive" in the above? If any one can see it, I confess they can see more than I can. I am contracting every

Figure 1. The first known drawing of a spearmint plant, identified as *Salvia Romana*, Speare Mint, by John Gerard in 1597. (J. Gerarde, *The Herball or Generall Historie of Plantes*, p., 552, J. Norton, London, 1597.)

Figure 2. The first known use of the word "Pepper-Mint" in the English language, by John Ray in 1696. (J. Raii, *Synopsis Methodica Stirpium Britannicarum*, 2nd edition, p. 124, S. Smith and B. Walford, London, 1696.)

Figure 3. The American peppermint plant, the common commercial variety in the United States during the nineteenth century. (C. F. Millspaugh, *Medicinal Plants: An Illustrated and Descriptive Guide to Plants Indigenous to and Naturalized in the U.S. which are Used in Medicine*, vol. 2, Plate 116, J. C. Yorston and Co., Philadelphia, 1892.)

Figure 4. The first known drawings of peppermint plants, those of James Petiver in 1713. (J. Petiver, *Herbarii Britannici Raji Catalogus cum Iconibus*, p. 31, London, 1713; taken from a reprinted edition, J. Petiveri, *Opera Historiam Naturalem Spectantia*, vol. 2, no page number, J. Millan, London, 1764.)

Figure 5. The American (Native) spearmint and the Scotch spearmint plants. The American variety was being commercially cultivated in Massachusetts by 1830. The Scotch variety was introduced into the United States as a commercial plant about 1908. Both types are cultivated today. (A. F. Sievers and E. C. Stevenson, *Mint Farming*, Farmers' Bulletin No. 1988, p. 7, USDA, April, 1948.)

Figure 6. The Black Mitcham peppermint plant, introduced into the United States about 1883, and the commercial variety cultivated today. (A. F. Sievers and E. C. Stevenson, *Mint Farming*, Farmers' Bulletin No. 1988, p. 5, USDA, April, 1948.)

Figure 7. A metal trunk of the type carried by the itinerant peddlers who set forth from Ashfield, Massachusetts, selling peppermint, spearmint, and other oils, and notions. The trunk is in the Ashfield Museum.

Figure 8. A metal receiving can used during the prosperous days of peppermint and spearmint production in the early nineteenth century at Ashfield, Massachusetts. The can, in the Ashfield Museum, bears the following label: "Tin still, given by Col. Ephraim Williams to Old Academy Museum."

Figure 9. A "Pepper Mint" oil bottle found in an Indian grave near Galesburg, Michigan, and dated about 1820. The oil was bottled by a British firm and probably distributed by early peddlers. The bottle is Item no. 60:490 in the Kalamazoo Public Museum, Kalamazoo, Michigan.

Figure 10. First known mention of American peppermint oil, in an advertisement by John Hart in 1800. (*The Sun*, p. 1, Pittsfield, Massachusetts, December 9, 1800.)

Figure 11. A "burr oak opening" in St. Joseph County, Michigan, where the first permanent plantings of peppermint were made in the state in 1838. The burr oak soils were brought into use since the prairie soils, first planted to peppermint in 1835, had not proved successful. (L. C. Wheeting and S. G. Bergquist *Soil Survey of St. Joseph County, Michigan*, Plate 1, USDA, 1921.)

Figure 12. A harvested peppermint field about 1890 near the Canandaigua Outlet at Lyons, New York, showing the cut hay in "cocks" prior to distillation.

Figure 13. First known mention of "Spear Mint" in the United States, by John Josselyn in 1672. (J. Josselyn, *New-Englands Rarities Discovered*, p. 89, G. Widdowes, London, 1672.)

Figure 14. Pages from the Jasper Bement ledger book. The ledger records the sale of oils and notions to the itinerant peddlers who figured so prominently in the early mint industry at Ashfield, Massachusetts. The ledger book is in the Ashfield Museum.

Figure 15. An early drawing of field distillation of various herbs in Europe. (H. Brunnschweig, *Liber de Arte Distillandi*, title page, J. Grueninger, Strassburg, 1500.)

Figure 16. An early 21 ounce bottle of H. G. Hotchkiss peppermint oil showing the label facsimiles of the many awards and medals.

Figure 17. Hiram G. Hotchkiss (1810-1898), the peppermint king of New York State, about 1890.

3 *Saluia Romana.*
Speare Mint.

Figure 1

Figure 2

5. Mentha ſpicis brevioribus & habitioribus, foliis Menthæ fuſcæ, ſapore fervido Piperis. *Pepper-Mint found by Dr.Eales*
in Hartfordſhire, *and communicated to us*; *ſince by Mr.* Dale *in*
Eſſex.

Folia Menthæ fuſcæ ſive vulgaris *Park.* folia valde refe-
runt, majora tamen ſunt & brevi lanugine hirſuta, ſpicæ in
ſummis caulibus & ramulis breves, laxiores, rubentes. To-
ta planta ſapore eſt acri & fervido Piperis.

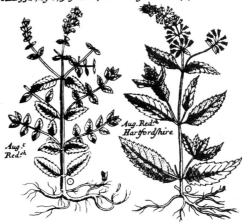

9 ESSEX Pepper MINT   10 EALES Pepper MINT
RAY 53 2 7. Syn. 79. 5. ed. 124. 2 RAY Syn. edit. 124. 5.

Figure 3

Figure 4

Figure 5

Scotch   Native

Figure 6

Figure 7

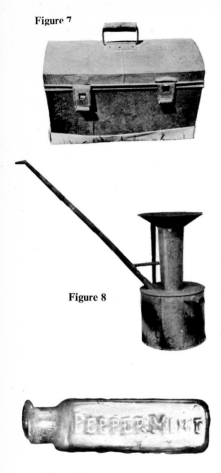

Figure 8

Figure 10

Diftillery & Brewery,

One mile Eaft of the MEETING HOUSE
LANESBOR UGH—

WHERE may be had, Beer
of the beft quality by the Hogf-
head, Barrel, or lefs quantity, as may fuit
the purchafer. *Alfo*, Eflence of Pepper
Mint, *American* and *Englifh*, warranted
genuine, in patent vials by the fingle, dozen, grofs or thoufand. Mint Cordial by
the Gallon.

Barley, Ryë, Indian Corn,
and Hops received in payment, and a
generous price given. Malt conftantly
on hand to be exchanged for faid articles
—Hams are taken in and fmoked in the
beft order, by the public's humble fer-
vant,

JOHN HART

N. B. Cafh paid for HOPS.

Lanefborough, Dec. 9, 1800.

Figure 9

Figure 11

Figure 12

Figure 13

New-Englands Rarities. 89

with a little Sugar and Spice, and so serve it to the Table in deep Basons, and it is altogether as good as a White-pot.

For People weakned with long Sicknefs.

It exceedingly nourisheth and strengthens people weakned with long Sicknefs.

Sometimes they make Water Gruel with it, and sometimes thicken their Flesh Broth either with this or *Homminey*, if it be for Servants.

Spear Mint.
Rew, will hardly grow.
Fetherfew prospereth exceedingly.
Southern Wood, is no Plant for this Country. Nor,
Rosemary. Nor
Bayes.
White Satien groweth pretty well, so doth
Lavender Cotton. But
Lavender is not for the climate.
Penny Royal.
Smalledge.
Ground Ivy, or *Ale Hoof.*
Gilly Flowers will continue two Years.
Fennel

Figure 14

Liber de arte distillandi. de Simplicibus.

Das buch der rechten kunst
zü distilieren die eintzige ding

von Hieronymo Brunschwygk/Bürtig vñ wund artzot der keiserlichē fryē statt straßburg.

un getruckt durch den wohlgeachte Johannem grueninger zu Strassburg
in den achte tag des meyen als man zelt von der geburt Christi
funfzehnhundert. Lob sy got. Anno 1500.

Figure 15

Figure 16

Figure 17

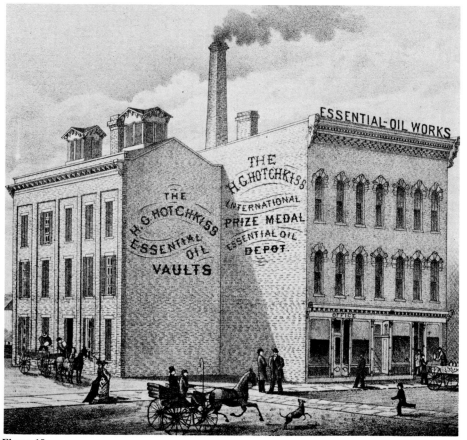

Figure 18

Figure 20

Figure 19

Figure 21

Figure 22

Sept. 10, 1904

Figure 23

Figure 24

Figure 25

Figure 26

Figure 27

Figure 28

Figure 29

Figure 18. The H. G. Hotchkiss essential oil works in Lyons, New York, about 1877. (W. H. McIntosh, *History of Wayne County, New York*, facing p. 103, Everts, Ensign, and Everts, Philadelphia, 1877.)

Figure 19. Alfred Hale of Alloway, New York, and one of his mint stills, about 1877. The firm of Hale and Parshall, Lyons, New York, was a Hotchkiss competitor for many years. (W. H. McIntosh, *History of Wayne County, New York*, facing p. 106, Everts, Ensign and Everts, Philadelphia, 1877.)

Figure 20. The present H. G. Hotchkiss building in Lyons, New York, 1969.

Figure 21. A scene along the Erie Canal, Lyons, New York, about 1890. The H. G. Hotchkiss plant is the white building between the barge and the rear horse.

Figure 22. A deposit slip from the Hotchkiss Peppermint Planters Banking House, Lyons, New York, dated 1853 (?).

Figure 23. A Todd Company letterhead in 1904 showing the head office in Kalamazoo, the large Campania muckland farm near Fennville, Allegan County, Michigan, the "Crystal White" trademark, and the medals awarded at various exhibits.

Figure 24. Albert May Todd (1850-1931), peppermint king of Michigan, founder of the A. M. Todd Company in 1869, and U. S. Congressman from Michigan, 1897-1898.

Figure 25. An early peppermint oil bottle of the "Crystal White" brand processed by A. M. Todd at Kalamazoo, Michigan.

Figure 26. Aaron P. Emery and farm at Mendon, St. Joseph County, Michigan, about 1877. The drawing shows the mint being harvested and distilled. Emery was a large mint grower and dealer in oils for many years. (*History of St. Joseph County, Michigan*, facing p. 220, L. H. Everts and Company, Philadelphia, 1877.)

Figure 27. The railroad station at Mentha, Van Buren County, Michigan, about 1935, named after the generic identity of the mint plants (*Mentha*).

Figure 28. Harvesting and distilling mint on the Henry Hall farm on the "Big Marsh" of Florence Township, St. Joseph County, Michigan, about 1890. ("The Peppermint Industry of St. Joseph County, Michigan," *Scientific American Supplement*, no. 748, May 3, 1890.)

Figure 29. An early newspaper advertisement for mint machinery in Lyons, New York. (*Lyons Republican*, June 3, 1869.)

day to build and furnish everything required to get up the Best Stills
Ever Built—notwithstanding the threats from this little original man—and
I guarantee parties afraid of this muttering thunder from the northeast,
against all trouble and damages whatever. His is simply a game of bluff.

It is not known if the United States Court heard any "muttering
thunder from the northeast."

Hotchkiss and Todd

Hiram G. Hotchkiss was a versatile man. Before 1850 he had been
primarily interested in the cultivation of peppermint. Following the
receipt of the prize medals granted at London in 1851 and New York
City in 1853 he became primarily concerned with establishing a reputation for a high quality product and attempting to control the New York
market. He exhibited his wares widely, winning medals in Vienna,
Hamburg, and Paris. At the *Exposition Universelle* held in Paris in
1867 Hotchkiss received the grand prize for highest quality peppermint
and spearmint oils.[68]

Hotchkiss imported sugar beets into New York to rotate with the
peppermint crop, was the first person in that state to cultivate red osier
for baskets and furniture, and had interests in mills, banks, canals, and
railroads. His tireless efforts on behalf of the essential oil industry made
Wayne County, New York (which always included the nearby counties
as well), peppermint and spearmint oils world renowned.

Albert M. Todd was also a versatile man. Almost single-handed he
had attacked the problem of quality in Michigan mint oils and waged
all-out war on the numerous adulterators and fraudulent operators. He
devised the first recognized tests for identifying impurities in mint oil
and circulated his findings widely through numerous appearances and
scientific papers. Largely through his efforts Michigan oils gained acceptance in the export trade.

Both men had developed new techniques of refining the oils to insure
better quality and, as their control of sources of supply were cemented,
both began to bottle, seal, and guarantee their products. Such activity
aided immeasurably in establishing the mint industry of the United
States as a reputable and trustworthy enterprise in the eyes of the world.
But the market was a competitive one and what had been a production
contest between New York and Michigan gradually merged into a
corporate contest between Hiram G. Hotchkiss and Albert M. Todd.
Developments were taking place in Michigan during the 1880's that
would soon tip the scales in favor of Todd.

Conclusion

As the year 1889 drew to a close American peppermint and spearmint oils had successfully entered competition in the world markets. Largely through the efforts of Hiram G. Hotchkiss in New York and Albert M. Todd in Michigan numerous problems involving the cultivation, distillation, and marketing of mint oils had been attacked and resolved. Steam power had been applied to the distillation process; new areas, notably Mississippi, had been involved in attempts to spread the industry; and new techniques in cultivation had been tried and adopted. A vigorous contest had been waged, and alternately won and lost, by the mint growers in New York and Michigan. As January 1, 1890, dawned across the wide stretches of the American landscape the mint industry began to enter one of its most active and hectic phases.

REFERENCES

[1]F. Stearns, "The Peppermint Plantations of Michigan," *American Journal of Pharmacy*, vol. 31, p. 38, 1859.

[2]*Ibid.*

[3]A. M. Todd, "The Essential Oil Industry of Michigan," *Proceedings of the American Pharmaceutical Association*, vol. 34, p. 121, 1886.

[4]D. C. VanSlyck, "Cultivation of Peppermint," *Report of the Commissioner of Patents for the Year 1849*, U.S. House of Representatives, Executive Document No. 20, p. 389, Part II, Agriculture, 1850.

[5]A. M. Todd, "The American Peppermint Industry," *V. Internationaler Kongress für Angewandte Chemie*, pp. 807-808, Deutscher-Verlag, Berlin, 1904.

[6]F. Stearns, *op. cit.*, pp. 39-41.

[7]D. C. VanSlyck, *op. cit.*, pp. 389-390.

[8]*Ibid.*, p. 390.

[9]F. Stearns, *op. cit.*, pp. 41-42.

[10]A. M. Todd, "Spurious Michigan Oil of Peppermint," *American Druggist*, vol. 15, no. 9, pp. 161-162, September, 1886; also his "The Essential Oil Industry of Michigan," 1886, *op. cit.*

[11]J. E. Todd and G. I. Todd (eds.), *The Todd Family in America*, pp. 248, 407-408, Press of Gazette Printing Co., Northampton, Massachusetts, 1920.

[12]In a brochure published by Albert M. Todd, Distilling Chemist, c. 1892.

[13]*Ibid.* As early as 1862, however, it was reported that L. B. Hotchkiss of Phelps had a "process of rectifying this oil unknown to any other person;" *Rochester Daily Union and Advertiser*, p. 2, Nov. 18, 1862.

[14]In addition to the above listed can be added the following references: *Proceedings of the American Pharmaceutical Association*, 1885; *Proceedings of the New York Pharmaceutical Association*, 1888; *American Journal of Pharmacy*, 1888; *Pharmaceutical Journal*, 1888; *Pharmaceutical Record* (London), 1888; *American Druggist*, 1886 and 1888; *39th Annual Report of the Secretary of the State Board of Agriculture of the State of Michigan*, 1900.

[15]S. B. McCracken, ed., *Michigan and the Centennial*, p. 490, State Centennial Board of Managers, Detroit, 1876.

[16]The judges were: Dr. Rudolf vonWagner, Germany; Dr. William J. Odling, Great Britain; M. F. F. Kuhlman, France; P. DeWilde, Belgium; Professor F. A. Genth, University of Pennsylvania, U.S.A.; Professor J. W. Mallet, University of Virginia, U.S.A.; E. Paterno, Italy; and Professor J. L. Smith, Louisville, Kentucky, U.S.A. Their names are shown on the Exposition certificates.

[17]F. A. Walker (ed.), *Reports and Awards*, Group I, p. 231, U.S. Centennial Commission, International Exhibition, 1876, J. B. Lippincott and Co., Philadelphia, 1878.

[18]*5th Annual Report of the Board of Agriculture of the State of Ohio to the 49th General Assembly for the Year 1850*, p. 322, S. Meday, Columbus, 1851.

[19]G. Everett, "Lake County," *8th Annual Report . . . for the year 1853*, p. 588, Public Document No. 21, 1854.

[20]*5th Annual Report. . . , op. cit.*, p. 530.

[21]*7th Annual Report . . . for the year 1852*, p. 344, Osgood and Blake, Columbus, 1853.

[22]D. C. VanSlyck, *op. cit.*, p. 388.

[23]F. Stearns, *op. cit.*, p. 42.

[24]M. B. Hillyard, "Peppermint in East Mississippi," *The Cultivator and Country Gentleman*, vol. 48, p. 696, August 23, 1883; G. Vasey, "Peppermint," *Report of the Commissioner of Agriculture: 1887*, p. 310, USDA, 1888.

[25]*Organization of the Agricultural Experiment Stations in the United States*, p. 27, Bulletin No. 1, Office of Experiment Stations, USDA, 1889.

[26]E. O. Eaton, "The Differentiation of Japanese and American Peppermint Oils," *Journal of the Association of Official Agricultural Chemists*, vol. 5, p. 597. 1922. *The Dispensatory of the United States of America* in its many revisions continued to list New England, Ohio, and New Jersey as sources of peppermint oil until 1892, although the evidence indicates that the revisions were, in many cases, simple reprintings of previous editions.

[27]A comprehensive discussion of attempts to raise peppermint and spearmint in the southern states is: J. E. Landing, "The Cultivation of Peppermint and Spearmint," *The Southeastern Geographer*, vol. 3, pp. 28-33, 1963.

[28]From Porcher in G. M. Hocking and L. D. Edwards, "Cultivation of Peppermint in Florida," *Economic Botany*, vol. 9, p. 80, 1955.

[29]M. B. Hillyard, *op. cit.*

[30]*Ibid.*

[31]*Ibid.*

[32]*Ibid.*

[33]*Ibid.*

[34]*Ibid.*

[35]Schimmel and Company, *Semi-annual Report*, p. 39, April, 1894; also, pp. 46-47, October, 1894. The Schimmel Co., of Leipzig, Germany, represented in the U.S. by Fritzsche Brothers, Inc. of New York City, was one of the leading European dealers in essential oils. Their comprehensive reports are a valuable source of information on world developments. An illustrated essay on the company appeared in *Chemist and Druggist*, pp. 11-18, April 26, 1913.

[36]A. Tschirch, *Handbuch der Pharmakognosie*, vol. 2, part 2, p. 941, C. H. Tauchnitz, Leipzig, 1917.

[37]*Census and Statistics of the State of Michigan, 1864*, p. 627, J. A. Kerr, Lansing, 1865; F. A. Fluckiger and D. Hanbury, *Pharmocographia*, p. 485, Macmillan and Co., London, 1870.

[38]C. Betts, "From St. Joseph County," *3rd Annual Report of the Secretary of the State Board of Agriculture of the State of Michigan for the Year 1864*, p. 69, J. A. Kerr and Co., Lansing, 1865.

[39]F. B. Hough (ed.), *Census of the State of N.Y. for 1865*, p. 410, Albany, 1867.

[40]"Peppermint," *6th Annual Report . . . of the State of Michigan for the Year 1867*, p. 69, Lansing, 1868.

[41]*Statistics of the State of Michigan, 1870*, p. 550, W. S. George and Co., Lansing, 1873. Stills and production were listed as follows:

Cass County (Marcellus Township)	1 still	285 lbs. oil
Ionia County (Lyons Twp.)	1 still	1,570 lbs.
Wayne County (Nankin)	3 stills	1,800 lbs.
St. Joseph County (8 townships listed)	39 stills	22,312 lbs.

8 of the St. Joseph County stills were in Lockport Township.

[42]*Census of the State of Michigan, 1874*, W. S. George and Co., Lansing, 1875; and *Census . . . , 1894*, vol. 2, p. 67, Robert Smith and Co., Lansing, 1896. The 1847 producing area in Hillsdale County was in Wheatland Twp. and in Berrien County near Riston. *Oil, Paint, and Drug Reporter*, June 21, 1948, mentions the peppermint association.

[43]F. A. Fluckiger and D. Hanbury, *op. cit.*, p. 485.

[44]*Statistics . . . 1870, op. cit.*, p. 550.

[45]Albert M. Todd, *Proceedings of the American Pharmaceutical Association*: *1876*, Appendix, p. 828. A Department of Agriculture bulletin in 1884 noted that Wayne County and area produced about 60,000 lbs. annually on 3,000 acres and "only a small quantity is grown outside Wayne County:" "Oil of Peppermint," *Statistical Reports*, New Series, no. 9, p. 28, USDA, July, 1884. In 1885 Wayne County production was estimated at 40,000 lbs.; *Rochester Daily Union and Advertiser*, p. 1, Sept. 28, 1885, Rochester, New York.

[46]M. E. Oaks, *Phelpstown Footprints*, pp. 58-59, Carpenter-He Prints, Geneva, New York, 1962; see also, *The Lyons Republican*, p. 3, August 20, 1868.

[47]F. G. Howes, *History of the Town of Ashfield, Massachusetts from Its Settlement in 1742 to 1910*, p. 104, published by the town, c. 1912.

[48]The Hotchkiss Papers, Feb. 15, 1847.

[49]S. B. McCracken (ed.), *op. cit.*, p. 490.

[50]Peppermint, "Cultivation of Peppermint," *Cultivator and Country Gentleman*, vol. 44, no. 1380, p. 437, 1879.

[51]"The Cultivation of Peppermint," *American Agriculturist*, vol. 25, p. 55, 1866.

[52]A. C. G., "Cultivation of Peppermint in St. Joseph County, Michigan," *The Rural New Yorker*, vol. 46, no. 1928, p. 19, Jan. 8, 1887.

[53]"Oil of Peppermint," *op. cit.*

[54]"Peppermint Culture," *Wayne Democratic Press*, p. 3, June 20, 1860.

[55]"The Peppermint Interest," *Lyons Republican*, p. 3, May 6, 1869.

[56]A. C. G., *op. cit.*

[57]S. T. Moore, "Journal of Paul Nelson Spofford," *Michigan History*, vol. 29, p. 331, 1945.

[58]*History of St. Joseph County, Michigan*, p. 191, L. H. Everts and Co., Philadelphia, 1877.

[59]*Ibid.*, p. 138.

[60]*Ibid.*, p. 221.

[61]*Ibid.*, pp. 106, 131, 138, 151, 156, 191, 209, 221, 228.

[62]*Portrait and Biographical Album of St. Joseph County, Michigan*, p. 482, Chapman Brothers, Chicago, 1889.

[63]"The Peppermint Industry of St. Joseph County, Michigan," *Scientific American Supplement*, no. 748, May 3, 1890.

[64]*Ibid.*

[65]*Ibid.*

[66]*Lyons Republican*, June 3, 1869.

[67]*Ibid.*

[68]*Rochester Daily Democrat*, p. 2, Jan. 24, 1854; *Rochester Daily Union and Advertiser*, p. 2, Nov. 18, 1862; *Ibid.*, p. 2, July 27, 1867. Also, from a Hotchkiss label which shows photos of the many medals awarded; and, W. H. McIntosh, *History of Wayne County, New York*, facing p. 103, Everts, Ensign and Everts, Philadelphia, 1877.

Chapter 6.

The Mint Industry Moves to the Mucklands

The Turbulent Decade

The last decade of the nineteenth century was an extremely active period for the American mint industry. Still centered in southwestern Michigan and western New York, and still represented in the market primarily by the Hotchkiss Company and Albert M. Todd, the industry continued to function mainly around the export market. Over 20 percent of the American production was shipped to a single European nation, Germany.[1]

Increasing acceptance of the American oils in the European market coupled with the decline of European mint production, especially in England, as a result of American competition, opened the doors for the domination of the export trade. Between 1891 and 1897 exports of American oil increased from 45,321 pounds to 162,492.[2] This represented an increase from less than half to about 55 percent of domestic production. By 1899 the export trade commanded over 65 percent.

The industry was further stimulated by a favorable series of import tariffs on foreign mint oils. Beginning in 1842 all imported essential oils were taxed at the rate of 20 percent. As a result of industry demand this was increased to 50 percent in 1884 and a specific import tax of 80 cents per pound was established on mint oil in 1892. This was adjusted downward to 25 percent in 1896 and set at 50 cents per pound in 1898.[3] With a great deal of protection for domestic producers, and a strongly improving market for export, the mint industry moved into a vigorous period of searching for newer horizons. This search centered primarily around the development of new producing areas, both in established states and elsewhere, and the introduction of new types of commercial mint plants.

The Search for New Areas

There were continued attempts to introduce mint cultivation in states other than Michigan and New York. Samples of peppermint oil were reported from New Jersey and Mississippi in 1893,[4] and an effort was made to establish both peppermint and spearmint production in the Kennewick area of Washington by a company which had a half-million roots shipped over the Northern Pacific Railroad and planted 19 acres in 1894.[5]

In 1898 it was suggested that "no more favorable sites can be found"[6] for peppermint culture than in Kentucky and, in 1899, a single farm in Stewart County, Tennessee, marketed 170 pounds of peppermint oil from two acres for $4.00 ($0.024 per pound).[7]

The only significant expansion, however, came in northern Indiana. It is possible that production had ceased for a time in the state because A. M. Todd, writing in 1900, stated that mint production spread into the northern counties of Indiana "perhaps twenty years ago."[8] Indiana production was estimated at 27,000 pounds in 1895, up considerably from 10 years earlier, but declined the following year to 20,000 pounds due to an "excess of rain and grasshoppers."[9] The amount of oil

Map 7. Counties of northern Indiana, showing the towns associated with muckland peppermint and spearmint oil production since 1846.

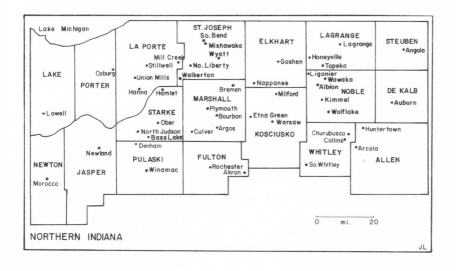

increased to 32,000 pounds in 1897,[10] and increased again to nearly 35,000 pounds in 1899.[11] The major producing areas of the state in 1899 were as follows:

St. Joseph County	10 farms	560 acres	15,280 pounds
Steuben County	11	103	3,100
Lagrange County	11	134	2,950

The remainder of the mint production was found in Elkhart and other counties (Map 7).[12] The growth of production in Indiana was directly related to the development of mint cultivation on the newly drained mucklands, a movement that resulted in a tremendous expansion of the industry in Michigan.

The Move to the Mucklands

Scattered across southern Michigan and northern Indiana are numerous small ribbons and pockets of highly organic soils known as mucklands. During the period of time following the retreat of the last glaciers from the area melt waters swirled across the landscape creating an entirely new set of drainage channels. Burdened by the tremendous quantities of loose debris from the glacial deposits many of the streams became temporarily dammed near their mouths and the waters began to back up. For a long time these sluggish streams were more like lakes and a great deal of vegetation began to sprout in the channels. Successive years of organic deposition created a thin veneer of black, silt-like soil known as muck. The same development took place in thousands of shallow lakes, ponds, and marshes.

During the last 15 years of the nineteenth century there was begun a great number of projects in both states designed to drain the mucklands and place them into productive cultivation. Peppermint was first grown on such soil in Michigan on the "Big Marsh" of Florence Township, St. Joseph County, by Henry Hall and found to be highly successful (Figure 28). Hall, who had been producing mint since 1868, planted as much as 400 acres annually and owned four distilleries.[13]

Lowland cultivation had been a practice in New York from almost the earliest days but the peppermint and spearmint fields were gradually shifted to the higher grounds.[14] In Michigan and Indiana the process was reversed, and the move from the burr oak openings to the newly drained mucklands, and the demonstration of profitable mint cultivation in Michigan, set off a dynamic period of expansion.

By 1893 mint production was taking place in 21 Michigan counties,[15] and practically all of it was on muckland. The producing areas were:

County	Major Townships	Acres	Number of Stills
St. Joseph	Florence, Mendon, Lockport	2,659	17
Muskegon	Moorland	709	0
Kalamazoo	Brady	635	0
Wayne	Romulus, Florence	550	1
Allegan	Clyde	451	1
Van Buren	Arlington, Bangor	225	1
Cass	Marcellus	200	3
Branch	Mattison	198	2
Calhoun	Burlington	171	4
Wexford	?	68	0
Hillsdale	?	38	1
Newaygo	?	30	0
Berrien	Royalton	27	0
Genesee	?	23	0
Oakland	?	18	0
Kent	?	12	0
Ingham	?	10	0
Ionia	?	9	0
Barry	?	3	0
Monroe	?	1	0
Cheboygan	?	1	0
Michigan		6,038	30

The newness of the movement is apparent from the limited acreages in most of the counties as well as from the fact that farmers in counties with relatively large acreages had not yet entered the distillery construction phase. Although the sudden expansion involved numerous muckland areas in a great number of counties only five, St. Joseph, Allegan, Van Buren, Calhoun, and Berrien, achieved and maintained significant production (Map 8).

Mint culture was introduced into Allegan County by Henry F. Severens who, by 1896, was reported to have "the largest peppermint field in the world," nearly a mile long, located on the Severensmarsh near Fennville.[16] Mint cultivation was introduced into several different sections of Van Buren County about the same time. In the Bangor area M. H. Hogmire had established production about 1886 from roots he had brought from near Mendon in St. Joseph County.[17] Other early growers near Bangor were Harvey and Stevens. Mint was introduced in the Decatur area about 1887 after nearly 3,000 acres of muck were drained into the Dowagiac River. Early growers were Neils Peterson, J. C. Dunnington, Lyscom Brigham, and W. H. Clark.[18] At one time nearly half the area was in peppermint.

It was in the Decatur area in this period that Lyscom Brigham who, by 1892, farmed nearly 400 acres and owned four mint distilleries,

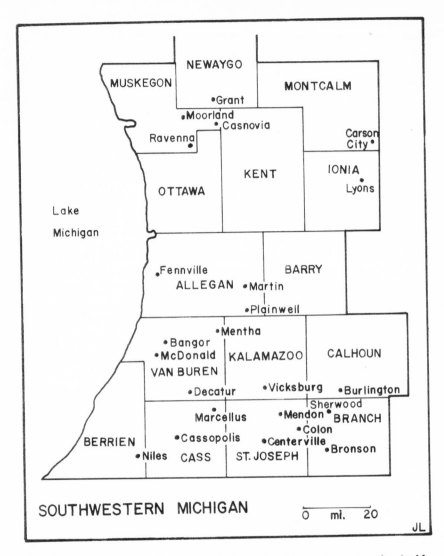

Map 8. Counties of southwestern Michigan, showing the towns associated with muckland cultivation of peppermint and spearmint since 1885.

patented the famous "muckland" or "Brigham shoe," large iron plates about twelve inches wide which, when bolted to the hooves of horses, made it possible for them to work in the soft muck ground.[19]

Muckland cultivation was not without its problems. The high water table and low elevations compounded the possibility of damage from winterkill and frost and the silt-like muck, when dry, was easily windblown. This latter problem led to the development of a very distinctive series of windbreaks, generally willows or Osage orange, which still mark these areas today. Strip-cropping of mint, generally with a form of rye, became common also as a method of reducing wind damage, and many fields were oriented north-south as further protection from the strong, prevailing southwesterly winds.

Muckland cultivation of mint proved so successful, with yields from 60 to 80 pounds per acre reported from new plantings,[20] that, by 1899, production in St. Joseph, Allegan, and Van Buren counties each exceeded the total from Indiana and New York combined.[21] The statistics for the three counties were as follows:[22]

County	Acres	Number of Farms	Pounds of Oil
Allegan	1,494	22	44,610
St. Joseph	1,827	164	35,892
Van Buren	1,641	127	34,170

St. Joseph County continued as a fairly important mint producing area for some time but gradually relinquished leadership to the newly developed areas which contained considerably more muckland. The development of muckland production in Indiana and Michigan was probably the most important advancement in the American mint industry since 1846 when steam distillation of the oil was introduced.

Albert M. Todd in Kalamazoo

Albert M. Todd was deeply involved in the shift of mint cultivation to the mucklands of Michigan. In the summer of 1891 he moved his distilling works from Nottawa to Kalamazoo, Michigan, where the Todd block was established at the corner of Kalamazoo Avenue and Rose Street. Todd had attempted, beginning in 1892, to develop extensive acreage in the Decatur area but was prevented from doing this by the high land cost.[23] As a result he turned his attention to the development of two extensive muckland farms, Mentha in northeastern Van Buren County, and Campania in central Allegan County (Figure 23).

At Campania, located on the Severensmarsh, ten miles of canals and drainage ditches were constructed, including the straightening of a natural stream flowing across the property. At Mentha (Figure 27), named for the generic identification of peppermint and spearmint (Genus *Mentha*), over fifteen miles of drainage ditches were dug which connected to a main ditch nearly four miles in length. At Mentha the first factory devoted to the manufacture of fuel briquettes processed from muck ground was built during the early twentieth century.[24] These two farms were the locales for a great deal of experimentation on various phases of mint cultivation.

During this period of farm development A. M. Todd not only devoted increasing time to the administrative affairs of the company but became actively engaged in politics. In 1894 he ran for the office of Governor of Michigan on the Prohibitionist ticket and polled 18,788 votes as a minor party candidate.[25] In 1895 he ran for Congress as a Democrat in a special election and, although he carried Kalamazoo County, he lost in the congressional district. In the regular election of 1896 Todd, with Democrat, Union Silver, and National Party support, won by 425 votes and went to Washington where he served a single term, the only Democrat representing the state of Michigan. He was defeated in the contest for re-election in 1898.

In Kalamazoo Todd continued his unceasing efforts to warn buyers of the great quantities of adulterated mint oil that wholesalers were continuously releasing on the market. So bad was the adulteration of much of the American oil that even large European buyers became wary of the local product. This development had two major effects: it concentrated much of the marketing of American oils through Todd and Hotchkiss, who would guarantee their products; and it acted to keep prices down at a time when the American industry was expanding and a steady price would have been desirable. Many of the smaller muckland mint producers were soon out of business.

In an effort to obtain peppermint oil of even higher quality, and to find plants of increased yield capacity, Todd was quite instrumental in the introduction of new commercial types of mint plants into the United States.

New Mint Plants Enter the Scene

The botanical nature of the mints, especially peppermint, is extremely complex. There are numerous subspecies of the peppermint plant and, within subspecies, various growth types exhibiting slightly different characteristics.[26] It is believed that the peppermint grown commercially in Massachusetts, New York, Ohio, and Michigan, as well as in other states, in the first days was the form imported by the early colonists which escaped from the kitchen gardens and became indigenous in most sections of the United States. This plant is known as American peppermint.

In the drug gardens of England, however, two very distinctive forms of peppermint were grown and their oil was in great demand. The first, known as Black Mitcham peppermint, was a type characterized by a deep purplish stem and very dark green leaves. The second, White Mitcham peppermint, had lighter colored leaves and stems and produced a very high quality oil.

New York legend relates that Hiram G. Hotchkiss "imported peppermint roots from Mitcham, England, to cross with native stock. This increased the native yield and developed what is known as Black Mint."[27] The exact nature of Hotchkiss' breeding experiments is not known, but Black Mitcham mint was long produced in England, needed no crossing, and none of the literature on peppermint indicates that the New York plants were any different from those being cultivated in other states.

About 1883, however, A. M. Todd imported a supply of Black Mitcham peppermint roots directly from England and planted them on his farm in St. Joseph County, Michigan.[28] It was discovered that the plants were hardier than the American peppermint and produced higher yields of a better quality oil. After Todd moved to Kalamazoo he made extensive plantings of the Black Mitcham on his holdings in Allegan and Van Buren counties.

The reputation of the Black Mitcham quickly spread, rootstock was sold and transferred, and peppermint growers began to shift production from American to Black Mitcham. In 1894 Todd marketed an oil known as "Rose Mitcham" advertised as being from Black Mitcham plants improved by cultivation in America.[29] At first, European dealers considered the American product as being of "poor quality,"[30] but this was largely due to the fact that Todd's oil came primarily from Michigan grown plants and many European dealers continued to prefer the New York product.[31] But Black Mitcham continued to spread, and at a rapid rate. In 1895 a "good deal" of the Michigan mint was of the Black Mitcham type.[32] This had increased to two-thirds the following year[33] and, by 1897, most peppermint fields in Michigan were Black Mitcham.[34] In the meantime the shift to the Black Mitcham plant also began in Indiana and New York. By 1900 Black Mitcham had become the dominant commercial peppermint plant in the United States.

White Mitcham peppermint was also produced in the United States for a short period of time, but its origins in this country are unknown. Todd does not mention the White peppermint in any of his many accounts of production. The plant was discovered to be less frost-resistant than the Black variety and produced considerably less oil, so never became popular among growers. The only known production of White mint was of 3,000 to 4,000 pounds produced in Michigan in 1897, the same year that observers noted a large acreage in Indiana.[35]

The advantages of raising the Black Mitcham variety undoubtedly kept the White mint from spreading into general cultivation.

The spearmint plant cultivated in the United States up to this time was, apparently, the same type imported by the early colonists which escaped from the home plantings and, like American peppermint, became indigenous throughout much of the country. The plant is known as American or Native spearmint.

The Great Rivalry Ends

The development of muckland cultivation coupled with the interest in growing the hardier and more productive Black Mitcham peppermint enabled Michigan peppermint production to reach new and undreamed of heights. In 1892 Michigan growers placed over 100,000 pounds of oil on the market and, in 1894 and 1897, nearly 175,000 pounds each year. Although New York oil was still preferred by many buyers the plentiful supply of Michigan oil, and the resulting price easing, placed it in great demand.

Michigan growers enjoyed a production advantage over those in New York. Labor costs were less, yields considerably higher, and new muck ground was being continuously brought into cultivation. Although the decade of the 1890's was not one of continuously increasing production in Michigan, the net trend was upward. As Michigan peppermint oil moved into the market in such plentiful amounts prices gradually lowered. The effects in New York were telling:[36]

Year	Michigan Production (pounds)	Average U.S. Price per lb.	New York Acreage
1892	100,000	$2.84	2,700
1893	75,000	2.68	2,200
1894	175,000	2.61	2,330
1895	108,000	2.22	1,940
1896	133,000	2.05	1,570
1897	172,000	1.58	1,300
1898	?	1.26	750
1899	145,000	1.01	300

By the end of the century some peppermint oil was selling for as little as $0.75 per pound.[37] In New York, where growers were producing peppermint on plots averaging about three acres, the competition was simply too severe and the peppermint lands were turned over to sugar beets. In the Wayne County area 25 distilleries were operating in 1898 but the number decreased to half that the following year.[38] The great rivalry had ended. Michigan now reigned supreme in the American peppermint industry.

Spearmint Production

The fortunes for American spearmint also began to change in a favorable direction. Prompted by a failure of European growers to produce the crop American farmers responded and, in 1894, there was a vigorous foreign demand for the "fine American distillate."[39] New York and Michigan combined produced nearly 12,000 pounds of spearmint oil in 1896,[40] which more than filled the demand and prices dropped precipitously. By 1898 spearmint production had virtually disappeared from New York and the oil prices which were now at "an all time low"[41] enabled Michigan growers to dominate the world spearmint oil market.[42]

Conclusion

As the first hundred years of the American mint industry drew to a close the major producing area was firmly established in the mucklands of the Middlewest. The local industry had become the major source of supply for peppermint and spearmint oils for the entire world. New plant types had been adopted and successfully brought into production. Cultivation and distilling technology had been significantly improved. Only the vagaries of the weather and the marketplace continued to plague American growers.

Hiram G. Hotchkiss passed away in 1898, the 59th year of the company he had founded. His passing was contemporary with the decline of the industry in the area for which he had so diligently worked and struggled. By this time Michigan and Albert M. Todd had become the new powers in the industry which moved forward toward its second century. That century, however, was to begin, for the American mint industry, on a rather somber and inauspicious note.

REFERENCES

[1]Schimmel and Company, *Semi-annual Report*, p. 43, October, 1897.

[2]U.S. Department of Treasury, *Foreign Commerce and Navigation of the United States For the Calendar Year ----*, for the years 1891 through 1897.

[3]Taken from *Foreign Commerce and Navigation of the United States . . . , op. cit.*, and *U.S. Import Duties Annotated*.

[4]*Semi-annual Report, op. cit.*, p. 39, April, 1894.

[5]"Western Peppermint," *The Cultivator and Country Gentleman*, vol. 60, p. 430, May 30, 1895, from the *Seattle Post-Intelligence*.

[6]G. L. Curry, "Peppermint Culture," *Proceedings of the Twenty-first Annual Meeting of the Kentucky Pharmaceutical Association: 1898*, p. 73.

[7]U.S. Census of Agriculture, 1899.

[8]A. M. Todd, "The Essential Oil Industry of Michigan," *39th Annual Report of the Secretary of the State Board of Agriculture of the State of Michigan*, p. 400, 1900.

[9]*Semi-annual Report, op. cit.,* p. 35, October, 1895; p. 56, October, 1896.

[10]*Ibid.,* p. 40, October, 1897.

[11]*Ibid.,* p. 45, October, 1899.

[12]*Ibid.;* "Peppermint," *Census Reports,* vol. 6, Agriculture, Part 2, Crops and Irrigation, pp. 522-523, 1899.

[13]W. C. Stebbins, *The Peppermint Industry,* B.S. thesis, Michigan State College, 1895; files of A. M. Todd Company; "The Peppermint Industry of St. Joseph County, Michigan," *Scientific American Supplement,* No. 748, May 3, 1890.

[14]W. VanFleet, *The Cultivation of Peppermint and Spearmint,* Bulletin 694, p. 3, Bureau of Plant Industry, USDA, 1915.

[15]*Census of the State of Michigan, 1894,* vol. 2, p. 67, Robert Smith and Co., Lansing, 1896.

[16]*Semi-annual Report, op. cit.,* p. 56, October, 1896.

[17]*Decatur Republican,* Dec. 30, 1926, Decatur, Michigan.

[18]R. Haefner (ed.), *Welcome to Decatur, A Centennial Souveneir Book of Decatur, Michigan, 1848-1948,* pp. 42-43, Decatur Agricultural Association, 1948; personal information from Otis Howe, 1967, retired Decatur peppermint grower.

[19]*Pictorial and Biographical Record of Kalamazoo, Allegan, and Van Buren Counties, Michigan,* pp. 543-544, Chapman Bros., Chicago, 1892; R. Haefner, *op. cit.,* p. 43. Other growers simply inserted a large piece of wood between the hoof and the regular shoe.

[20]Personal information from Otis Howe, *op. cit.*

[21]"Peppermint," *Census Reports, op. cit.*

[22]*Ibid.*

[23]R. Haefner, *op. cit.,* pp. 42-43.

[24]A. M. Todd, "The American Peppermint Industry," *V. Internationaler Kongress für Angewandte Chemie,* pp. 808-809, Deutscher-Verlag, Berlin, 1904; O. W. Rowland, *A History of Van Buren County, Michigan,* vol. 1, pp. 110, 597, Lewis Publishing Co., Chicago, 1922.

[25]W. F. Dunbar, *Kalamazoo and How It Grew,* pp. 116-117, faculty contributions, Western Michigan University, 1959.

[26]For an overview of the taxonomy and botany of the peppermint and spearmint plants, see: O. A. Farwell, "The Correct Name for the Spearmint," *Rhodora,* vol. 26, pp. 19-22, 1924; G. M. Hocking, "Scotch Mint and Spearmint. A Comparative Study of Cultural, Morphological, and Histological Characteristics of Species of *Mentha* Growing in Florida," *Journal of the American Pharmaceutical Association,* vol. 38, pp. 394-402, 1949; and, G. M. Hocking and L. D. Edwards, "Nomenclature of Peppermint and Its Varieties," *Journal of the American Pharmaceutical Association,* vol. 33, pp. 333-342, 1944.

[27]L. O'Connor, "Peppermint King of the World," *Yankee,* pp. 92-93, April, 1958.

[28]A. M. Todd, *op. cit.,* p. 806, 1904.

[29]*Semi-annual Report, op. cit.,* p. 47, October, 1894.

[30]*Ibid.,* p. 8, April, 1895.

[31]*Ibid.,* p. 39, April, 1894.

[32]*Ibid.,* p. 35, October, 1895.

[33]*Ibid.,* p. 56, October, 1896.

[34]*Ibid.,* p. 41, October, 1897.

[35]*Ibid.* Mention of White Mitcham peppermint in 1943 being "sparsely grown in the United States" could have been a reference to some experimental plantings: E. Guenther, "A Survey of American and European Peppermint Oils," *Manufacturing Confectioner,* vol. 23, p. 23, October, 1943.

[36]Figures compiled from various sources cited in the text, but especially from *Semi-annual Reports, op. cit.,* 1894 to 1900.

37*Semi-annual Report, op. cit.,* p. 34, April, 1899. On November 20, 1897, Lyscom Brigham of Decatur, Michigan, received the following prices for peppermint oil from A. M. Todd: English (Black Mitcham), 72½¢ per lb., American, 85¢ per lb., mixed, 75¢ per lb. In 1895 Henry F. Severens of Allegan County, Michigan, received the following peppermint oil prices from Todd: English, $1.62½ per lb.; American $1.65 per lb. Despite the price differential, however, most Michigan growers switched to production of Black Mitcham peppermint (from the files of A. M. Todd Co).

38*Ibid.,* p. 44, October, 1899.

39*Ibid.,* p. 50, April, 1894.

40*Ibid.,* p. 69, October, 1896.

41*Ibid.,* p. 47, April, 1898.

42*Ibid.,* p. 42, April, 1899.

Chapter 7.

Perspective on A Century

The first hundred years of the American mint industry was a classic period in the development of a new industry. From an experimental peppermint planting project in western Massachusetts the cultivation of peppermint and spearmint had grown to such an extent that American growers dominated the world market.

Acceptance of the American product was slow in coming. Having a limited domestic market in the drug trade, the bulk of the processed oil moved into the European export trade where early prejudices against the American product had to be overcome. This was done successfully largely through the marketing efforts of Hiram G. Hotchkiss of Phelps, and later Lyons, New York, where the industry had been established by settlers from the early mint districts of Massachusetts. The same type of acceptance battle was waged for the mint oil later produced in the Middlewestern states of Indiana and Michigan, and was achieved primarily through the efforts of Albert M. Todd of Nottawa, and later Kalamazoo, Michigan.

American growers were largely on their own regarding the cultivation and processing of the mint crops, since they had little experience to draw upon for such matters as cultivating large plantings and distilling the oil on the farm. The experiences and cultivation migrated westward with the vanguard of American settlers, moving from Massachusetts to New York, then into Ohio and New Jersey, and finally into Michigan and Indiana.

Great impetus was given to the foundling industry in Michigan between 1847 and 1849 when a successful monopoly, engineered by

Hotchkiss, temporarily removed the New York competition. But the New York oil had gained acceptance in the world market, local growers activated mint cultivation once again and, for a half century, growers in New York and Michigan waged a production battle that was finally decided in favor of the latter by the development of muckland cultivation and a tremendous expansion of acreage.

Technological developments were not lacking. From the simple copper kettle stills of Massachusetts mint growers eventually adapted steam to the farm distillation process which enormously increased the capacity that an individual grower could handle. By the end of the century the sophisticated mint distilleries of the American farms had become ingenious structures of efficient and rapid production.

Marketing had become significantly stabilized. The industry, plagued by speculation, sale of adulterated oils, and fraudulent advertising, began to establish its reputation largely through the dedicated marketing enterprises of Hotchkiss and Todd. Their vigorous efforts to bring honesty and trust into an industry largely controlled by speculative brokers of the east coast cities eventuated in their primary control of the source of supply. The bulk of the domestic oil passed through their hands and they, in turn, guaranteed its quality and purity. Their reputations established, brokers and users began increasingly to turn to their companies with orders. "H.G.H." and "Crystal White" became the most widely accepted brands of mint oil sold throughout the world.

But the first hundred years were to end on a dour note. The development of muckland production in Michigan and Indiana, and the resulting overproduction, so depressed the market that prices of oils were about as low as at any time since the founding days. The result was the virtual elimination of the commercial industry in New York and the concentration of production in a few muckland areas of southwestern Michigan and Indiana. This new localization enabled A. M. Todd to become the primary force in the industry. At this stage the American mint industry began its second century.

PART II:

THE GOLDEN PERIOD: TOWARD THE SECOND HUNDRED YEARS

Chapter 8.

Toward A Domestic Market

A Troubled Beginning

The second century of the American mint industry did not begin with the same note of enthusiasm demonstrated by Mr. John Hart of Lanesborough, Massachusetts, who had so diligently advertised his peppermint essence and cordial in 1800. Plagued by low prices and a series of bad weather years even the growers in Michigan and Indiana, now the only two important producing states, began to feel the squeeze. The pressure, however, was greatest on the smaller producer. The farmers controlling larger acreages, and there were many in Michigan and Indiana, could withstand the market for an unfavorable season or two. But even at $1.00 per pound Midwestern growers could make some money as estimated production costs amounted to only 50 cents per pound.[1]

During the winter of 1899-1900 the Michigan mint fields were "devastated by frost,"[2] and the harvest the following summer was most unsatisfactory. There was still an abundance of oil from previous years in circulation so prices did not immediately respond. But when the 1901 harvest in Michigan and Indiana also proved to be disastrous, and growers still gained little price benefit, many closed out their fields.

In St. Joseph County, Indiana, 1901 yields of peppermint oil were off 50 percent from the preceding year and fields near Mishawaka were so bad that it hardly paid to harvest the crop.[3] In Elkhart County, near Goshen, there was wholesale abandonment of mint cultivation and distilleries were dismantled.[4]

The situation was ripe for speculation as was always the case in the industry when prices were low at the same time supplies were short. Ninety percent of the world's supply of peppermint oil, and practically the entire supply of spearmint oil, was cultivated in an area extending within a radius of ninety miles from Kalamazoo, Michigan.[5] A decade of low prices and overproduction, a series of bad crop years culminating in 1900 and 1901 with very meager harvests, and diminishing supplies of available oil laid the foundation. In the autumn of 1901 the first rumors of a speculative movement began to circulate.

Monopoly Again Rears Its Head

During the winter of 1901-1902 Albert M. Todd sent buying agents throughout the mint producing areas of Michigan and Indiana and they were successful in buying up nearly the entire production. This procedure was not so unusual, for it was a normal routine of the Todd buying operation. After receiving the oil, however, Todd simply stored it in warehouses, releasing none for sale. Market stocks continued to decline and the monopoly was insured further success when floods and heavy rains decimated the Michigan and Indiana fields in 1902.[6] On one of the Todd farms expected production of 5,000 pounds of oil dropped to a meager 600 pounds. Michigan production was further reduced to 40 percent of that of 1901.[7] By the autumn of 1902 it was rumored that Todd had control of a quantity of oil equal to 90 percent of the total American supply.[8] Peppermint oil prices doubled; but Todd would not sell.

In November, 1902, peppermint prices jumped suddenly to $5.00 per pound, and Todd was accused of releasing only enough oil to meet necessary demands and continuing to hold his supply in an effort to drive the price to $6.00.[9] By the winter of 1902-1903 the agitated period had resulted in a virtual standstill of trading in the industry.

The market broke with sudden fury. A different Michigan dealer had attempted to sell 7,000 pounds of peppermint oil to New York brokers at $4.65, but could find no buyers. The attempt, however, convinced the brokers that the Kalamazoo monopoly was easing and they held firm.[10] The dealers would not buy and Todd could not sell. Growers, who were not benefitting from the possible increased prices, decided to move their 1903 oil directly to the hands of New York brokers. The brokers were determined to wait. As a result it was estimated Todd had accumulated a supply of nearly 150,000 pounds of oil and could not market it at a price to meet expenses. In less than two years Todd had gained a virtual monopoly of the American mint industry, but had overextended his finances, and the company passed into a period of considerable financial difficulty.

The Todd maneuver, as might be expected, was looked upon with great disdain by eastern brokers and users of mint oils. Variously described as a "secret syndicate," "a clique," "American bulls," "a gang of speculators," and "Hotspurs,"[11] Todd had completed one of the shrewdest marking strategies since the Hotchkiss-Patterson monopoly of 1847, yet it ended in failure.

Growers Attempt to Organize

The after-effects of the 1902 monopoly were manifold. Exports dipped to a meager 13,000 pounds in 1903, a severe blow to a foreign-oriented industry, one which had exported over 145,000 pounds of mint oil in 1898. Not until 1907 was an equivalent amount shipped overseas.

Oil prices fluctuated for a time then began to level off between $2.00 and $3.00 per pound. The 1903 harvest was a good one but the 1905 and 1906 crops were hard hit by severe cold. Greatly dissatisfied by the speculative reports which plagued the industry during this time, one of the leading trade journals commented:[12]

> gently prepared as they were by the sorrowing epistles in which Western distillers of peppermint oil have for the past few months poured out their grief over the damaged crop, the buyers of peppermint oil will hardly be shocked by the first quotations for the new crop oil. In fact, these quotations, which are about thirty to thirty-five per cent above last year's Fall values, afford some relief from the uncertainty which the aversion of distillers to naming prices had caused in the local and foreign markets. The leading factors in the Michigan-Indiana peppermint oil industry still refuse to declare their views as to values, but the quotations to hand appear to be made in good faith; that is to say, on the basis of saddling on the purchaser whatever damage the elements caused to the crop of the parties quoting. . . In the meantime the local market is being manipulated with much zeal by both those who believe that a high market for peppermint oil is essential to the country's economic weal and by those who take pride in low quotations, whatever their motives might be. . . There are those "spreadeagle" economists who assert that because peppermint oil is largely an article of export, patriotism calls for "bullish" views as to values. No worse service could be rendered to the welfare of the product in the markets of the world.

This general strategy, predicting short crops, buying the oil at a low price, then selling when the market advanced, was such a common procedure among eastern brokers and many oil buyers that the growers of the crop began to evidence interest in organizing. Finding succor from the American Society of Equity, a circular prepared by George C. Wattles of Sherwood, Michigan, was forwarded to mint growers in 1906 calling upon them to organize, issue accurate production reports, fix minimum prices, and condemn adulteration.[13] A meeting of growers was held at Kalamazoo on September 5 and the following resolution adopted:[14]

whereas the principal producers of peppermint oil have carefully considered the cost of producing the said commodity throughout the entire oil producing belt and have ascertained systematically the available quantity for consumption during the coming year,

And whereas the present high price of labor and unfavorable natural conditions have tended to both reduce the acreage and also largely increase the cost of production,

And whereas there has been considerable agitation among the New York and other buyers regarding the fixing of a minimum price by the growers and primary owners and holders of essential oils,

And whereas there is a feeling among the said growers that the initial price of oil of peppermint should be materially higher than last year,

And whereas it is deemed by competent judges that oil peppermint ought to be placed upon the market at from $3-to-$4-per lb. in order that growers may receive a fair compensation for capital and labor invested,

Therefore be it resolved, that we do recommend that the minimum price of oil peppermint in the producing districts throughout this jurisdiction be not less than $2.75 to $3.- per lb. as per quality,

And further resolved, that even higher prices are justifiable under the circumstances.

Whereas this branch of the American Society of Equity is known and recognized as the essential oil branch,

And whereas at this time nothing has been done or said in regard to any other essential oil produced in marketable quantities in this jurisdiction other than oil peppermint,

And whereas it is not deemed advisable at this time to make recommendations regarding prices or productions of said other essential oils.

Therefore be it resolved that we do not deem it advisable or necessary at this time to take into consideration matters pertaining to the production and marketing of such essential oils other than oil peppermint produced within our jurisdiction, but stand ready to consider all matters of this nature as circumstances and conditions seem to demand.

A further circular from the Society, dated September 24, left little doubt as to what the growers had in mind.[15]

THE AMERICAN SOCIETY OF EQUITY
of North America

(seal)

Essential Oil and Mint Growers Branch
MARKET SITUATION.

September 24th, 1906.

To all Mint Growers, Greetings:

It is deemed advisable that all growers of Essential Oils should know the market and price situations, this being the time that local buyers acting with New York and other speculators to depress prices in order to cover short sales (futures) at too low figures, and stock up for speculative purposes. Now the public does not practically get any benefit out of these low prices to the growers, and the grower is expected to rush in with his oil and sell at a lower price than he should in order to carry out the scheme to fill the pocket of the speculator.

At the Kalamazoo meeting, Sept. 5th, a price of from $2.75 to $3.00 was recommended and even higher prices justifiable, taking into consideration consumption, cost of growing, shortage of crop and other natural disadvantages to the grower, local buyers and representatives of New York and other handlers of oils, were unanimous that $2.75 was not too high to the grower and only equitable for peppermint to the grower this season. Buyers admitting that the grower should have received $2.50 for last years crop. It has turned out however that speculators will speculate as long as the growers will lay himself liable to speculation by being unorganized and uneducated as to the tricks that are played upon him, making the farmers the dupes of all others.

The plan at present is to scare the grower into selling his oil for a low figure, telling him the price is going down, and that there is more oil grown than was expected, staying away from the grower making him believe they do not want oil or any other story to scare in the oil, so the buyers have chopped from $2.75 to $2.40. Now candidly is this not a pernicious practice and should not every grower set himself against such practices and systematic robbery? New York papers read about like this: "While prices on peppermint are lower, the New York selling prices are unchanged." So you see it is like the millers, no matter how low wheat goes the price of flour remains about the same.

There is surely a remedy for the growers, and this is organization. As the crop is short and so admitted by all who read and are in touch with the situation a little bit, follow the plan of the American Society of Equity, hold your oil until the demand comes. Every pound of oil sold at a low figure will stand against the grower until consumed, and even then buyers may claim New York has lots of oil in stock. New York advises this summer have been about like this: Peppermint did not winter well; old stock short; prices higher.

This was when they were selling. Why don't they carry out their declarations and give the growers some benefit of the true situation?

No oil is being sold to speak of where growers are organized and now it rests with the growers to take care of themselves by simply holding for the price until the demand comes, which will not exceed 60 days, as not one tenth of the oil needed has been bought nor is in stock, and above all things do not be scared into throwing away your hard earnings. Come together and talk over the matter. Read up-to-date literature and get the true situation of the markets and prices of all farm products. Wayne and Seneca counties, N.Y. report only half crop.

Muskegon county, Mich., which has been known to have 600,000 pounds has only 10,000 pounds this season. Growers in all mint growing districts report short crop more or less, with but few exceptions. Conditions have been bad most of the summer and so reported in farm papers where they had the truth, one paper reports 50 pounds to the average. This is preposterous and never was known, except here and there a little. Indiana has suffered more than Michigan, these are facts and generally admitted by those who know.

Now get a hustle and get organized, take membership in the Society, including the Essential Oil Branch only $2.00 per year, giving you information from time to time and the official paper, *Up-to-Date Farming,* published at Indianapolis, Ind., in the interests of profitable prices on all farm crops.

Remember if anything is done to help the farmer he must attend to it himself and he will always be duped until he does it.

October 11th—This circular has been withheld from going out to learn if possible the case of the depression in the market. The foregoing are the facts from reliable authority. "Some speculators in the east as well as west depressed the market for the very purpose of lowering it, and partly to the fact that a number of small dealers as well as growers, made a large number of offers promiscuously, offering the same amount of oil to a number of houses which further hurt the market. The conditions accordingly are very unsatisfactory." What has been said in this circular is all in order and a good demand must come as all admit the crop is much less than last year.

For information or membership write to any of the undersigned,

T. J. G. Bolt, Ravenna, Michigan	R. E. Osborn, Secretary
Pres. and Chairman of Board	Sherwood, Michigan
of Essential Oil Branch	Geo. C. Wattles, General
	Organizer, Sherwood
	Michigan

Although few persons begrudge the farmers adequate prices for their products it is interesting that the peppermint growers found no hesitancy in recommending procedures which they wholeheartedly condemned when practiced by others; holding oil on speculation, controlled acreage and production, price fixing, and issuing promises as guarantees. This attempt at cooperative marketing, with no regulatory machinery, proved a complete failure primarily because the rights of the superior farmer were not adequately protected. There was always a premium on high quality oil from the farm but the cooperative venture offered this man the same benefits as accrued to the poor farmer who marketed weedy, dirty oil. As a result organization attempts lasted less than a single year.

Following the attempt to organize the growers, the basic marketing pattern which has served the industry until the present day had become well crystallized. Farmers marketed their oil, for the most part, through several well organized country dealers who, in turn, processed the oils to meet customer specifications and delivered it to the trade and export market.[16] The Todd Company weathered its financial crisis and, at the same time, expanded its position in the industry. A. M. Todd continued to exhibit interest in the business but gradually turned over active management of the firm to his eldest son, Albert J. Todd, who served as President until 1956. Two younger sons, Allman A. Todd and Paul H. Todd, also served in the business following completion of their education, and a son-in-law, E. L. Woodhams, joined the company in 1910 as manager of the farming operations. The Todd Company and the Hotchkiss Company of Lyons continued to be the major country dealers buying and processing natural peppermint and spearmint oil from the growers.

Increasing the Domestic Market

The marketing machinery, thus stabilized, was a significant step forward in aiding the establishment of a stable industry. Based on the integrity of the country dealers, growers developed a basic faith in the marketing procedures, increasing reliance was placed on the country dealers, and the tumultous speculation which had plagued the industry began to decline. The dealers, with their wide grower contacts, their specialized equipment for processing and blending the natural oils, and their knowledge of the oil market, became the middle-men through which the bulk of the supply was channelled. Brokers, exporters, and users of mint oils began to deal primarily through the country dealers. A stable marketing pattern had become firmly established.

In the early part of the century there began a gradual shift from the primary importance of the export market. This trend was centered around what, at the time, appeared to be a rather insignificant item of commerce, chewing gum. Materials for chewing dated back to ancient days and early American products of the type used a wide variety of flavoring bases, especially spruce oil. In the middle part of the nineteenth century the technique of manufacturing chicle-based gum was developed and the gum business slowly began to grow.

In 1891 William Wrigley, Jr., a 29 year old Philadelphia soap dealer, moved to Chicago with $32 in his pocket and established a business centered on the distribution of soap and baking powder.[17] Chewing gum was added to Wrigley's interests but the first two brands, Vassar and Lotta, met little public response. Wrigley then introduced Juicy Fruit and Spearmint gum which became very popular. By 1910 the spearmint flavored chewing gum was the nation's top seller.[18] Four years later Wrigley began marketing Doublemint, flavored with peppermint oil, and it was destined to become the nation's favorite.

Wrigley was not alone. In 1891 the Beech Nut Packing Company of Canajoharie, New York, was incorporated (originally under the name of Imperial Packing Company) and began marketing a successful line of preserved foods. Soon chewing gum was added to the product list as well. Other early gum producers were Fleer, Sen Sen, American Chicle, Beemans, Adams, White, Zeno, Mansfield, Dunn, Blood Berry, and Curtis. Soon Wrigley, Beech Nut, and the American Chicle Company (a merger of the Adams and White companies) dominated the gum business and the increased consumption of peppermint and spearmint oils not only had significant effects on the cultivation of the plants but was primarily responsible for reorienting the industry from emphasis on the foreign drug market to emphasis on the development of high quality mint oils for domestic consumption by the gum and candy companies.

Another seemingly insignificant development of the day was the adaption of peppermint and spearmint oil as a flavoring in tooth paste. Led by such companies as Colgate, Pepsodent, and Kolynos, the flavored pastes soon found wide acceptance among the consuming public, added a significant outlet for the mint industry, and further aided the move to a secure domestic market.

Spearmint Gains a Hold

The fortunes of spearmint also began to change. Never too significant a crop, always dominated by the greater demand for peppermint, the chewing gum and toothpaste emphasis brought spearmint into much wider use and increased cultivation. In 1903 only 17 acres were planted in Indiana.[19] Indiana and Michigan combined cultivated 800 acres in 1908.[20] Spearmint oil had come into such demand that the country dealers began negotiating contracts with the farmers for guaranteed delivery of their crop, a process which further aided in establishing a stable industry.

In 1909 extensive new plantings were laid down in Indiana. By 1911 cultivation had increased to 1,727 acres in Indiana and Michigan with 2½ acres in New York.[21] But yields were so low during the season that several growers were forced to "purchase the annulment of their contracts for delivery."[22]

The increased American consumption of spearmint oil was looked upon by Europeans with some amusement because of a long established preference for peppermint. This development caused one firm to comment that

> judged by European standards of taste, it seems scarcely credible that employment of this oil should be steadily increasing in the United States. That, however, is the fact.[23]

But spearmint consumption continued to increase and, in 1912, 2,057 acres were planted in Indiana and Michigan, 1,000 acres of that by a single grower.[24]

The fortunes of spearmint were additionally aided by the introduction of a new type plant. About 1908 A. E. Beebe, a mint grower near Niles, Michigan, had found plantings in a Wisconsin garden of a type of spearmint from Scotland which was not too well known. He obtained some roots and set them out on his own land near Niles, Michigan, but met some resistance when he attempted to market the oil. Todd secured roots from Beebe in 1910, set them out on his large Mentha plantation and had several hundred acres under cultivation in a few years.[25] The new plant, Scotch spearmint (*Mentha cardiaca* G.), proved to be more productive than the Native spearmint, by as much as 50 percent, but slightly less tolerant to frost.[26] Since frost and winterkilling were major concerns in muckland cultivation the new plant gained in favor only slowly but, with the interest and support of Todd, eventually became commonly cultivated throughout the producing areas of Indiana and Michigan. Scotch spearmint had apparently been introduced into the eastern United States at an earlier date, since it was reported growing wild from Nova Scotia to the District of Columbia in 1913.[27]

The demand for spearmint oil had become so steady by 1918 that the Todd Company negotiated three year contracts through 1920 with growers for $3 a pound. Although spearmint cultivation never has exceeded that of peppermint in acreage it has continuously been a significantly important crop since it gained a foothold in the chewing gum and toothpaste industries.

Cultivation Developments

For the first quarter of the twentieth century Michigan and Indiana continued to be the only important states in the production of pepper- and spearmint oils. But, as had been the history throughout the nineteenth century, numerous attempts to introduce cultivation into new areas were carried out.

Ohio. Mint production in Ohio apparently disappeared in the latter half of the nineteenth century but, in 1919, a single farmer cultivated 100 acres and obtained 1,200 pounds of oil for which he obtained $6,000.[28] There were also reports about 1901 of production near Burton (Map 9).

Louisiana. Shortly after 1920 cultivation of peppermint on reclaimed lands near Raceland, Louisiana (La Fourche Parish), proved to be unsuccesssful due to contamination with "odoriferous weeds."[29]

Iowa. Peppermint cultivation was introduced into Hancock County, Iowa, by Robert Ulrath who "netted" $65 from four acres grown in 1907 and planned expansion in 1908.[30] Cultivation apparently lasted until about 1911,[31] but a report on peppermint published by the Iowa Horticultural Society in 1931 makes no mention of the production.[32]

Maryland, Virginia, South Dakota. Between the years 1908 and 1912 Frank Rabak of the U.S. Department of Agriculture conducted cultivation experiments on peppermint in three widely scattered sections of the country on different types of soil. The three experimental locations were: Glenn Dale, Maryland (light, sandy soil); Arlington Farm, Virginia (heavy clay soil); and Webster, South Dakota (rich, black loam soil). The Maryland soils were rated as best with those in South Dakota ranking next.[33] Despite these experiments and findings the commercial cultivation of mint in the three states never developed.

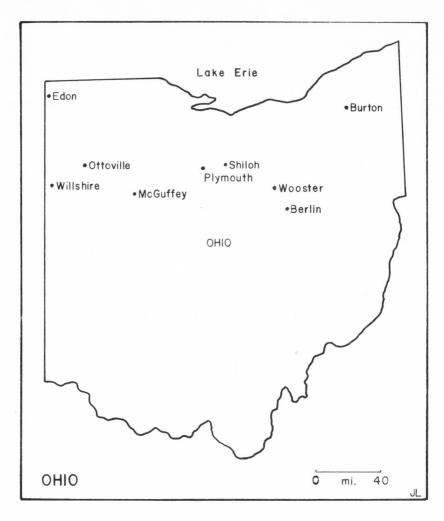

Map 9. Ohio, showing the towns associated with peppermint and spearmint oil production since 1900.

Wisconsin. Mint cultivation was reported in Wisconsin in 1904 and 1917 but neither of the attempts proved to be successful.[34] In 1922, however, the Todd Company granted funds to Edward Kremers of the University of Wisconsin to conduct research experiments on the chemistry of peppermint and spearmint oils. Kremers, one of the leading authorities on the chemistry of the essential oils, published his findings in a number of publications.

Texas. In 1908 peppermint and spearmint were reported to have been successfully cultivated at Sherman (Grayson County).[35] The outcome of the plantings is unknown.

California. The state of California was mentioned as a peppermint producer in a report published in 1910.[36]

North Carolina. About 1920 a group of Amish and Mennonites from Indiana and Michigan settled in Currituck County, North Carolina, in the vicinity of the Dismal Swamp where a great deal of muckland was being developed through drainage.[37] John Slabaugh, one of the settlers, had brought peppermint roots from the Middlewest and planted them in his garden. Rootstock was taken from the garden and commercial plantings were established. By 1927 nearly 70 acres were under cultivation with Slabaugh and a Mr. Kurtz controlling about 60 of the acres. A single distillery, on the Kurtz farm, handled the area production. New acreages were established through transplants instead of the usual method of digging and replanting roots.

Idaho. The introduction of peppermint cultivation into Idaho in 1903 was undertaken by Oliver H. Todd (Figure 58), brother and one-time partner of Albert. The development was described by Todd:[38]

> in 1903 my nephew, Will Price of Fairfax, Michigan, at my request sent me a box of mint roots which I planted on a vacant lot in Couer d'Alene, Idaho, where I was living. They seemed to do well and I extended them till, in 1905, I had enough roots to plant about two acres near St. Maries, Idaho. That fall I built a small distillery and distilled the oil from my crop. Though the yield was not heavy the quality of the oil was super-fine. Tho I had a fine crop the next year, I did nothing more with it in Idaho, due to a lack of sufficient suitable land.

Oregon. O. H. Todd moved from Idaho to Eugene, Oregon, where he was also successful in the development of peppermint cultivation along the Willamette River Valley in that state. "In the spring of 1909, my son, Victor, who was living in St. Maries (Idaho), sent me at Eugene, Oregon, where we were then living, a barrel of mint roots which I planted in my garden. The next year I extended my acreage and in 1913 I planted about 20 acres near Albany, Oregon. The land was unsuitable except for a fourth of an acre on bottom land where it grew magnificently. We put up a distillery near Albany, and sold roots to the farmers about there. Within the next two or three years, the mint industry was well established in the Willamette Valley with several hundred acres planted and more than a dozen distilleries in operation."[39]

Peppermint cultivation spread quickly throughout the Willamette Valley, especially in the area between Eugene and Salem (Map 10), a

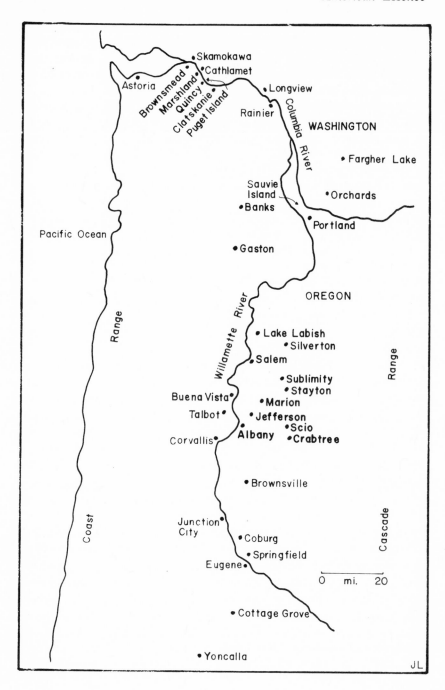

factor aided immeasurably by higher prices resulting from the World War. Todd, acting as a buyer, promoter, instructor, and organizer, was primarily responsible for the development of the industry in what has become, today, one of the major producing regions of peppermint oil in the world. Such an accomplishment, however, did not come at once.

At least two stills operated in the Valley in 1913, both near Albany; that of Todd and another built by Emory Wallace and a Mr. Marshall at Knox Butte.[40] The following year, 1914, W. J. Turnidge began growing mint and built a still at Crabtree and Clyde Sidwell originated production in the Coburg area. In 1916 plantings were extended north near Hillsboro where S. B. Reasoner planted 5½ acres, and near Dallas where about 20 acres were set out.[41] An estimated 4,000 pounds of peppermint oil was produced in 1916, the bulk of it bought by O. H. Todd for shipment to his brother's firm in Michigan.[42]

By 1917 plantings had been established in a large muckland development at Lake Labish and, about 1920, Charles Hermo established plantings on diked land along the lower Columbia River near Quincy with roots obtained from nearby Puget Island (Map 10).

The growth of the industry had been quite rapid but, plagued by several years of bad drought and easing prices near the end of the War due to sharp export decreases, nearly 50 Oregon growers met on January 13, 1917, and resolved to form the Willamette Valley Mint Growers Association.[43] A special committee met on February 13, wrote a constitution and a set of by-laws and elected O. H. Todd first president. Plans called for pooling of oil, establishment of prices, and marketing only through the association, an arrangement not at all unlike that of the Society of Equity's attempt in Michigan in 1906. The Association planned to build a distillery at Corvallis to handle the 1921 crop. A national convention of mint growers was held in Cassopolis, Michigan, in 1920 but support of middlewestern growers for the Oregon movement did not come about due to a considerable disagreement over the selling prices that would be asked for the oil. For many reasons the association, although it existed for a considerable time, did not succeed. Most growers preferred to market independently, especially during periods when prices were rising. But the association also faced a more severe problem, loss of interest in mint cultivation. By 1919 only 14 farms were producing mint in Oregon, involving 116 acres, producing 2,089

Map 10. The Willamette River Valley of Oregon and the lower Columbia River Valley of Oregon and Washington, showing the towns associated with peppermint oil production since the beginning of commercial plantings near Albany, Oregon, in 1913.

pounds of oil for a revenue of $10,455.[44] The industry continued to decline until, by 1924, even O. H. Todd was caused to wonder "whether the mint industry will revive."[45]

Washington. Commercial peppermint production spread from Oregon to the state of Washington about 1917 when plantings were established on drained land on Puget Island in the Columbia River near Quincy, Oregon (Map 10).[46] For "six or seven years" experiments were carried out at the Medicinal Garden of the University of Washington,[47] but expansion did not take place from the immediate vicinity of the Columbia River.

Michigan, Indiana and *New York.* As new cultivation experiments took place in the other states, Michigan and Indiana continued to dominate the production. The census of agriculture for 1909 revealed the following:

State	Farms	Acres	Pounds	Value
Michigan	446	6,360	121,169	$194,391
Indiana	78	1,814	36,621	58,110
New York	?	21	301	499

The decline of the industry to such a limited extent in New York was remarkable in that, as late as 1911, oil brokers in the east were advertising Wayne County peppermint oil "in any quantity."[48] The Hotchkiss Company had no alternative but to turn to the western fields for a source of supply. Despite this fact there continued to be a steady demand from the foreign users for H.G.H. peppermint oil, to some extent based on the assumption that it was the preferred New York oil.

The immediate after-effects of World War I were felt quite deeply by mint growers in Michigan. Troubled to some extent by bad weather, and concerned by falling prices, Michigan growers cut their acreage nearly 40 percent between 1909 and 1919. The census of agriculture for that year tells the story:

State	Farms	Acres	Pounds	Value
Indiana	407	7,107	171,085	$855,425
Michigan	342	3,878	113,135	565,675
Oregon	14	116	2,089	10,445
Ohio	1	100	1,200	6,000
New York	3	9	745	2,980

In this 10 year period, 1909 to 1919, over 100 Michigan growers had abandoned the mint industry and, for the first time in nearly a half century, the commercial mint production lead shifted to a new state,

Indiana. This was a victory Indiana growers would maintain, however, for a slim thirty year period.

There were a number of new plantings in Michigan during this period, but the one that proved to be most important took place in 1913. Charles Sprague, who owned a farm near St. Johns in Clinton County, planted two acres of peppermint roots on his farm. The following year, J. E. Crosby, living just south of St. Johns, purchased the crop from Sprague and had the mint hay distilled about six miles northeast of Carson City in nearby Gratiot County.[49] Other growers soon followed Crosby's lead; "Peppermint Bill" Smith, Eugene Livingston, and John Martis being among the first. From this limited beginning the cultivation of peppermint began to spead into nearby counties and, in a decade, the central Michigan district centered around St. Johns was destined to become the most important mint producing region in the history of the state (Map 11).

Several technological developments of some importance took place in Michigan about this time. Root planting machines (Figure 34), designed to reduce the labor involved in the standard hand-planting techniques, began to come into use on a limited basis, and there was a search for more efficient means of loading and unloading hay for processing at the distillery. Instead of hauling the hay on wagons large cylindrical tanks (forms), which could be placed directly into the distilling tubs, were hauled into the fields and filled (Figure 33). After processing the tanks were removed from the tubs and emptied. This considerably shortened the distilling time since a filled tank could be removed without the delay of hand emptying of the tub. It was also an important forerunner of the mounted, portable distilling tub that came into use about 1940.

During this period most of the distillery equipment was being manufactured by the Star Tank Company of Goshen, the Pioneer Company of Middlebury, both in Indiana, and the Freeland Company of Sturgis, Michigan.

In Indiana major producing counties continued to be St. Joseph, Noble, Lagrange, and Elkhart. Extensive muckland acreages, however, were put into mint in LaPorte, Marshall, Kosciusko, and Starke counties and acreage increased annually:[50]

Year	Acres
1919	7,107
1920	12,383
1923	19,333
1925	20,400

Indiana muckland farmers were finding mint a quite profitable enterprise at the same time that their counterparts in Michigan were aban-

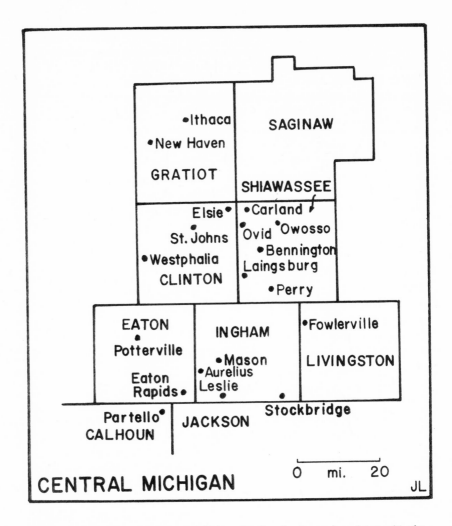

Map 11. Counties of central Michigan, showing the towns associated with the production of peppermint and spearmint oil since the beginning of commercial plantings near St. Johns in 1913.

doning the industry. Some, but not all, of the reason can be attributed to the fact that the acreage in Indiana was being put into new ground with subsequent higher yields. The Indiana farmers would soon discover, however, that the yields from new acreages were not a permanent asset. Michigan fields had also been bothered by a new pest, the mint flea-beetle,[51] and the first hint of an entirely new menace to the mint crop was heard in 1924 when an unknown form of disease was discovered on the Todd plantation at Mentha.[52]

Developments in New York were not at all encouraging during this period and the industry never did revive. By 1904 all mint in New York was of the Black Mitcham type and, the following year, major production areas were centered around Newark, west of Lyons.[53] From 1910 there were only several growers in the entire state. About 1920, stimulated by a short crop and rising prices, there was a revival of interest in mint. John Hutchby of Newark obtained roots from Michigan and plans were made to build two new distilleries near Lyons.[54] There was also some expansion of the industry into the Montezuma Marsh area and in the mucklands around Fairville.[55] The net result, however, was nil, and New York, for all practical purposes, ceased to be a commercial mint oil producer.

Conclusion

As the year 1924 drew to a close, the mint production lead had shifted from Michigan to Indiana but both states continued to be the only significant producers. Numerous attempts had continued to be made to introduce cultivation in new areas but only the development in Oregon seemed to hold any significant promise. The mint industry in the United States had become considerably more stabilized with the establishment of a workable and orderly marketing program which continued to be dominated by the Hotchkiss and Todd companies.

The increasing favor of peppermint and spearmint oils in chewing gum, candy, and toothpaste opened a lucrative domestic market for producers and dealers, and the industry slowly changed from one with an export emphasis to one with increasing attention to the local market. Spearmint came into more common cultivation as a result of its favor among gum and toothpaste manufacturers, and American growers had successfully captured the world market.

A new and more productive type of spearmint had been brought under cultivation and slowly began to dominate the industry. Growers had twice attempted to organize and market their oil in a form of cooperative scheme, and both times met failure because the system did not adequately protect the interests of the superior farmer. Within the apparatus of the accepted marketing program there was still a premium placed on high quality production. Only the poor farmer stood to benefit from the cooperative marketing societies.

As the year 1925 opened there was absolutely no reason to believe that the mint industry in the United States would not continue the basic pattern established during the first quarter of the twentieth century.

REFERENCES

[1]Schimmel and Company, *Semi-annual Report*, p. 45, October, 1899.

[2]*Ibid.*, p. 34, April, 1900.

[3]*Ibid.*, p. 42, October, 1901.

[4]*Ibid.*

[5]A. M. Todd, "The American Peppermint Industry," *V. Internationaler Kongress für Angewandte Chemie*, p. 804, Deutscher-Verlag, Berlin, 1904.

[6]*Semi-annual Report*, op. cit., p. 64, October-November, 1902.

[7]*Ibid.*

[8]*Ibid.*, p. 65.

[9]*Ibid.*, p. 58, April-May, 1903.

[10]*Wayne County Review*, p. 3, February 19, 1903, Lyons, New York.

[11]*Semi-annual Report, op. cit.,* p. 65, October-November, 1902; p. 57, April-May, 1903; p. 55, October-November, 1903; p. 71, April-May, 1904.

[12]"Peppermint Oil Vagaries," *Oil, Paint, and Drug Reporter*, July 6, 1906.

[13]*Semi-annual Report, op. cit.,* pp. 54-55, April-May, 1906. For elaboration of the attitude of the trade toward the growers' attempt to organize, see the following: *Oil, Paint, and Drug Reporter*, September 3, 1907 and Septembr 10, 1906; *Chemist and Druggist*, September 22, 1906, p. 465; October 3, 1906, p. 589.

[14]*Ibid.*, pp. 55-56; *Kalamazoo Telegraph*, Sept. 5, 1906, Kalamazoo, Michigan.

[15]*Ibid.*, pp. 56-57.

[16]J. E. Landing, "Mint Oil Marketing," *Drug and Cosmetic Industry*, vol. 94, no. 1, pp. 34-35, 63, January, 1964.

[17]"Sticking With Gum," *Wall Street Journal*, August 16, 1967.

[18]*Ibid.*

[19]*Semi-annual Report*, op. cit., p. 72, October-November, 1903.

[20]*Ibid.*, p. 114, October-November, 1908.

[21]*Ibid.*, p. 84, October, 1911.

[22]*Ibid.*, p. 117, April, 1912.

[23]*Ibid.*, p. 106, April, 1911.

[24]*Ibid.*, p. 103, October, 1912.

[25]G. M. Hocking, "Scotch Mint and Spearmint. A Comparative Study of Cultural, Morphological, and Histological Characteristics of Species of *Mentha* Growing in Florida," *Journal of the American Pharmaceutical Association*, vol. 38, p. 396, 1949.

[26]E. Guenther, "Oil of Spearmint," *The Manufacturing Confectioner*, vol. 23, no. 8, p. 12, August, 1943.

[27]From Britton and Brown in G. M. Hocking, *op. cit.*, p. 396.

[28]U.S. Census of Agriculture, 1919.

[29]R. Glenk, "Perfumes and Aromatic Chemicals," *Journal of the American Pharmaceutical Association*, vol. 13, p. 1025, 1924.

[30]"Peppermint in Iowa," *Country Gentleman*, vol. 72, no. 2854, p. 956, October 10, 1907.

[31]A. Henkel, *American Medicinal Leaves and Herbs*, Bulletin no. 219, p. 28, Bureau of Plant Industry, USDA, 1911.

[32]H. H. Gardner, "Peppermint for Muck Soils," *Iowa State Horticultural Society Reports: 1931*, pp. 239-242.

[33]F. Rabak, *The Effect of Cultural and Climatic Conditions on the Yield and Quality of Peppermint Oil*, Professional Paper, Bulletin No. 454, USDA, Dec. 9, 1916.

[34]*Paint, Oil, and Drug Review*, vol. 44, p. 18, 1904, in G. M. Hocking, *op. cit.*, p. 340; A. Tschirch, *Handbuch der Pharmakognosie*, vol. 2, p. 930, C. H. Tauchnitz, Leipzig, 1917.

[35]J. Long, "Drug Cultivation in Texas," *Meyer Brothers Druggist*, vol. 39, p. 206, 1908.

[36]A. Tschirch, *op. cit.*, p. 930.

[37]A. F. Sievers, *Travel Report*, pp. 2-5, unpublished manuscript, USDA, 1927.

[38]O. H. Todd, *Memoirs*, unpublished, 1924; through the courtesy of Mrs. Vera Todd McDonald, Eugene, Oregon, daughter of O. H. Todd.

[39]*Ibid.*

[40]G. Shields, "Oregon's First Mint Grew at Jefferson," *Valley News*, Jefferson, Oregon, from the files, not dated. See also, *Sunday Oregonian*, Dec. 26, 1926, Portland, Oregon.

[41]"Oregonians Distilling Peppermint," *Pacific Drug Review*, p. 74, December, 1916.

[42]*Ibid.*

[43]M. D. Butler, "Oregon Peppermint Men Organize," *Market Growers Journal*, vol. 20, p. 228, March 1, 1917; A. G. B. Bouquet, *"Mint Growers Pool Product,"* *Ibid.*, vol. 27 p. 146, October 1, 1920, mentions that Oregon growers pooled their oil and offered it for $8 per pound. By 1921 the Willamette Valley Association had been superceded by the Oregon Mint Growers Co-operative Association with G. Moisan of Gervais as secretary: C. W. Johnson and R. Wilkes, "A Study of Pacific Coast Peppermint Oil," *Journal of the American Pharmaceutical Association*, vol. 12, pp. 782-785, 1923; A. F. Sievers, *op. cit.*, pp. 38-39.

[44]U.S. Census of Agriculture, 1919.

[45]O. H. Todd, *op. cit.*

[46]A. F. Sievers, *op. cit.*, p. 17.

[47]C. W. Johnson and R. Wilkes, *op. cit.*, p. 783.

[48]*Semi-annual Report, op. cit.*, p. 68, October, 1911.

[49]*The Republican-News*, St. Johns, Michigan, special centennial issue, 1956, section 11, p. 4. Other mint articles are: section 8, p. 4; section 11, p. 3. See also: F. Pritchard, "Peppermint: Michigan's Magic Carpet", *The State Journal*, Lansing, Michigan, October 18, 1936.

[50]*Indiana Crops and Livestock*, No. 99, p. 20, Purdue University, 1933. An extensive account of the Woodward Brothers farm near Grovertown, Indiana, can be found in: W. B. Throope, "Mint on Marsh Land," *The Country Gentleman*, vol. 80, pp. 624-625, March 27, 1915.

[51]Extensive studies on this beetle were undertaken by L. G. Gentner of Michigan State College who published a number of reports: e.g., *The Mint Flea-beetle (Longitarsus waterhousei Kutschera): Its Habits and Measures for Control*, Circular 125, Agricultural Experiment Station, Michigan State College, 1929.

[52]R. Nelson, "Verticillium sp. (?) wilt," quoted by G. H. Martin in "Diseases of Forest and Shade Trees and Miscellaneous Plants in the United States in 1925," *The Plant Disease Reporter*, supplement 50, p. 474, December 1, 1926.

[53]*Semi-annual Report, op. cit.*, p. 54, April-May, 1905.

[54]A. H. Pulver, "Peppermint Revival Promised," *Market Growers Journal*, vol. 27, no. 1, p. 12, July 1, 1920.

[55]C. VanDuyne, N. M. Kirk, W. Seltzer, J. P. Gum, and H. W. Erde, *Soil Survey of Wayne County, New York*, p. 282, Bureau of Soils, USDA, 1923.

Chapter 9.

The Great Price Rise

The 1924 Crop[1]

As the distilling season of 1924 drew to a close in Michigan and Indiana it became apparent that production was going to be considerably reduced from 1923. Final estimates were that the crop was off from ⅓ to ½ and the supply of oil would fall nearly 10 percent short of meeting just the domestic needs not to mention the entire export market. Because of the short supply prices of peppermint and spearmint oil gradually advanced to new highs. A quotation chronology of natural oil prices, per pound, was as follows:

August 27, 1924		February 2, 1925	
peppermint	$4.50	peppermint	$13.00
spearmint	2.60	spearmint	4.50
October 3, 1924		March 2, 1925	
peppermint	7.50	peppermint	15.00
spearmint	3.50	spearmint	4.50
December 24, 1924			
peppermint	9.75		
spearmint	4.35		

By early spring practically all the available supply had been sold by farmers and country dealers, but the price rise had attracted the attention of many new growers and a considerable expansion of acreage was expected during 1925.

The supply of peppermint oil was further reduced when it became necessary for some of the large American manufacturers to begin using increased quantities of oil to obtain natural menthol since the normal supply had been considerably disrupted as a result of the Japanese earthquake of 1923.

By May of 1925 the expected acreage increases had been realized. Buyers looked forward to a banner production year of nearly 600,000 pounds of oil, far in excess of the domestic demand of about 400,000 pounds annually. Buying eased, prices began to slump a little, and all parties waited for the new crop to come in. Their wait was shortly shattered by an unexpected event.

The Great Frost

On Sunday and Monday, May 24 and 25, 1925, a severe killing frost hit southern Michigan and northern Indiana and decimated the mint fields. The plants were already late owing to an extremely cold winter and a spring marked with excessive rain and high winds. The frost was immediately followed by a period of high heat and drought. Although growers were quick to recognize the extent of the damage, estimating that not more than 200,000 pounds of the expected supply would be harvested, dealers and brokers interpreted the reports as another scare tactic to drive prices even higher. For a time the market was at a standstill as interested parties gathered to assess the true situation. Contrasting reports were given, a favorable one from a trade journal:[2]

> careful survey of the situation in the peppermint growing regions enables the *Oil, Paint and Drug Reporter* to form the opinion that in the absence of further unfavorable weather conditions, the production of peppermint oil this year will be larger than that in 1924. But the crop will be several weeks late; as the setback by the frosts in May will not permit distillation to start until the second week of August. . . Under the most favorable growing conditions, the total yield of oil would be, perhaps, 50 percent greater than the 1924 production.

Such optimistic reports brought a sharp rejoinder from an Indiana grower and dealer:[3]

> Editor,
> We have refrained from writing you on your bits of "foolish ideas" on the Oil Peppermint situation; but you have persisted in talking wisely on a subject of which it seems to us you know nothing of. In your various articles on Oil Peppermint you state or hint that you receive many different opinions or advice as to the crop situation on this article, and it leaves you in an uncertain state of mind. So from this wouldn't you believe that the wisest policy is to thoroughly investigate the situation yourself, and thereby eliminate the "guesswork."
> In many of your statements you hint as if the Primary dealers are a banded organization whose main purpose in life is to take advantage of the Consumer. But no monopoly exists amongst the dealers here, this matter was investigated by the Department of Justice and not a thing wrong

was found by them. Further the primary dealers are not speculators, but apply to their business the soundest of economic principles.

In brief our final analysis shows that the peppermint yield will at the maximum not exceed 200,000 pounds, and a very probable minimum of 160,000 pounds; also to be taken into consideration is that we enter the new crop year without any carry-over of oil. The above figures are backed by us, and will aid anyone who cares to have these figures verified. Kindly take the above facts into consideration before publishing anything further on Oil of Peppermint.

Bremen, Ind.   M. Brown and Sons
Sept. 21, 1925   M. Brown

The conservative estimates proved to be the more correct. By June 22 peppermint prices had advanced to $17.50 a pound, reached $19 on June 29, and went over $20, an all time high, on July 13. Since growers had reacted primarily to the peppermint market, spearmint acreage was considerably reduced and the impending shortage of that product drove prices to $14 a pound on August 17.

As the 1925 distilling season opened in late July it appeared for a time that even the most optimistic estimates would be too low. But such hopes were soon shattered as the actual limited nature of the 1925 crop became increasingly apparent. There simply was not enough mint oil to meet all the demands.

The Great Price Rise

The shortage of mint oil even reached the shores of Japan as menthol producers in that country, expecting a flood of orders from American users, increased their prices. A leading gum manufacturer purchased over 40,000 pounds of the 1925 mint oil crop, further depleting available supplies. By November it was estimated that only 50,000 pounds of mint oil was available to last for the remainder of the season until the 1926 crop came in. Peppermint oil was now selling at $29 a pound and spearmint oil for $15 (Figure 36). Growers rejoiced in their good fortune. A single Indiana mint farmer was reported to have netted $75,000 from his mint crop, and many others between $15,000 and $30,000. The net income of Michigan and Indiana growers was estimated at nearly $6,000,000.[4]

Mint oil had become such a valuable commodity that many Michigan and Indiana farmers, in order to protect themselves from theft, stored their supply in local bank vaults.[5] The holding of this oil in hopes that prices would go even higher acted further to deplete stocks. The situation had become so critical that Secretary of Commerce Hoover was urged to investigate the mint industry to determine if the shortage was a real one or the result of a monopolistic enterprise. But a more serious problem that faced the industry was the possibility that many of the users of mint oils would turn to substitutes, especially Japanese mint oil and synthetics.

The Japanese Mint Problem

Japanese mint (*Mentha arvensis* L.) had been cultivated in the Orient for centuries and was the chief source of natural menthol. Japan was the major world supplier. With the menthol removed the resulting de-mentholized oil has an odor and a taste not unlike natural peppermint oil but is much ranker, coarser, and less desirable.

For many years it had been the custom of fraudulent peppermint dealers to adulterate their oil with de-mentholized Japanese mint oil. This enabled peppermint stocks to last longer and also increased profits since the Japanese oil generally sold at a price well under American peppermint oil. Major users of peppermint would also turn to the Japanese oil in times of short supply since the Japanese mint oil represented the best known substitute.

As a result of pressure from the American industry the Department of Agriculture, acting under the statutes of the Pure Food and Drug Act, made a ruling in 1923 that any product labelled "mint" or "mint flavored" must contain natural peppermint oil and could not be flavored with that of Japanese mint. The Department's rationale was that the Japanese mint plant had been identified by the American botanist Asa Gray as Corn mint, was specifically distinct from the peppermint plant and, therefore, was not a true peppermint. As a result, the de-mentholized Japanese oil had to be referred to as corn mint oil or field mint oil and all products containing the material had to be labelled accordingly. This development was a distinct advantage for the American mint industry. Peppermint was further protected in that the *United States Pharmacopeia* specifically designated that anything compounded from natural peppermint oil had to use material distilled from the plant *Mentha piperita* L. This automatically eliminated the Japanese product.

At the same time, however, there were no such stringent regulations regarding peppermint oil in the major European importing countries. When the American supply was short, or too high priced, users naturally turned to the Japanese product and American exports fell off sharply. Many British importers were accused of mixing a small quantity of American oil with that of the Japanese and labelling it "American blended." This was a major reason why the shift from export to domestic consumption was so important for the American industry.

The developments of 1924 and 1925 also brought attention to the possibility of developing synthetic mint oils. A synthetic menthol had been perfected but the work of drug and flavoring chemists had not yet been able to compound a suitable substitute for peppermint or spearmint oil. In order to ease the plight of large American users of mint oils, however, the Department of Agriculture did allow the designation "peppermint flavor, non-alcoholic, fortified with synthetic menthol" to be used on any product containing a mixture of synthetic menthol, mineral oil, and 3 percent peppermint oil.

But the American industry was not content to rest entirely on the protection of the pure food and drug laws. As the use of flavoring substitutes increased, and since imports of Japanese mint oil had risen from 375 pounds in 1924 to over 50,000 pounds in 1925, trade restrictionists began to apply pressure on the government for increased tariff rates on the Japanese product.

The Protectionists Rally

In 1911 the tariff rate on imported peppermint oil had been lowered from 50c to 25c a pound. Since this rate applied to most essential oils it was an advantage to the users of Japanese mint oil. In 1922 the tariff rate on imported essential oils was changed to 25 percent of value,[6] and was the rate prevailing during the great price rise.

Indiana and Michigan farmers became increasingly concerned with activities of Japanese mint oil dealers. Convinced that the foreigners were conspiring to regulate American exports and develop a monopolistic combine to capture all the American business, they called their Congressmen to action.[7] The growers' concern was looked upon in the trade with some humor, and the entire idea labelled a "Japanese Romance" story.[8] Nevertheless, Indiana growers were able to convince Congressman Hickey of LaPorte who, in April, 1926, introduced a bill to amend the 1922 tariff law and increase the rate on Japanese mint oil from 25 to 100 percent. The bill died.

The Market Breaks

In some manner, the industry weathered the winter of 1925-1926. The total mint oil production for 1925 proved to be nearly 350,000 pounds, a compromise between the optimists and the pessimists. After reaching prices of nearly $32 a pound for peppermint oil and $16 a pound for spearmint oil the heavy buying season came to a close and the demand eased (Figure 36). Prices dropped some then firmed throughout the winter at about $15 for peppermint and $8 for spearmint. By this time, however, there was practically no oil available for sale. The high prices had attracted such attention among farmers that preliminary estimates placed the 1926 potential production at double that of 1925. It seemed that every farmer in the nation was determined to reap some of the benefits of the prevailing shortage. As buyers and users looked forward to a peak production year and a return to more normal pricing and business activity, however, the growers in Michigan and Indiana once more turned their attention to cooperative marketing in an effort to maintain higher prices.

The Association Flurry

During the spring of 1925 a South Bend, Indiana, banker, George Knoblock, aware of the potential advantages of a new cooperative marketing law passed by the Indiana state legislature, suggested the possibilities of such an organization to several peppermint growers.[9] The idea took root and the St. Joseph Valley Mint Growers Cooperative Association was formed with Claude Nettrower of Lakeville as President, Edward D. Getz of South Bend as Vice-president, and S. J. Stuart of Elkhart as Secretary. About 20 members were recruited during the 1925 season and the Association was able to market its first supply of oil in the fall for $14.25 a pound. Coming before the great price rise, this marketing success attracted the attention of more growers and membership slowly grew.

The Association officers were energetic and mission-minded men. They made plans to build a warehouse in South Bend to hold 100,000 pounds of oil, and 100 carloads of coal and large supplies of potash were ordered to enable growers to handle the processing of the 1926 crop. Spurred by the high prices and expecting the coming season to produce additional high revenues, despite buyer predictions of overproduction and lower prices, the officers conducted a vigorous membership campaign throughout Indiana and Michigan.

By February, 1926, membership had increased to over 200, and South Bend banks had placed a $500,000 credit at the disposal of the Association to finance the crops and sales of the members.[10] Through the activities of the Association it was possible to enlist the aid of Congressman Hickey who introduced the bill to raise the tariff on Japanese mint oil. As the 1926 season approached the Association proposed that all members pool their oil and allow the organization to attend to marketing. With adequate financing, facilities, and grower cooperation, success was not to be denied.

Growers were attracted to the Association for many reasons. A number had sold their supply of 1924 and 1925 oil under a contracted price and were, therefore, denied the full benefits of the buying season price advances. Others, trying to outwit the dealers, had held their oil too long and had to sell at a price much less than the peak. It appeared logical to many of them, especially the smaller acreage producers, that the only possible way of beating the market was to pool the oil and sell it cooperatively. The idea was attractive enough that the Association had more than 600 members in Indiana, Michigan and Oregon, by September of 1926.[11] As the distilling season progressed most of the growers held their oil and stored it in bank vaults or shipped it to the Association warehouse in South Bend.

The Association Dies

John Getz of South Bend, son of the Secretary, was hired by the Association in 1926 to serve as field representative. Getz first promised the growers that a $15 asking price would be requested for their oil. When the fall market opened at about $12 a pound asking prices were eased downward. The Association began disposing of oil, but prices had to be continuously adjusted downward since 1926 production proved to be spectacularly successful. The input of new acreages combined with a favorable growing season placed more than 650,000 pounds of mint oil on the market from the 1926 crop. There was enough oil available from non-members that the Association was hard pressed to hold prices.

In a last ditch effort to control the market Getz obtained financing from the Morris Company of South Bend to build up a pool of 100,000 pounds of oil for which growers would be guaranteed $5.50 a pound on peppermint. Growers, disgruntled at the tumbling prices, responded. Getz held rallies, placarded the mint areas with posters cautioning the growers against selling too soon (Figure 37), and set about to get grower pledges for their oil. When the deadline was reached, however, the Association was 22,000 pounds short of the pool goal and the Morris Company withdrew its offer. Undaunted, Getz obtained different financing and set out in early December to obtain pledges to build a pool of 150,000 pounds. Getz was convinced that with this amount of oil held by the Association the market would react favorably and growers could realize greater profits than they expected. Again growers responded.

Fifty-four farmers from the Decatur, Michigan, area pledged nearly 15,000 pounds for Getz's pool, and 11 Berrien County, Michigan, growers pledged an additional 20,000 pounds.[12] With the added Indiana total it looked as if the pool might succeed. In early December disaster struck.

Dr. J. E. Maxwell, a large mint grower in the Decatur area, and a member of the Association, had not pledged his 1926 oil to the pool. According to the rules this left him free to market his oil independently. After holding his oil until late November, Dr. Maxwell concluded that the Association goals were unrealistic and the prevailing prices could not be maintained. Accordingly he sold his entire crop of 2,400 pounds of oil to the Todd Company for $5 a pound.[13] Several days later unknown "criminals" planted a charge of dynamite under Dr. Maxwell's distillery which destroyed the boiler, tanks, and condensing worm, and blew off the east side of the still shed. This "malicious crime, one of the worst perpetrated in Decatur in recent years,"[14] caused an explosion that shook the houses of the neighborhood and was plainly heard in the village two miles away. The Van Buren County sheriff, after conducting an investigation, offered the following reward on December 2, 1926 (Figure 35):[15]

$100

I will give a reward of $100 for information which will lead to the arrest and convinction of the person or persons guilty of dynamiting the peppermint distil of Dr. J. E. Maxwell.

Glenn Weaver,
Sheriff of Van Buren County.

It was believed that the crime was committed in revenge for Dr. Maxwell's failure to support the Association. Within days, however, other growers became convinced that Maxwell was correct. C. L. Brooks of Fennville, Michigan, had deposited 200 pounds of peppermint oil with the Association in South Bend for which he received a bank loan of $3 per pound. In early December he was notified by the bank that he would have to sell his oil and repay the loan. Since the Association had not yet reached its goal of 150,000 pounds it refused to market his oil, leaving Brooks considerably distraught.[16] Similar episodes occurred in other producing areas involving many growers. Soon a flood of oil was being released by growers and prices dropped even lower. The Association then became embroiled in a slander suit against the Leman-Gerber Company of Bremen, Indiana, representatives of which had criticized the Association as being inefficient and mismanaged.

The end came quickly for Getz. Realizing that his promises were completely unrealistic, officers of the Association deposed the glib field representative whereupon he promptly filed suit and asked the court to place the Association in receivership.[17] After hearing a series of heated arguments from both sides Judge J. Fred Bingham of South Bend superior court denied the receivership and declared the Association solvent enough to continue to transact business.

The Association rebounded from the Getz disaster and moved on to even greener pastures. At a meeting held in South Bend in January, 1927, the Association set forth ideas to inaugurate a five year plan of compulsory cooperative marketing, to make South Bend the center of the peppermint and spearmint business, to construct massive facilities for storing, grading, and processing oils, and to build pharmaceutical plants to utilize the oil.[18] South Bend was to become the financial mint center of the world, adding more than $4,000,000 to local revenues. The grandiose scheme never came to pass.

In March the American Trust Company filed suit against the Association for an overdue note. Growers, disenchanted with the failure of their organization to successfully market the crop according to their expectations, failed to renew memberships. There were too many growers outside the organization to enable it to succeed. In the meantime peppermint prices had dropped below $4 a pound, 1927 acreage predictions signalled another record crop, and all indications were that prices would go even lower. The seller's market was over and, instead of banding together in a cooperative association, many growers decided to abandon the business altogether. Mint growers had discovered again that cooperative marketing organizations do not work unless the members cooperate.

Conclusion

The years 1924, 1925, and 1926 had been tumultous ones in the mint industry. The great price rise had set off a chain reaction that threatened, for a time, to reorient the entire marketing pattern. Great attention had been concentrated on export problems and Japanese competition. Increasing attempts to develop synthetic mint oils were made. The St. Joseph Valley Mint Growers Cooperative Association had attempted to corner the peppermint and spearmint market, but a resulting plethora of law suits brought about its demise.

When the dust had settled the position of the country dealers had been strengthened, growers had become convinced that cooperative marketing had more disadvantages than met the eye, prices returned to low levels, supplies were more than adequate, and distilleries began to be dismantled at almost the same rate that they had been constructed. This tremendous involvement, however, of American farmers from coast to coast, all wanting to be in on the killing, a process by which they killed themselves, was an amazing story of the adaptability of American agriculture.

REFERENCES

[1]Unless otherwise specified the material for this chapter was taken from the essential oil sections and market quotations for the years 1924, 1925, 1926, and 1927, from the following publications: *Oil, Paint, and Drug Reporter, Drug and Chemical Markets, New York Commercial,* and *Commerce Monthly.*

[2]"The Peppermint Oil Outlook," *Oil, Paint and Drug Reporter,* p. 20, June 8, 1925.

[3]"Disagrees on Peppermint Situation," *Drug and Chemical Markets,* Oct. 7, 1925.

[4]*Decatur Republican,* Decatur, Michigan, January 21, 1926.

[5]*South Bend Tribune,* South Bend, Indiana, October 28, 1925.

[6]*U.S. Import Duties Annotated,* U.S. Department of Commerce, 1926.

[7]"A New Crop for Indiana Farmers," *The Unafraid Republican,* Mt. Vernon, Indiana, January 27, 1926.

[8]"A Japanese Romance," *Drug and Chemical Markets,* p. 314, February 4, 1926.

[9]"New 'Klondike' Region Produces 80 per cent. of Peppermint Oil Sold to Markets of World," *Indianapolis News,* January 18, 1926.

[10]"Peppermint Oil Speculation Forces Growers to Organize," *New York Commercial,* February 3, 1926.

[11]"Peppermint Oil to Have Banner Production Year," *South Bend Tribune,* September 1, 1926.

[12]"Forming New Mint Oil Pool," *Decatur Republican,* December 2, 1926.

[13]"Maxwell Peppermint Distil Dynamited," *Ibid.,* December 2, 1926.

[14]*Ibid.*

[15]*Ibid.*

[16]"Peppermint Oil Market Weak," *Decatur Republican,* Dec. 9, 1926.

[17]"John Getz Makes War on St. Joseph Valley Mint Association," *Decatur Republican,* February 3, 1927.

[18]"Pass Resolution for Cooperative Selling," *South Bend Tribune,* January 28, 1927.

Chapter 10.

The Great Response

The reaction to the great price rise period of 1924-1926 was intense, occasionally dramatic, and wide-reaching. In addition to the trade and cooperative marketing responses described in the previous chapter the great price rise also provoked a good deal of study and research, innovation, and, of great significance, one of the most massive acreage expansions in the history of the American mint industry.

Study and Research

The tremendous interest aroused by the very high mint oil prices resulted in a number of professional surveys and experimental plantings designed to increase general knowledge of the industry. The U.S. Department of Agriculture sent Arthur F. Sievers, a senior biochemist in the Bureau of Plant Industry, on a tour of the mint producing areas during the summer of 1927. This trip, and the resulting travel report, eventuated in a special bulletin devoted to the raising and processing of peppermint and spearmint,[1] the third federal government publication concerning mint production.[2]

The agricultural experiment station in Indiana had published a bulletin on mint production in that state as early as 1917,[3] but the price rise prompted similar publications by experiment stations in Oregon (1925),[4] Michigan (1926),[5] and Washington (1936),[6] and by the Iowa State Horticultural Society (1931).[7]

In 1926 experimental plantings for research purposes were set out in Washington and Florida. About 1/20 of an acre of peppermint was established at the Prosser Irrigation Experiment Station in Washington,[8] and the medicinal garden at the University of Florida was stocked with a number of different types of mint plants including peppermint and spearmint.[9] In relation to the research on peppermint at Florida a newspaper quoted a government source as saying that "experiments under way predict a great possibility for a wide development of the peppermint industry in Florida where there are thousands of acres of favorable soil."[10]

Research specialists in the agricultural experiment stations of the major producing states began to become increasingly involved in studies concerning the cultivation, harvesting, distilling, and marketing of mint oils, and considerable attention was paid to such problems as water needs, fertilizers, insect, weed, and disease control. Since that time there has been a steady flow of bulletins, reports, technical studies, and marketing statistics published by the states of Indiana, Michigan, Oregon, and Washington.

Innovation

A rural Indiana newspaper in 1928 very neatly summarized the major technological advancements in the mint industry that had occurred within recent years.[11] The writer itemized the advancements as follows: introduction of low pressure boilers; submerged condensers; improved hoisting equipment, and new mint planters. To this list could also have been added the increasing acceptance of the Black Mitcham peppermint and the Scotch spearmint, and the gradual transition from horse power to tractors.

Planting new acreages of peppermint and spearmint had always been a problem and required considerable hand labor. It was a general practice to extend new plantings by digging out the established rootstock in the spring from a particularly healthy section of a two or three year old field (Figure 38). Although the number of roots varied considerably a good stand would supply about 1,000 grain sacks of roots from an acre, enough stock to replant an additional 50 acres. The roots were usually forked to the surface, the soil shaken off, the stock trimmed, and then laid out in the furrows by hand, the planter covering the root with soil as he walked along (Figure 39).

Another expansion technique, not uncommonly practiced, was to pull some plants, roots and all, from an established field and transplant them on the new acreage. Both procedures, however, were time consuming and labor committing and there was a constant search for machines that would do the task more efficiently and economically. For a considerable period of time, converted potato planters which would feed out the roots in a long, straight line served quite satisfactorily, although they were employed by only the larger operators. For transplanting, a wagon, similar to that used for planting cabbage, was rigged with a low platform so that a seated operator facing to the rear could insert the mint plants one by one into the soil as he was pulled forward by the tractor. In the mucklands of Indiana and Michigan it was not uncommon to dig out the roots in the fall, place them in large piles and cover them with dirt. This "pitting" technique occasionally protected the rootstock from severe winter weather, especially when snow cover was light, leaving the fields bare and exposed.

On his 1927 trip Sievers visited a farm in Oregon on which roots were dug out by cutting the field into squares about 15 to 18 inches wide with a machine something similar to a sod cutter. The squares were then lifted whole and the roots shaken clear.[12]

There was a tremendous demand for rootstock during the spring months of 1925 and 1926 as farmers throughout the land sought to get in on the mint killing (Figure 41). Newspapers in the major producing areas were filled with advertisements such as the following from the *Decatur Republican:*[13]

For Sale

5 acres English peppermint roots plowed under last fall, are very thick and large as they are on old celery ground, price $1.00 per square rod.
Earl L. Whitmore   Glenwood, Michigan

C. J. Moisan of Gervais, Oregon, undoubtedly established some sort of record in 1925 when he sold 17,000 sacks of mint roots from 20 acres for $1.25 an acre.[14] This many sacks would enable the buyers to plant 350 new acres of peppermint.

Weeding also required great amounts of hand labor because machine cultivation damaged the plants, except when they were very young, with resulting losses of oil. The problem was greater on old fields since mint, being a perennial herb, would grow in a random pattern and obscure the rows set out the first year. New mint, known as "row mint," has always been easier to cultivate than old mint, known as "field mint" or "meadow mint." The general practice of hand weeding and hoeing was continued, although some growers experimented with animals; cows, goats, and sheep were turned into the mint fields. The animals would avoid eating the spicy mint plants but would quickly glean off the grass and other weeds. Hoof damage to the mint plants was so excessive that the practice never became too widespread. Later, geese were used as weeders and were found to be efficient enough that the practice spread and became particularly important in Washington.

When harvested the mints were cut like any hay crop and placed in small cocks or windrows which, after drying for a day or so, would be placed on wagons and hauled to the distillery (Figure 42). The general middlewestern practice of cutting with large hand scythes never became too common in the west (Figure 40), various forms of mowers being employed to cut the crop. Sievers found one grower near Coburg, Oregon, who harvested by chopping each plant with a sharp hoe, a tedious process, but justified on the basis that mowers knocked off too many leaves and reduced profits.[15] During favorable seasons the cutting of a second crop was generally practiced but many growers felt this depleted the vitality of the roots to such an extent that it was not recommended.

Changes in the distillery equipment were always being made (Figure 45). The wooden stilling tubs costing around $90 (also known as vats or retorts), gradually gave way to large, 7 foot, galvanized steel tubs costing $100, generally circular but occasionally rectangular in shape. Small motors began to replace the hand pulleys by which the hay was lifted into and out of the tubs. Submerged multitubular condensers in which the tubes or pipes passed through a rectangular tub filled with water slowly began to replace the drip-type worm condensers commonly employed for so many years. Such condensers were generally horizontal in layout but vertical units were also employed.

Hand fired boilers for generating steam represented the single most expensive item in the distillery. As acreages planted by single growers in Michigan and Indiana became extremely large it was necessary to have a high capacity boiler. High pressure units, employing from 80 to 110 pounds of steam pressure, generally constructed in pairs, became increasingly common, but were expensive. Smaller growers more frequently constructed a lower pressure boiler, employing 15 to 25 pounds of steam pressure. This unit, known in the western states as the "fog boiler," required a much longer time for distilling a load of mint hay than the high pressure types but was popular due to its more reasonable cost (Figure 44).

Many of the early distilleries used in the western states had been shipped from Indiana and Michigan, and quite a number of steam boilers had been secured from old logging camps since the latter were slowly shifting to gas power. But the Eastman Brothers Manufacturing Company, located at Silverton, Oregon, became an important local supplier. A conspicuous feature of the distilling tub manufactured by the company was the "water seal" which prevented steam escaping from the tub. The cover fitted into a trough on the tub about 4 inches wide and 8 inches deep, which was filled with water. This sealed the tub and was effective as long as steam pressure did not build up sufficiently enough to force the lid upward. Other designs utilized gaskets of various materials to seal the tubs.

During the prohibition era mint distillery operators were required to have federal and state permits to operate. An Indiana newspaper commented succinctly on this necessity.[16]

> Affidavits must be made and filed with the federal officials, showing that the stills are not to be used for the illegal "production of distilled spirits for beverage purpose." Just how a galvanized iron mint still could be used to produce "moonshine" is not made clear; but the federal prohibition authorities have set up a system of "red tape" that is going to cause great confusion and much delay for peppermint growers, and for the makers and retailers of mint stills.
>
> A number of firms in Elkhart, St. Joseph, Marshall, and other nearby counties are engaged in the manufacture of these stills. According to the new regulations, the following procedure must be carried out:
>
> "The manufacturer must notify in writing the Collector of Internal Revenue of the district in which the still is manufactured, requesting a permit for the removal of the still, stating by whom it is to be used, its serial number, capacity, material of which it is made, the time when the same is to be removed, and the place where it is to be set up.
>
> "This request must be accompanied by an affidavit in triplicate from the purchaser of the still. This affidavit must show:
>
> 1. Name of manufacturer and address.
> 2. Place where still is to be set up and by whom.
> 3. Capacity of still per hour.
> 4. Material from which it is made.
> 5. Purpose for which it is to be used.
> 6. A statement that it is not to be used for the production of distilled spirits for beverage purposes.
>
> "One copy of the affidavit is to be retained by the manufacturer or former owner of the still, the other two copies are to be sent by the manufacturer to the Collector of Internal Revenue, with a letter requesting a permit to remove the still to the party making the affidavit.
>
> "After the still is set up, the owner must then apply to the Prohibition Administrator of the district in which the still is set up for Form 26, with which to register the still before it can be used."
>
> Just how long it will take to go through all this official red tape is not known, but dealers in mint stills in this region declare it will seriously delay farmers in getting new equipment ready for use this summer, and will work great hardship and expense upon manufacturers and farmers.

A most ingenious experiment on peppermint cultivation was carried out on the A. M. Todd farm at Mentha in 1929, involving the use of mulch paper, an item which attracted wide attention from vegetable growers in the United States about this time. In a letter describing the results to his employer, the farm superintendent, Richard F. Stroud, left little doubt regarding the future of mulch paper and peppermint.

Today the purity of ones Peppermint Oil goes a very long way with the manufacturers of the lowly chewing-gum. So much so that it occurred to one of them, after reading the Mulch-paper advertisements, and noting the absolute absence of weeds, that here was a panacea for weedy oil.

They accordingly asked a grower to make the test for them and it fell to the lot of the writer to carry out the experiment in spite of its very evident misgivings.

A plot was prepared and a perfect tilth obtained. Ten rolls of paper eighteen inches wide and three hundred yards long were purchased and then the fun began.

With the aid of three men and every variety of tool the paper was well and truly laid in strips three feet from centre to centre, its edges buried two inches deep. It might be well to state at this juncture that this work was done by an American, an Englishman, an Austrian and a naturalized Italian. The names that paper was called during the process of laying would not be found in any of their respective dictionaries.

It might also be well to advise that up to this point some fifty dollars per acre had been invested.

The day was hot and the surface soil dry but the writer was tempted to set half a dozen plants just for the hell of it. With an iron-shod dibber a hole was made in the centre of a strip and a plant placed therein. There was nothing for it but to punch another hole alongside in order to tighten the plant in the ground. The paper had a temperature of about 150° F which fried the six plants in about as many minutes.

So we waited until it had cooled off the next morning and then worked fast and furiously. Even so it took at least four times as long to plant the area through paper as it would have to plant in the bare ground.

With the planting completed we looked with pride on the long straight rows of plants with the neat and weedless background of placid paper.

Tis well we did not reserve our admiration for another day for that same evening a wind-storm sprang up. The next morning the sight was enough to discourage the most ardent Mulch-paper enthusiast.

Strips were torn up, rolled up, blown up; some in ditches, some hanging in festoons around a nearby telephone pole and some maybe over in the next county, who knows? Anyway it was a mess and there was absolutely no way to replace the paper. About ten percent had been removed and much of the remainder loosened at the edges. A great deal of this damage might have been averted had the ends of each roll been buried instead of lapped over the preceding roll.

Experience sure makes fools wise.

Rain followed the wind and from then on all was well. Plants thrived and grew faster than other plants set in the bare ground. Weeds in the spaces between the strips and in the many holes made in the paper grew likewise and had to be removed entirely by hand work as no horse-drawn tool could possibly navigate without upsetting the whole outfit.

The number of hand-weedings would at least double or even treble this expense item as compared with bare ground planting.

Eventually the crop was raised and the delicate question arose as to how to harvest it. A mowing machine was out of the question so men with scythes did this work. A horse-drawn rake was likewise impossible so men with hand rakes were necessary and even then some paper got into the cocks. By this time the paper was pretty well chopped and torn up and disclosed a mass of runners as white as macaroni between the paper and the soil. Sun, wind and early frosts dried up quantities of these before a plow mercifully buried roots, runners and paper and put an end to the most unhandy procedure for raising weedless peppermint ever attempted.

Looking back at the experiment in the cool of a January blizzard it is quite plain that first-year mint needs no Mulch-paper as this crop is very rarely weedy at the time of distilling.

So the real problem of producing second and third year mint free from weeds by the use of Mulch-paper has never been attempted.

It is a problem to baffle the ingenuity of Professor Lucifer Butts and the writer of this paper is happy to hand over its solution to some budding professor of that description.

Next problem please!

Black Mitcham peppermint continued to grow in importance. It was the only type grown in the Pacific coast states and, by 1922, had completely supplanted American peppermint in Michigan.[17] By 1917 it accounted for more than half of the Indiana acreage.[18] Scotch spearmint, on the other hand, expanded outward from Michigan more slowly and accounted for only 50 percent of the American acreage as late as 1943.[19]

The Vast Expansion

The price rise had stimulated interest of farmers in mint cultivation throughout the land. State and federal agricultural agencies were deluged with inquiries and requests for roots. Much of the expansion was purely speculative, involving land developers and growers with no more interest in mint than the money they thought they might make. In most cases a conspicuous lack of knowledge of both cultivation and marketing was more apparent than successful yields of oil. Whatever the case, the great price rise stimulated for several years one of the most significant acreage expansions in the history of the American mint industry. This expansion pattern fell into two major categories: the introduction of mint into states where it was not then being grown, such as Virginia, Missouri, Idaho, Iowa, Arkansas, Texas, Ohio, and California; and the expansion of acreage and development of new producing areas in the major mint states of Indiana, Michigan, Washington, Oregon, and New York.

Virginia. In 1926 the U.S. Department of Agriculture announced that peppermint fields had been developed in Virginia.[20] Nothing further is known although the state was listed as a producer, probably erroneously, as late as 1955.[21] For many years the Department of Agriculture carried out experiments on mint plants at the experimental farm near Arlington.

Missouri. Peppermint cultivation was successfully introduced into Missouri in an unspecified location in 1925.[22] A trade journal reported that "Missouri's first peppermint crop, an experiment by a Mennonite colony, was grown this year, and the first cutting yielded 50 pounds of oil to the acre. It is estimated that the second cutting will yield 30 pounds to the acre."[23] It is possible that the Missouri development was related, in some way, to the industry in Indiana where a great number of mint growers were Old Order Amish and Mennonites, especially in Elkhart, Lagrange, and Kosciusko counties. The close kinship and constant communication among the members in various states probably attracted interest wherever Amish and Mennonites lived at the time. It is known that peppermint cultivation was re-introduced into Iowa and Ohio primarily through the involvement of Indiana Amish farmers.

Idaho. Peppermint growing was established along the Snake River in Canyon County near Caldwell, Idaho, and, by 1929, two farmers were cultivating 19 acres from which were obtained 800 pounds of oil worth $2,200.[24] For some unknown reason, probably low prices, both the Missouri and Idaho plantings, despite high yields, lasted only several years.

Iowa. About 1926 several Old Order Amish farmers in the settlements near Hazleton and Kalona, Iowa, obtained some mint rootstock from relatives in Indiana. Plantings were made but no serious effort to move into a commercial phase was ever attempted.

Arkansas. According to the U.S. Census of Agriculture for 1929 there was a single mint farm in Arkansas consisting of two acres of plantings from which 133 pounds of oil worth $366 were produced.

Texas. In a letter from a University of Texas professor, dated January 15, 1947, it was stated that "about 20 years ago there were about 100 acres of peppermint under cultivation in Galveston County, Texas."[25] Nothing further is known.

Ohio. Only in Ohio and California was mint cultivation actually introduced on any large scale. Following the price rise peppermint was introduced into three distinct sections of Ohio (Map 9).

1. *Holmes-Wayne Counties.* In 1926 Eli Kandel of Berlin Township, Holmes County, made contacts through relatives of his wife with several Old Order Amish mint growers in Indiana and secured some roots. Production was started in 1927 on a small section of organic soil known locally as The Plains about two miles northwest of the village of Berlin. Kandel built a 2 tub mint still and sold rootstock to neighbors as well as growers in adjacent Wayne and Stark counties. The Kandel still processed most of the mint in this

area as few others were built. Small acreages were the rule and, according to the 1929 census of agriculture, county production was as follows:

County	Acres	Pounds of Oil	Farms
Holmes	20	365	5
Wayne	30	500	1
Stark	12	250	1

Growers in the Plains area were Kandel and his two brothers, John and Will, Eli and John Reighenback, and two Old Order Amish farmers, E. Y. and Jacob Miller. The oil was sold to Chris Schrock, known as the "peppermint king" of Indiana, who annually sent a truck into the area for pickup. Production continued in the Plains area until 1938 but was ended when Eli Kandel retired. The family discontinued the cultivation duè to difficulty in obtaining labor to weed and still the crop. Production continued on the Oberholtzer farm near Wooster in Wayne County until 1945. The entire production of this area was peppermint except for several acres of spearmint planted by Kandel and Oberholtzer.

2. *Richland County.* Peppermint and spearmint production was commenced in Richland County near Shiloh in 1928 on the farm of Rudy Rader although there may have been earlier plantings in the Plymouth Marsh area along the Richland-Huron-Crawford counties boundary. In 1929 R. R. Howard began cultivation in the same area. Both men had secured mint roots from Atlee Miller, an Old Order Amish farmer living near Honeyville, Indiana. Other growers in the area were Bloom, Davis, England, and Roland. Several stills were built in the area but most of the growers gave up cultivation of mint in the late 1930's, although some small acreages were maintained as late as 1944. In 1939 the census of agriculture enumerated 2 farms in nearby Crawford County·

A letter from the A. M. Todd Company to R. R. Howard on July 18, 1933, included the following information:[26]

> For strictly choice 1932 crop PEPPERMINT we are now paying $2.25 per pound and for strictly choice SPEARMINT 90¢ per pound.
> The quality of your PEPPERMINT last year was excellent and we know your fields must have been perfectly free from weeds. The presence of native weed oils in PEPPERMINT deducts as much from the price as almost any impurity and we sincerely hope it will be your purpose this year to see that your oils are quite as clean as they were last year. Doing this you will get top prices and will find a ready market.

3. *Hardin County.* In 1926 Allie Moore, then living on a farm in Hardin County two miles south of McGuffey, obtained some pepper-

mint roots from Old Order Amish farmers near Middlebury, Indiana. He had his first hay crop distilled in Indiana but built a two tub still in 1927. The roots were apparently diseased and Moore's production was never successful. After several years he sold part of his equipment to J. Rumbaugh who continued mint production until 1943. Other growers in the area were J. B. Stambaugh, Finley Huston, Hall, Tuttle, and the Scioto Land Company. Huston had obtained three peppermint roots from Indiana growers and developed his acreage from that limited supply.

This development took place on the extensive Scioto Marsh, a vast, level tract of muckland which had been brought into use by the Land Company. The Company's mint production lasted until 1954 when it was terminated due to subsidence of the muck soil. After that date only the Huston farm remained as a mint producer in Ohio.

There were several miscellaneous attempts to introduce peppermint in other areas of Ohio as well. The census reported 3 acres in Logan County in 1929. In 1937 Lingle and Sons planted 2 acres near Edon in Williams County, and Herman Meyers planted an acre near Willshire in Van Wert County in 1937 but it never proved successful.

During the decade 1926-1936 Ohio was not an important mint producer. Although there were a number of growers, especially in the Holmes-Wayne, Hardin, and Richland county areas, state acreages seldom exceeded 700 and were generally quite less. The agriculture censuses for 1929 and 1939 showed the following state totals:

Year	Farms	Acres	Pounds of Oil	Value
1929	9	140	2,465	$7,101
1939	7	213	2,513	4,901

New York. When Sievers visited New York in 1927 he found less than 50 acres of peppermint and a single mint distillery in Wayne County (Figure 43).[27] He found one farm and a still in adjacent Seneca County. Much of the acreage had been established from roots secured in Indiana and the plantings were made because of interest resulting from the great price rise. It was rumored that a great effort would be made to restore Wayne County once again to an important position in the mint industry,[28] but such ambitions were never realized. The census of agriculture in 1929 showed the low state of mint production in New York.

County	Acres	Farms	Pounds of Oil
Wayne	2	2	50
Oswego	10	1	500

The state total of 550 pounds with a value of $1,485 has not since been exceeded.

In an interesting account of the Wayne County peppermint industry written by Linda J. Gaylord of Ontario, New York, a list was compiled showing the names of nearly 100 mint farmers known to have been involved in the industry in that county since 1816. Her list shows:[29]

Arcadia-Fairville
George Arhart
L. J. Benton
H. B. Filkins
Charles Fritz
H. B. Price
George Scheer
Jacob Scheer
P. R. Sleight

Galen
E. Smith

Huron
Ishmael G. Gardner
Oscar Weed

Lyons
Archibald Burnett
Cody Burnett
Nahum Burnett
D. W. Dillingham
Alfred Dunn
James Elmer
J. E. Fellers
Alfred Hale
Hiram G. Hotchkiss
W. H. Houghteling
Henry Jennings
David McClelland
J. H. Merchant
Elias Patten
Isaac Roy
B. P. VanMarter
S. J. Wright
Conrad Young

Macedon
Charles H. Plumb

Marion
Edward W. Croncher
Tom Farnsworth
William Howell
William Lookup

Palymra
John Beals
John Frey
J. Gerard
Anson Hillimire

Rose
Gilbert Brown
Charles Deady
William Fisher
Linus Osgood
James Phillips
John Phillips
Joel H. Putnam
Fred Ream
William Rodwell

Sodus
Henry Ackerman
Riley B. Belden
Peper Clicquennoi
Lou Corey
Jacob Geither
Samuel B. Greene
Edwin Pultz
Theodore Pultz
Phillip Rankert
Henry Walhizer
Merritt White

Williamson
Jay Adams
J. E. Ameele

Wolcott
Nelson Cromwell
Levi Morris

Although the list may not be complete it will undoubtedly provoke many fond memories for the people of Wayne County.

California. Besides Ohio, California was the only new producing state in which the great price rise stimulated what amounted to a significant development. It began in 1925 when John Irmer planted about 16 acres of peppermint on flood-irrigated sandy loam in the San Joaquin Valley near Tulare,[30] the first specific account of an attempt to produce irrigated mint in the United States (Map 12). It is believed that he made

Map 12. California, showing the towns associated with commercial mint oil production since 1925.

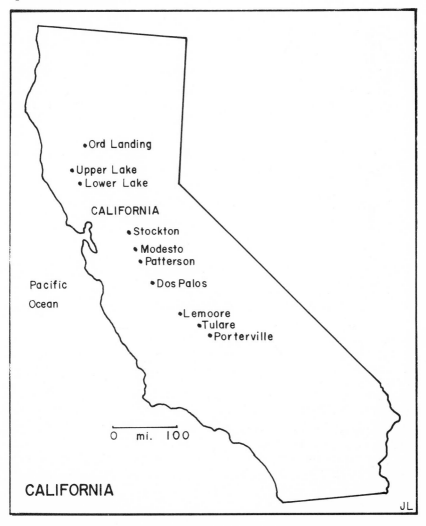

more than $7,000 profit from his 6 acres.[31] The foliage was lush and the leaves quite large and two cuttings were obtained with yields averaging about 60 pounds to the acre. Irmer's experiment, coupled with nearby developments of Japanese mint fields, established by John Davies of Oregon, attracted considerable attention. The following year five acres of peppermint were planted by Ray Vincent near Porterville and yields averaged nearly 50 pounds to the acre (Figure 47). Several acres of spearmint were set out by Bonine in the same area and three cuttings were taken. As a number of additional growers planned to move into mint production a California newspaper was led to run the following article commenting on the development.[32]

> Peppermint is being planted everywhere, wherever land is thought suitable. Like all things that have made good, it is being rushed to the limit. Where will it end? Like cotton, grapes, potatoes, onions, etc., that have had their ups and downs? Prof. R. L. Adams, the present marketing commissioner, once said in his classroom: "Plant what the other fellow isn't." Which is certainly good advice.
>
> Overproduction will not come this year in California, for there are not enough roots of either variety to cause overproduction. But how about Michigan and Indiana, or Japan, if they have bumper crops? But if the people planting this winter make good, the demand for roots next winter will be enormous, and I fear a good many thousand acres will be planted, for the eyes of farmers are turned their way. The one good thing about peppermint oil—it will keep and can be stored in one's bedroom.
>
> There are agents in this valley from Oregon who are soliciting business to sell roots of the English black stem variety, and they are receiving orders. Some of them even bringing in sacks of dirt asking advice, "Is this the right kind of dirt for peppermint?"
>
> Trucks are going by on the highway loaded down with sacks of peppermint roots. Fourteen hundred sacks went to a place five miles south and west of Modesto, to plant 60 acres of the Japanese variety. Another truck went to Laton, Kings County, with a load, and a number of trucks are hauling to the Island district west of Hanford. Tipton, Tulare County, received its share. Ten acres are going into the English black stem variety on the Gist Brothers ranch north of Tulare. John Irmer, west of Tulare, who made such a wonderful success on six acres, is planting about 40 more.
>
> About June, 1927, mint stills will be in demand. Will they be as much in demand in 1928, and how about 1929?

The conservative columnist was not heeded and, in 1927, there were more than 16 growers in the Tulare-Porterville area, Ormer, Gist, Mastin, and Rounsaville at Tulare, and Larsen, Cloer, Fiske, Vincent, Vossler Brothers, Green, Alexander, Saak, Helm, Adamson, and others at Porterville.[33] A large distillery was built by the Essential Oil Products Company at Lemoore and processed much of the mint grown in the area which totalled about 150 acres. A mint growers association devoted to aid in processing and marketing the crop, was founded in Tulare County.

In 1928 peppermint fields were developed at Dos Palos by a half dozen growers, McClarren, Redfern, Petersen, Galtsch, Hardman, and others; at Upper Lake on reclaimed lake bed by the Essential Oil Products Company; and near Ord Landing in Glenn County where farmer A. A. Bushee found that peppermint did not take to rolling, non-irrigated terrain.[34]

A careful observer, partially amazed and partially amused at all the mint activity taking place, visited a number of farms and interpreted the California cultivation in the following words:[35]

> plants cost about $100 per acre, and are set out in January or early February on well levelled ground with small checks because of the shallow root system and the fact that it is a waste of water when deep penetration occurs. Hence, a rapid "flushing" over small checks.
>
> Buyers are now making contracts and playing safe, with one eye on possible expansion in acreage, and the prices named in these documents are $6 in 1927, $5 in 1928, and $4 in 1929—this for English peppermint.
>
> According to local experience, one should not start without first having secured a piece of rich, sandy loam soil, relatively high in humus, and without alkali; also a good pump, capable of throwing 750 gallons a minute per 40 acres, and the will to take care of the patch and fight weeds, because they not only weaken the stand but spoil the oil. (No cheeseweed flavor is wanted in peppermint candy or chewing gum, stated Mr. Wrigley in a recent interview with our Household editor).
>
> Irrigation is applied every 15 days in spring and fall, and speeded up to 10-day intervals in hot weather. Now, with all this fancy irrigating, and frequent, too, and with old-fashioned weeding and careful curing, not too dry and without losing the leaves, then distilling to top it off, we can readily see where the dilatory farmer gets it in the neck. Lady Luck is likely to stick a pin in his rose-colored balloon.
>
> One big drawback is the cost of starting. There is a matter of $100 an acre for plants, and the mere trifle of $1,000 for a still. You must have one of these, you know, and one slightly used, purchased from the sheriff will hardly do. A mint still isn't that kind, you know. Of course, in case of a "bust" it might be converted, but who wants to be driven to the life of a bootlegger because of an unsuccessful wooing of the Peppermint Siren?
>
> And the price of oil may drop to $3 if Michigan and Japanese crops are good. The trade will take just so much, unless Mr. Kimmel and his Kings County cohorts can make the great American jaw chew more gum or the temperamental nostril demand more mentholatum!
>
> We don't profess to know all about it, but hogs and alfalfa, yea, even prunes, have a strong counter-attraction. But to the brave "Minters" and distillers of the potent and aromatic breath-disguising and halitosis-cheating oil, we offer best wishes, provided there aren't too many of them.

But there were too many. Not in California, but also Indiana, Michigan, Oregon and Washington growers had responded, and all the Mr. Kimmels in the country could not persuade the great American jaw to chew sufficient gum to dispose of the tremendous supply of mint oil that was made available. But California expansion continued.

In 1927 the Western Mint Company, formed in Oregon, secured several thousand acres near Dos Palos and offered farmers one of the most spectacular mint opportunities of all time. A few quotations from their newspaper advertisement quickly reveal the nature of the offer (Figure 46).[36]

> California growers will get millions from mint. Destiny points to California as the future mint producing state. Just think what profits are awaiting California mint growers. You need not be a farmer to share in the profits of mint culture. Californians who are alert for profits will be given an opportunity to join a syndicate, which is already formed, by purchasing one or more acres of this land. The Western Mint Company will do all the work; plant the roots, irrigate, cultivate, harvest the crop and distill the oil. All this is done for a flat fee of $75.00 per acre. The entire profits from the oil—less this fee, are returned to the individual who owns the land. No longer is it necessary to wait until fruit trees come into bearing, or vines are matured. Mint growers get their profits now. Acreage in this syndicate will earn big returns for many owners. Desirable economies of operation can be effected when hundreds of acres are cultivated by one organization. Cooperation pays! Arrangements for buying an acre or more in the syndicate on deferred payments have been perfected. You can pay out of profits! But begin to get profits this spring! Let peppermint be your mint.

To the great credit of California farmers this blatant land speculation scheme proved to be a complete failure.

Experimental plantings were established in 1927 near Delevan, spearmint was introduced into Upper Lake in 1929, and cultivation at Lower Lake was inaugurated in 1930 by Coldren and Rogers, and in the Stockton Delta area on the ranch of J. O. Hayes, Jr. But the California industry was short lived. The Porterville plantings were discontinued in 1929 due to difficulties of controlling the weeds, and the other areas were slowly taken out of cultivation because of resulting low prices and the general poor quality of the California oil.[37] By 1939 only a single mint farm, that of Hayes near Stockton, remained in the state. "Destiny" had failed California, and the millions of dollars of presumed profits never arrived at the banks.

Washington. When Sievers visited Washington in 1927 he found considerable expansion in the original producing area along the lower Columbia River and also observed farms in two areas in which mint culture was introduced resulting from the great price rise; the Puget Sound area between Tacoma and Burlington, and the Lower Yakima Valley including the Richland-Kennewick area near the junction of the Yakima, Snake, and Columbia rivers (Map 13). Estimated state acreage in 1927 was 1,750, about half of which was in the lower Columbia district, with 500 acres owned by Alexander Brothers at Woodland,

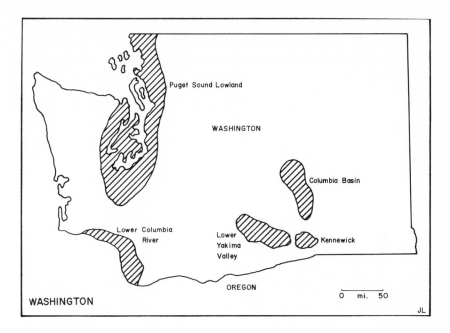

Map 13. Location of the major mint oil producing districts of Washington. Although the Puget Sound Lowland covers the largest area, the plantings were small and widely scattered and the district has been, historically, the least important.

150 acres on Puget Island, nearby islands, and the adjacent mainland around Skamokawa and Cathlamet, and about 100 acres in the Long-view-Kelso area.[38]

New acreages were established along the Nisgally River near Mc-Kenna, at Lake Stevens east of Everett, and in the lower Skagit River valley around Burlington, all in the Puget Sound lowland. New plantings were placed in small pockets of organic soil at Orchards and Fargher Lake just north of Vancouver. The remaining acreage in the state was related to irrigated lands in the Yakima Valley and the Columbia Basin irrigation project with the plantings in a number of localities near Kennewick.

The original plantings in the Yakima Valley resulted from a promotional scheme engineered by the Pacific Coast Mint Company headed by W. J. Turnidge in 1926. Turnidge, who had been involved in mint growing in Oregon since 1914, prepared a prospectus which was circulated throughout the Valley and was based primarily on the high prices prevailing for mint oil in 1924 and 1925. He solicited cooperators to plant plots of roots from which a considerable expansion of acreage was envisioned for 1927. These experimental plots were located near Sunnyside, Kennewick, Richland, and Walulla.

There were no distilleries in eastern Washington in 1926, so Turnidge had the hay trucked to Portland, Oregon, for distilling, then built a still near Sunnyside which went into operation the following year. Similar to the land development scheme originated in California a little later by the West Coast Mint Company, Turnidge's proposal set forth the following requirements: the Pacific Coast Mint Company would furnish all the roots at $1.00 per sack, the cost to be paid out of the first year oil production; all roots would remain the possession of the company and could not be moved; if growers wished to discontinue the crop, the company would remove all the roots; and distillation would be handled by the company on the basis of a sliding scale originating with a charge of one-half the value of the oil produced the first year.[39] Nearly 200 acres were contracted by Turnidge during 1927, but general grower dissatisfaction with the arrangement coupled with the sudden decrease of oil prices caused the company to be dissolved within several years.

Independent developments near Richland were quite successful, and early growers were Joe Lindskog, Ben McGhan, and Fred Johnson. Lindskog had started under Turnidge's plan in 1926, but built his own still the following year and continued his production independently.

Expansion in Washington was quite rapid. From a few growers and about 100 acres in 1925, the industry involved over a hundred farms by 1929. The census of agriculture for that year showed the breakdown by counties as follows:

County	Number of Farms	Acres	Pounds of Oil
Benton	4	6	219
Clark	5	233	10,100
Cowlitz	7	231	3,656
Pierce	2	16	550
Skagit	1	1	20
Wahkiakum	42	203	10,024
Yakima	52	156	4,163
State	113	846	28,732

Nearly 700 of the state's 846 acres in mint were concentrated in the lower Columbia River district in Clark, Cowlitz, and Wahkiakum counties, and this area continued to be the major production region for several decades.

In 1927 mint growers in this district organized the Woodland Mint Growers Incorporated,[40] but general disinterest in cooperative marketing prevented the society from reaching any effective proportion.

Oregon. The mint industry in Oregon expanded considerably. From several hundred acres in 1924 mint plantings exceeded 2,000 acres by 1927. When Sievers visited Oregon that year he found the producing regions located around the original centers at Clatskanie, Lake Labish, Eugene, and Salem, and newly developed areas in the highlands near Roseburg (Yoncalla, Sutherlin, Dillard, Camas Valley, and Coquille), the alluvial flats near Portland, and small plantings along the Columbia River near Rainier directly across the river from Woodland, Washington (Map 14).[41]

Expansion was most notable near Coburg and at Lake Labish and the surrounding area. Peppermint was placed on the E. A. and J. O. Hayes farm at Lake Labish in 1926 and 700 acres were planted in 1927.[42] The Willamette Valley and the Columbia River area near Clatskanie and Portland contained nearly 1,700 of the state's 2,000 acres in 1927.[43] W. J. Turnidge had attempted to promote mint cultivation on irrigated land in north central Oregon in 1925 but local and state officials discredited his promotion scheme and it was not implemented. Peppermint was introduced on irrigated land in Oregon, however, in 1926, when two growers planted over 15 acres near the

Map 14. Location of the major mint oil producing districts of Oregon and western Idaho.

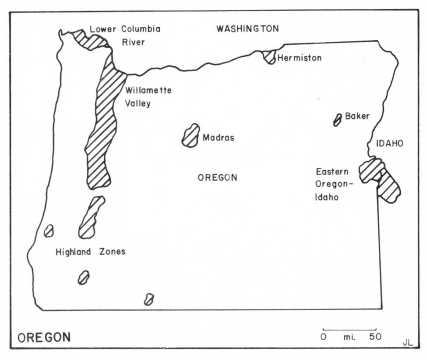

town of Hermiston.[44] By 1929, according to the census of agriculture, mint cultivation was found on 160 farms in 11 Oregon counties:

County	Number of Farms	Acres	Pounds of Oil
Benton	1	2	33
Clackamus	8	102	3,767
Columbia	12	243	6,771
Douglas	13	97	1,574
Lane	45	400	11,409
Linn	21	214	5,701
Marion	52	1,015	47,983
Morrow	1	3	56
Multnomah	2	69	4,075
Washington	4	132	2,914
Yamhill	1	8	50
State	160	2,285	84,333

By this time Oregon and Washington combined were producing nearly 12 percent of the mint oil supply of the United States, a remarkable achievement in a period of less than five years.

Hopes were entertained that the Oregon cooperative marketing association could be revived and a plan was devised that would insure quality oil production. Field inspectors would travel to the various farms and check for weeds. If the fields did not pass inspection the association would either reject the oil or admit it to the market pool at a reduced price.[45] But the general disinterest in cooperative marketing, after the number of unsuccessful attempts that had been made, prevented the idea from being implemented.

Michigan and Indiana. Despite the proliferation of attempts to introduce mint cultivation in other states the most significant expansion resulting from the great price rise came in the chief producing states of Indiana and Michigan. Between 1923 and 1927 acreage in Indiana doubled to 38,500 acres. It reached 40,000 acres in 1928, and went to the all-time high for the state in 1930, 42,630 acres.[46] By 1929 Michigan acreage had tripled over 1919 and 11,141 acres were grown. In 1929 the two states had over 2,700 of the nation's 3,000 mint farms, were growing nearly 46,000 of the total 51,000 acres, and produced 735,000 pounds of oil of the total national output of 882,000 pounds.[47] But the industry was concentrated even more than the figures indicate. Nearly 80 percent of the total acreage was in a single state, Indiana, and 10 percent of that state's total acreage was found in a single county, St. Joseph. What person, at this time, would have made any prediction that the two states would ever be anything but the nation's leading producers of mint oil?

But there had been subtle shifts of the industry in both states. By

1929, 24 Michigan counties each had some land devoted to mint cultivation, but in only six did the amount exceed 1,000 acres and five of the counties were muckland areas in the southwestern section of the state, Van Buren, Branch, Allegan, Berrien, and Cass (Map 6). Only in Clinton County in central Michigan was the industry in any way successful outside of this basic producing region.[48]

In Indiana, by 1929, cultivation had been extended all the way to the Ohio River and 36 counties reported some mint oil production, the greatest number ever recorded in the state. Of these, however, only 8 exceeded 1,000 acres and they were all in the northern portion of the state adjacent to the Michigan boundary, St. Joseph, Kosciusko, Lagrange, Marshall, Starke, LaPorte, Elkhart and Noble.[49]

The great price rise had also made it possible for new country dealers to become established in the business and the Hotchkiss and Todd companies found new competitors in Indiana. William Leman, born near Peoria, Illinois, in 1885, had moved to a farm just north of Bremen, Indiana, where he began raising perppermint and became an agent of the Todd Company. In 1911 Leman began, in a small way, to deliver oil to the New York brokers, then formed a partnership with his brother-in-law, Louis Gerber. The firm of Leman-Gerber rented a warehouse at Wyatt then, in 1926, moved its facilities to Bremen, in the heart of the mint district of Marshall County, where the company is still located.

Bejamin Brown came from Chicago and settled on a farm just west of Bremen near Lake of the Woods in 1906. Two years later he began growing peppermint in the area and entered the business as a buyer in 1920 in partnership with his brothers, Max and Samuel. The firm, M. Brown and Sons, named for Benjamin's father, Morris, was located in Bremen just one block south of Leman-Gerber. The strategic location enabled both firms to become important buyers and dealers in peppermint and spearmint oils.

The tremendous expansion of acreage resulted in a 1929 oil production of nearly 900,000 pounds, almost triple that of 1925. The great response, of course, killed the market, sent prices tumbling, nullified all the land speculation themes, and made cooperative marketing a ridiculous superfluity. Peppermint oil prices were now down to about $3.50 per pound yet farmers, demonstrating that cussedness for which they are well known, continued to concentrate their efforts on peppermint. Spearmint in the meantime, neglected as a crop, was in somewhat short supply and prices were nearly $5.00 per pound.

The price dislocations threatened the stability of the industry to such

Figure 30. An early mint distillery of the type utilized after the introduction of steam distillation in 1846. Parts identified are as follows: a and b, plank boiler top; c, brick boiler foundation; d, water funnel; e, steam pipe; f, g, h, i, and j, distilling tub; k and l, condenser pipes and tub; m, receiving can. Estimated cost in 1892 was about $25. (J. B. Ellis, "The Growth and Manufacture of Peppermint," *American Agriculturist*, vol. 51, no. 7, p. 421, July, 1892).

Figure 31. Some mint scenes from Michigan about 1898. From top: weeding a mint field; the mint distillery; boiler and condenser pipes; farmer holding demi-johns, cans commonly used to store mint oils in the early days. (D. Malloch, "American Peppermint Culture," *Rural New-Yorker*, vol. 57, no. 2540, p. 669, October 1, 1898.)

Figure 32. A mint distillery in New York about 1890, estimated to have cost from $500 to $1,000. The boiler is at left, tubs at right, and the condenser tank and receiving can in the foreground. (T. Greiner, "Peppermint —Its Culture and Distillation," *American Agriculturist*, vol. 49, no. 1, p. 13, January, 1890.)

Figure 33. An early truck-mounted mint hay tank on a farm in Michigan. The portable tanks, introduced into Michigan about 1925, were inserted directly into the distilling tubs and were the predecessors of completely mounted portable distilling tubs which came into use about 1940.

Figure 34. The patent diagram of a mint root planting machine designed by J. H. Shirley of Kalamazoo, Michigan, in 1907.

Figure 35. A notice which appeared in the *Decatur Republican*, Decatur, Michigan, December 2, 1926.

Figure 36. Market quotations and news notes from various trade journals in November, 1925, the peak of the great price rise period. The quotation at lower right is from the St. Joseph Valley Mint Growers' Cooperative Association, October, 1926.

Figure 37. Placards posted in the mint producing districts of Michigan and Indiana in 1926 by the St. Joseph Valley Mint Growers' Cooperative Association.

Figure 38. Forking out the mint roots for spring planting on a Michigan farm about 1935.

Figure 39. Hand planting mint roots on a Michigan farm about 1935.

Figure 40. Harvesting mint with scythes in Michigan about 1935.

Figure 41. Various advertisements for mint rootstock which appeared in the *Decatur Republican*, Decatur, Michigan, during the spring of 1926.

Figure 42. A large tractor pulling wagons of spent hay on the Campania Farm, Allegan County, Michigan, about 1920.

Figure 43. A mint distillery near Lyons, New York, about 1925. The "drip type" condenser is shown at left.

Figure 44. A mint distillery and "fog" boiler near Quincy, Oregon, about 1934. The tub is the "water seal" type manufactured by Eastman Brothers of Silverton, Oregon.

Figure 45. A. M. Todd visiting the mint distillery during harvest time at the Mentha plantation, Van Buren County, Michigan, about 1930.

Figure 46. Many speculative schemes were developed following the great price rise period. This advertisement appeared in the *San Francisco Examiner* on December 8, 1927.

Figure 47. A mint distillery near Porterville, California, in 1927. (A. F. Sievers, *Travel Report*, facing p. 9, U. S. Department of Agriculture, 1927.)

Figure 48. Numerous attempts to form cooperative marketing associations for mint growers have been made, but none has proven successful. This circular was mailed to Indiana and Michigan farmers in 1930.

Figure 49. The critical shortage of peppermint oil in the early part of World War II led the federal government to issue the famous Food Distribution Order 81 by which the entire national supply of peppermint oil was to be set aside for sale to the government.

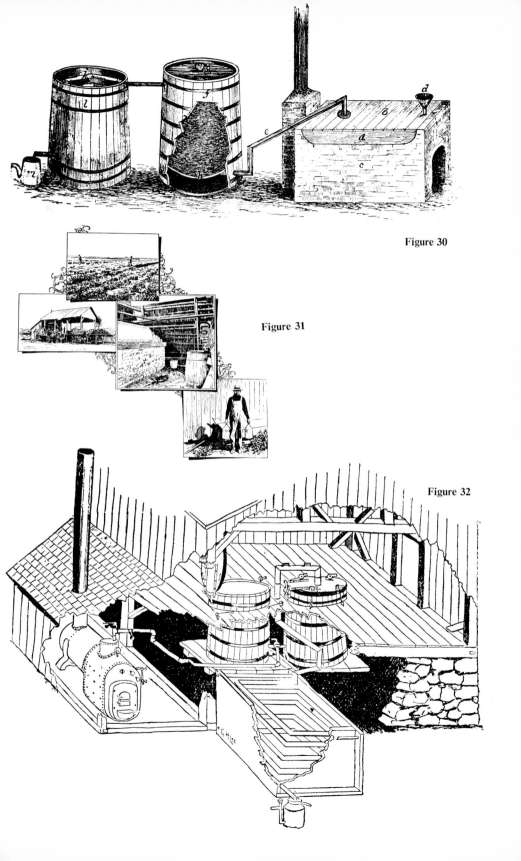

Figure 30

Figure 31

Figure 32

Figure 33

Figure 34

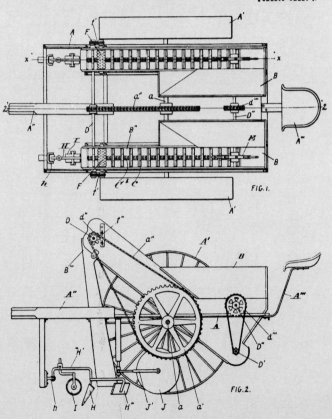

No. 870,693.

PATENTED NOV. 12, 1907.

J. H. SHIRLEY.
ROOT PLANTING MACHINE.
APPLICATION FILED MAR. 6, 1906.

2 SHEETS—SHEET 1.

FIG. 1.

FIG. 2.

John H. Shirley Inventor

Witnesses

Figure 35

Figure 36

Oil Peppermint—Has maintained its firm position, but prices have marked time during the past week at $28.00 to $30.00 ℔. Only business in a small way has been done, owing to the high price. Shows no signs of receding at present.

Oil Peppermint—True to predictions in the trade here, the price of peppermint kept climbing after it passed the $25.00 mark last week.' Prices appeared to harden at $27.00 and $28.00 for a few days, but then went still higher and sales were made early this week at $28.00 for natural and $29.00 for U. S. P. Control of the market is still closely guarded in the Mid-West, where factors apparently have the situation well in hand in spite of the high price. Whether the price will go over $30.00 remains to be seen. Demand is steady, but confined to small quantities as might be expected.

PEPPERMINT.—This article was rather quiet during the period, there not being a great deal of demand current during the week. For the most part, local stocks were very light and there was no disposition to increase them. The primary market stood pat most instances, but found demand hardly up to a point of satisfaction. Quotations held at $28 to $29 per pound for natural and $29 to $30 per pound for redistilled.

Peppermint, natural, single distilled, cases ....lb.	28.00	@29.00
redistilled, U.S.P., tins.....lb.	29.00	@30.00
Petitgrain, Paraguay, tins...lb.	2.15	@ 2.25
Pimento, berries, tins.......lb.	4.50	@ 4.75
Pine needle, Siberian, cans..lb.	.40	@ .50
Rose, natural, coppers.......oz.	9.50	@13.50
artificial, bottles ....oz.	2.00	@ 3.00
Rosemary flowers, USP, tins..lb.	.50	@ .55
technical, tins ....lb.	.37½	@ .40
Safrol, drums, tins ....lb.	.31	@ .33
Sandalwood, E.I., U.S.P., tins.lb.	7.10	@ 7.25
Sassafras, natural, tins.......lb.	.85	@ .95
artificial, drums ....lb.	.27	@ .29
Savin, tins..................lb.	2.10	@ 2.25
Spearmint, U.S.P., cases......lb.	13.75	@14.00

SPEARMINT. — Demand has been light of late and the rising trend of values has been checked at $14 to $15 per pound. However, resumption of buying would find stocks very light and in strong hands.

Oil Spearmint—Up to $14.00 ℔ this week and likely to go higher as the quantity available is extremely small.

PEPPERMINT—		
Nat'l ...29 00 a	..
U. S. P..31 00 a	..
Pet grain.2 15	a2 25
Pimento.. 4 75	a5 00
ROSE—Oz.—	
Nat'l ..9 50	a 13
S'thetic .2 00	a6 00
ROSEMARY Fl.—	
French.. 45	a 55
Spanish. 37½	a 40
Rue 3 00	1 6 00
Safrol .. 31	a 33
SANDALWOOD—	
E Inc..7 00	a7 25
W. Ind..1 75	a3 00
Austra-	
lian ..5 00	a ..
SASSAFRAS—	
Nat'l ... 90	a1 00
Artif ... 27	a 29
Savin ...2 10	a2 25
Sp'mint ..14 00	a 14 25

Essential Oils.

(Quotations by St. Joseph, Valley Mint Growers' association, 163 North Walnut street.)

Peppermint—New York, natural, $6.35 to $6.75, in cases; redistilled U. S. P., $7.00 to $7.75; local market nominal.

Spearmint—New York, U. S. P. $5.50 to $5.75; local market nominal.

Peppermint Growers
NOTICE!

AUG 30 1926

Attend the big Rally!

HAMLET SCHOOL

Friday Eve., Aug. 27

Eight O'Clock

Figure 37

BEWARE!
Mint Growers

The Speculator, armed with unlimited funds is throwing his whole strength against your Courage and Foresight.

A STUDIED PURPOSE ON TH PART OF THE SPECULATORS. BANDED TOGTHER IN A POWERFUL GROUP, IS BEING FOSTERED TO DESTROY YOUR MORALE. THERE HAVE BEEN BOASTS MADE THAT PEPPERMINT OIL WILL SELL (AND THEY WILL BUY IT) FOR LESS THAN FIVE DOLLARS A POUND. THROUGH THEIR ACTIVITIES. THEY HAVE ALREADY COWED NUBERS OF GROWERS TO THROW THEIR OIL ON THE MARKET THIS SEASON AT PRICES LESS THAN HALF WHAT THE CONSUMER WILL PAY THEM FOR IT WHEN THE CONSUMER IS READY TO BUY. THE CONSUMER OF LARGE QUANTITIES OF OIL DOES NOT GET INTO THE MARKET IN EARNEST UNTIL THE MIDDLE OF SEPTEMBER AND THEREAFTER. THE SPECULATOR IS TELLING YOU THE CONSUMER WILL NOT PAY WHAT YOU ARE HOLDING OUT FOR. THE SPECULATOR HAS NOT BEEN ASKED FOR OIL EXCEPT IN FEW INSTANCES.

There is no Over-supply of Oil

YOUR TRADITIONAL ENEMY HAS TOLD YOU THAT BECAUSE OF A LARGE PRODUCTION THE PRICE IS BOUND TO BE SMALL. THAT THERE IS NOT SUFFICIENT MARKET TO TAKE CARE OF ALL THE OIL IN THE COUNTRY. TWO YEARS AGO HE TOLD YOU THE THE SAME THING. MANY OF YOU BELEIVED HIM. HE BOUGHT YOUR OIL FOR THREE TO SIX DOLLARS PER POUND AND SOLD IT IN THE SPRING TO THE CONSUMER TO NET HIM $9.50& $10. NORMALLY WE HAVE A CARRY-OVER FROM 15 per cent TO 25 per cent OF OLD CROP. LAST YEAR WE HAD SUCH A CARRY OVER. THIS YEAR WE HAVE NO CARRY OVER. THE CONSUMERS DRUMS ARE DRY. THEY WILL CONSUME MORE OIL THIS YEAR THAN LAST YEAR. THE BEST INFORMATION IS THAT THE PRODUCTION THIS YEAR DOES NOT EXCEED LAST YEARS BY OVER 10 per cent. WITHOUT THE CARRY-OVER IT MEANS PRACTICALLY THE SAME SUPPLY AS LAST YEAR.

The Consumer must have Oil or Close Shop

He will pay a reasonable price for it when his demand for it is insistent

Hold your Oil and you will get the Price

SELL YOUR OIL AND THE SPECULATOR WILL GET THE PRICE THAT IS RIGHTFULLY YOURS

Get your information from

St. Joseph Valley Mint Growers' Co-operative Ass'n

Phone L. 5789 Cor. Washington & Walnut Sts., South Bend Indiana

READ THIS AGAIN

Figure 38

Figure 39

Figure 40

Figure 42

Figure 41

Figure 43

Figure 44

Figure 45

Figure 46

Figure 47

Figure 48

Mint Growers
ATTENTION!

There will be a meeting of the Mint Growers of Northern Indiana and Southern Michigan held in the Court House at South Bend, Ind., at 1:00 o'clock p. m. on

Tuesday, January 28, '30

A representative of the Federal Farm Board of the Division of Co-Operative Marketing from Washington, D. C., will be present. Also a representative of the Indiana Farm Bureau.

Mint Growers:

It is important that you attend this meeting. Your attitude will determine the future possibility of Co-Operative Marketing of Mint Oil.

Help the Federal Farm Board!

For by co-operating with this Board you will be helping yourself.

WAR FOOD ADMINISTRATION
AGRICULTURE

[FDO 81]

PART 1445—ESSENTIAL OILS

OIL OF PEPPERMINT

The fulfillment of requirements for the defense of the United States will result in a shortage of the supply of oil of peppermint for defense, for private account, and for export; and the following order is deemed necessary and appropriate in the public interest and to promote the national defense:

§ 1440.1 Restrictions relative to oil of peppermint—(a) Definitions. When used in this order, unless otherwise distinctly expressed or manifestly incompatible with the intent hereof:

(1) The term "oil of peppermint" means the volatile oil distilled by steam or processed by any other means from any variety of the peppermint plant, including, but not being limited to, the varieties Mentha piperita and Mentha arvensis.

(2) The term "person" means any individual, partnership, association, business trust, corporation, or any organized group of persons whether incorporated or not.

(3) The term "Director" means the Director of Food Distribution, War Food Administration.

(b) Restrictions. Without regard to the rights of creditors, existing contracts, or payments made, every person who owns, controls, or has in his possession oil of peppermint on the effective date hereof or any time subsequent thereto shall promptly set aside 100% of said oil of peppermint for sale and delivery to the Food Distribution Administration, War Food Administration, including but not restricted to the Federal Surplus Commodities Corporation or to any person or agency designated by the Director: Provided, That any person who owns and has in his possession a quantity of oil of peppermint on the effective date of this order and who used oil of peppermint during the year 1941 in the manufacture of any product may during the corresponding portion of the year 1943 use 30 per centum of the quantity of oil of peppermint used by him during such corresponding period in 1941.

(e) Report required. Every person owning 25 pounds or more of oil of peppermint on the effective date of the order shall, within 15 days from said date, report to the Director on form FDO No. 81-1 the number of pounds of oil of peppermint owned by him on the effective date of this order and furnish such other information relative to said oil of peppermint as may be requested in said form.

(d) Provisions of Food Distribution Regulation No. 2 not applicable. The provisions of Food Distribution Regulation No. 2 (8 F.R. 7523), issued June 4, 1943, by the War Food Administrator, shall not be applicable to this order.

(e) Audits and inspections. The Director shall be entitled to make such audit or inspection of the books, records and other writings, premises or stocks of oil of peppermint of any person, and to make such investigations, as may be necessary or appropriate, in his discretion, to the enforcement or administration of the provisions of this order.

(f) Records and reports. (1) In addition to the reporting requirement contained herein, the Director shall be entitled to obtain such information from, and require such reports and the keeping of such records by, any person, as may be necessary or appropriate, in his discretion, to the enforcement or administration of the provisions of this order.

(2) Every person subject to this order shall, for at least two years (or for such period of time as the Director may designate), maintain an accurate record of his transactions in oil of peppermint.

(3) The record-keeping and reporting requirements of this order have been approved by the Bureau of the Budget in accordance with the Federal Reports Act of 1942. Subsequent record-keeping or reporting requirements will be subject to the approval of the Bureau of the Budget pursuant to the Federal Reports Act of 1942.

(g) Petition for relief from hardship. Any person affected by this order who considers that compliance herewith would work an exceptional and unreasonable hardship on him may apply in writing for relief to the Director, setting forth in such petition all pertinent facts and the nature of the relief sought. The Director may thereupon take such action as he deems appropriate, which action shall be final.

(h) Violations. The War Food Administrator may, by suspension order, prohibit any person who violates any provision of this order from receiving, making any deliveries of, or using oil of peppermint, or any other material subject to priority or allocation control by the War Food Administrator, and may recommend that any such person be prohibited from receiving, making any deliveries of, or using materials subject to the priority or allocation control of other governmental agencies. In addition, any person who wilfully violates any provision of this order is guilty of a crime and may be prosecuted under any and all applicable laws. Further, civil action may be instituted to enforce any liability or duty created by, or to enjoin any violation of, any provision of this order.

(i) Delegation of authority. The administration of this order and the powers vested in the War Food Administrator, insofar as such powers relate to the administration of this order, are hereby delegated to the Director. The Director is authorized to redelegate to any employee of the United States Department of Agriculture any or all of the authority vested in him by this order.

(j) Communications. All reports required to be filed hereunder and all communications concerning this order shall, unless instructions to the contrary are issued by the Director, be addressed to the Director of Food Distribution, War Food Administration, Washington 25, D. C. Ref. FD-81.

(k) Effective date. This order shall become effective at 12:01 a. m., e. w. t., September 13, 1943.

(E.O. 9280, 7 F.R. 10179; E.O. 9322, 8 F.R. 3807 E.O. 9334, 8 F.R. 5423)

Issued this 10th day of September 1943.

MARVIN JONES,
War Food Administrator.

Press Release Immediate:
Saturday, September 11, 1943.

The War Food Administration has acted to assure an equitable distribution of oil of peppermint—an essential oil now limited in supply but important in both food preparations and pharmaceutical uses—by reserving all such oil for Government action. Most of the U. S. supply of this oil is produced in Michigan, Indiana, Ohio, California, and Oregon. All persons now owning, controlling, or having in their possession Oil of Peppermint must set aside for Government action, 100 percent of their holdings. This is required under Food Distribution Order 81, effective September 13, 1943.

Manufacturers, druggists and others who used Oil of Peppermint in the manufacture of any product in 1941, however, may use quantities now in their possession up to the equivalent of 30 percent of the quantity used in the corresponding period of 1941.

GPO—WFA 110—p. 1

Figure 49

an extent that the Beech-Nut Company of New York, in an effort to induce quality growers to remain in cultivation, empowered the Todd Company to contract with growers on a three year basis for the first 50 percent of the crop at prices of $6 per pound in 1927, $5 in 1928, and $4 in 1929. The remainder of the crop would be purchased at the prevailing market price. This strategy proved to be good insurance, for users, dealers, and growers, but only the best producers were signed to contracts. Those that were not found themselves facing a glutted market with little chance of selling, or selling at a price barely above profits. The great response had ended. Marginal growers and profitminded artists abandoned the industry as quickly as they had entered.

Conclusion

As the great depression began to creep across the American landscape in late 1929 the American mint industry had just passed through one of its most frantic five year periods. The great price rise had stimulated a tremendous acreage expansion including a plethora of attempts to introduce mint cultivation in new areas. A number of land speculation schemes had been centered around peppermint, and all had been found wanting. A good deal of research had been originated in the agricultural colleges and new techniques and equipment had been applied to mint cultivation and distillation by the growers. One of the most comprehensive cooperative marketing programs ever devised in the industry had been developed, tried, and cast aside. Oil prices had tumbled from all-time highs to a point where profits barely exceeded costs. It was on this somber note, overproduction and low profits, that the decade of the 1920's ended and the industry passed into an extremely troubled period.

[1]A.F. Sievers, *Peppermint and Spearmint as Farm Crops,* Farmers' Bulletin No. 1555, USDA, February, 1929. The *Travel Report,* 1927, a comprehensive account of mint farms in the states of North Carolina, New York, California, Oregon, Washington, Michigan, and Indiana, was never published.

[2]The first two were: A. Henkel, "Peppermint," *Miscellaneous Papers,* pp. 19-20, Bureau of Plant Industry, USDA, Bulletin no. 90, 1906; W. VanFleet, *The Cultivation of Peppermint and Spearmint,* Farmers' Bulletin 694, USDA, October, 1915.

[3]C. B. Sayre, *Mint Growing in Northern Indiana,* Circular No. 65, Purdue University, Agricultural Experiment Station, August, 1917.

[4]A. G. B. Bouquet, *Peppermint Production for Oil,* Circular 221, Oregon State College, Agricultural Experiment Station, mimeo, 1925.

[5]J. R. Duncan, *Peppermint Growing in Michigan,* Special Bulletin No. 153, Michigan State College, Agricultural Experiment Station, March, 1926.

[6]O. Johnson and J. C. Snyder, *Peppermint Oil Production in Washington,* Extension Bulletin 227, State College of Washington, June, 1936.

[7]H. H. Gardner, "Peppermint for Muck Soils," *Iowa State Horticultural Society Reports: 1931,* pp. 239-242.

[8]"Experiment Station to Grow Peppermint this Year," *Pasco Herald,* p. 5, Pasco, Washington, May 6, 1925.

[9]The results of the Florida experiments were published in a variety of reports in a number of journals. See, especially: G. M. Hocking and L. D. Edwards, "Cultivation of Peppermint in Florida," *Economic Botany,* vol. 9, pp. 78-93, 1955; G. M. Hocking, "Scotch Mint and Spearmint. A Comparative Study . . . Growing in Florida," *Journal of the American Pharmaceutical Association,* vol. 38, pp. 394-402, 1949; G. M. Hocking and L. D. Edwards, "Nomenclature of Peppermint and Its Varieties," *Ibid.,* vol. 33, pp. 333-342, 1944.

[10]"Japanese Mint Producers Reach for American Trade," *New York Commercial,* Jan. 21, 1926. An article in the 1928 *Homestead Enterprise* also predicted successful mint culture in Florida: see G. M. Hocking and L. D. Edwards, 1955, *op. cit.,* p. 91. Experimental plantings were also made at Penney Farms and by the U.S. Sugar Corporation near Clewiston (*Ibid.,* p. 83).

[11]"Peppermint," *The Farmers Exchange,* New Paris, Indiana, June 15, 1928.

[12]A. F. Sievers, *Travel Report, op. cit.,* p. 21.

[13]*Decatur Republican,* Decatur, Michigan, date uncertain but about April 22, 1926.

[14]"Mint in the Northwest," *Aromatics,* p. 21, November, 1927.

[15]A. F. Sievers, *Travel Report, op. cit.,* pp. 26-27.

[16]"Peppermint," *The Farmers Exchange,* New Paris, Indiana, June 15, 1928.

[17]Schimmel and Company, *Annual Report,* p. 57, 1922.

[18]C. B. Sayre, *op. cit.,* pp. 1-2.

[19]E. Guenther, "Oil of Spearmint," *Manufacturing Confectioner,* vol. 23, no. 8, p. 12, 1943.

[20]"Japanese Mint Producers Reach for American Trade," *op. cit.*

[21]A. Osol *et al* (eds.), *The Dispensatory of the United States of America,* 25th revision, 1955, pp. 1033-1039, J. B. Lippincott Co., Philadelphia, 1960 edition, 1960.

[22]"New Klondike Region Produces 80 Percent of Peppermint Oil Sold to Markets of World," *Indianapolis News,* January 18, 1926.

[23]*Drug and Chemical Markets,* date unknown.

[24]U.S. Census of Agriculture, 1929.

[25]G. M. Hocking and L. D. Edwards, 1955, *op., cit.,* p. 81.

[26]Letter supplied by R. R. Howard.

[27]A. F. Sievers, *Travel Report, op. cit.,* p. 61.

[28]*Drug and Chemical Markets,* February 25, 1926.

[29]L. Gaylord, *A Survey of the Peppermint Industry of Wayne County,* historical paper, Wayne County, New York, Historical Society, pp. 49-51, April, 1965.

[30]C. F. TenEyck, "Peppermint Oil Development in California." *Proceedings of Conference on the Cultivation of Drug and Associated Economic Plants in California,* p. 54, December, 1943.

[31]W. C. Tesche, "Please, Sir, It's Only Peppermint," *Pacific Rural Press,* p. 3, January 1, 1927.

[32]The San Joaquin Valley newspaper is unidentified; taken from the files of the A. M. Todd Company.

[33]C. F. TenEyck, *op. cit.,* pp. 54-55. It is also known that small acreages of White Mitcham peppermint were planted in California.

[34]*Ibid.,* p. 55.

[35]W. C. Tesche, *op. cit.*

[36]*San Francisco Examiner,* December 8, 1927.

[37]C. F. TenEyck, *op. cit.,* pp. 54-55.

[38]A. F. Sievers, *Travel Report, op. cit.,* pp. 12-13.

[39]*Ibid.,* pp. 45-46.

[40]C. S. Anderson, *The Mint Industry: Price Effecting Factors and Future Possibilities,* economics term paper, Washington State University, p. 7, 1927.

[41]A. F. Sievers, *Travel Report, op. cit.,* pp. 12-13.

[42]"Mint in the Northwest," *op. cit.,* p. 21.

[43]A. F. Sievers, *Travel Report, op. cit.,* p. 14.

[44]*Drug Markets,* Nov. 30, 1926.

[45]*Ibid.,* pp. 39-40.

[46]*Indiana Crops and Livestock,* Purdue University, 1930.

[47]U.S. Census of Agriculture, 1929.

[48]*Ibid.*

[49]*Ibid.*

Chapter 11.

The Mint Industry Faces the Depression

The Market

The depression was a good designation for the American mint industry during the decade of the 1930's, but it was a depression of prices and not of production. In fact, the production for the 1930's remained fairly stable, generally hovering around the 1,000,000 pound mark for the entire decade. The fact that the chief domestic outlets for mint oils, chewing gum, toothpaste, and candy were more or less luxury items did not prevent the American public from continuing their consumption in some quantity. But consumption never exceeded production.

There were, therefore, serious price dislocations or depressions due to the overproduction. By 1935 peppermint oil had dropped to $1.74 per pound and spearmint oil was selling off the farm for $1.30 and had even been below $1. Peppermint oil went to $2 in 1936 then levelled off for the remainder of the decade. Spearmint oil continued low but was at $1.77 by 1940. For many farmers these figures were far below their production costs. In the Middlewest mint production was continued as a cash crop by many only because it was part of the rotation system and growers had considerable investment in distillation equipment. By rotating growers could hedge their acreage against the prevailing market.

The export demand was a boon to the industry during this troubled period. Having dropped to a meager 67,809 pounds in 1926 the expected European substitution for American oil never materialized and the market quickly rebounded. Over 200,000 pounds were exported in 1927 and the amount increased to 386,000 in 1936, representing over one-

123

third of the national production. In 1939 nearly half the American oil produced moved into the export trade.

Although the national demand remained somewhat stable the over-production and resulting low prices forced farmers to come to grips with their production costs. Only by maintaining high yields, thus decreasing expenses, could growers expect to weather the low market period. Any factor that contributed to decreased yields proved to be a severe problem. Such a factor assumed significant proportions in Michigan during the decade.

Conditions in Michigan

The disease that had been discovered on the Mentha plantation in 1924 proved to be a form of Verticillium wilt caused by a soil borne fungus destructive to many agricultural crops. Because mint roots had been so freely transported from one producing region to another the disease was soon found throughout the fields in southwestern Michigan. Erratic, causing severe losses in some years, absent the next, the disease baffled experts who were unable to discover any type of recommended procedure or formula for its control.[1] It was generally believed that water availability was a key to successful cultivation but the severity of the disease was recognized in that a control program included the development of wilt resistant strains of mint plants as the best possible solution.[2]

Wilt is a complex disease and mainfests itself in a bewildering array of differing symptoms. The plants may dwarf, twist, curl, blanch, develop asymetrically, and lose leaves; cankers develop on the roots with resulting rot and loss of vitality or death. Yields, of course, are seriously reduced.

The early research on the wilt disease was done almost entirely by Ray Nelson, a plant pathologist from Michigan State University. As the technological battle began the disease was becoming excessively spread throughout the mucklands of the southwestern producing district. Many sections devoted to peppermint cultivation, especially in Branch, Berrien, Van Buren, and Allegan counties, were abandoned. Less susceptible spearmint was substituted but the generally poor marketing conditions prevailing prevented any great expansion. Having come at a period of low prices, growers were unable to profit from a crop with erratic yields. Gradually much of the muckland was turned into cultivation of more profitable vegetables.

The central producing region, centered around St. Johns in Clinton County, was a newer area and was not, at first, troubled as greatly by the disease. By 1936 the central district, especially Clinton and Shiawassee counties, was the chief producing region in the state and accounted for more than half of the total acreage in 1939.[3] By this time the large Gun Marsh along the Gun River in Allegan County had been drained and put into cultivation. A whole host of new towns began to appear in the Michigan mint literature: Elsie in Clinton County; Ovid, Owosso, Carland, Corunna, Bennington, and Laingsburg in Shiawassee County; Plainwell, Martin, and Hopkins in Allegan County (Map 11). As the older muckland acreages went out of cultivation the newer sections expanded. Between 1935 and 1940 the central Michigan district produced nearly one-third of the entire national peppermint and spearmint oil supply. Michigan regained the lead from Indiana and, once again, reigned supreme in the mint industry.

But the victory was a temporary one. Wilt disease control was not perfected and the newer areas began also to suffer from the accumulative consequences. To further complicate the problem a new disease, mint anthracnose (leopard spot), which was already a problem in Indiana, was first reported in the state in 1935.[4] Fortunately, adequate control measures were soon developed and left Verticillium wilt as the major cultivation problem facing Michigan growers.

The central Michigan district quickly incorporated the importance of the mint industry into its local lore. When the town of Laingsburg celebrated its centennial in 1938 a special contest was held and Miss Catherine Colby was elected to reign over the holiday parade as "Peppermint Queen," attended by princesses Myrtle Veith and Elaine Trombley.[5] The "Peppermint King" was Ralph Cortright who had introduced mint culture in the area in 1926.[6] At this time there were more than 15 mint distilleries in the Laingsburg area alone, including those of Cortright, Albert Phinney, Ed Lee, and Roy Hooper.

Growers, disenchanted at the low market prices, began once again to evidence interest in cooperative marketing. The trend developed as a result of the dissatisfaction of several growers in the central district with their buying relations with the Todd Company. The growers accused Todd of having a monopoly of the Michigan oil business and in 1935 appealed to their Congressman, Fred L. Crawford of Saginaw. Crawford, in turn, requested the Federal Trade Commission to conduct an investigation.[7]

> Peppermint growers are in for some pertinent information regarding the prices they get for their crop, and possibly, for a better price, it was learned today at the Federal Trade Commission.
> The commission, acting upon the request of Congressman Fred L. Crawford of Saginaw, who said that "one firm" seems to exercise a monopoly

over the price the farmer in Michigan gets for peppermint oil, stated today that they had detailed "men" to start an investigation in the peppermint price situation. A request was also made of Crawford's office to furnish the commission with the names of growers or dealers who have expressed dissatisfaction with the present price of the oil.

This was taken to mean that the commission would like those who believe undue restraint is being exercised to depress the price of peppermint oil to come forward and supply it with any information it may use in its investigation.

Crawford said in his letter to the commission that when the present marketing season opened the price of the oil was around $2.50 per pound and the best any farmer in the state could get today would not exceed $1.25.

He also contends that if this situation is not improved "I cannot see much future for the industry."

The chairman of the commission in his reply to Mr. Crawford stated that the commission would include the situation in the Michigan peppermint industry in the investigation which it is now carrying on regarding other agricultural products. It was stated definitely that the matter had been turned over to the chief examiner's office and that it would be gone into thoroughly.

The situation which Crawford cited to the commission was that the farmers were "forced" to sell to one firm, there being no other market for the product locally that was open to the farmer. This results in the farmer being obliged to take whatever price the "one firm" offers the growers, he said.

Throughout the winter the Federal Trade Commission conducted its investigation, which involved discussions with farmers, dealers, including Todd, Leman-Gerber, and Brown, and some of the major oil users like Wrigley and Beech-Nut. In April, 1936, the investigation was closed and the entire industry was given a clean bill of health. The crux of the situation appeared to be that the dissatisfied growers had marketed oils with Todd that were not choice quality and resented the reduced prices which they were paid.

Many growers, however, felt that concrete steps should be taken to insure better marketing conditions. Convinced that there was some skullduggery by which brokers and dealers conspired to keep accurate production statistics from growers, nearly 150 mint farmers met at St. Johns on April 7, 1936, and voted to form the Michigan Peppermint Growers Association whose purpose it was

> to promote the marketing of peppermint and spearmint grown by members and the collective purchasing for the members of the commodities used in the growing and distilling of peppermint. The association will also furnish members with information on the control of parasites, drought, moisture, and other crop conditions that arise from time to time.[8]

Named to temporary positions were: Roy Peters, Leslie Brown, Emil Lee, Norman Gute, A. J. Herscher, William Britten, Myron War, E. A.

Livingston, and A. J. Manly.[9] Nearly 300 growers met on the following May 1 and approved permanent incorporation of the organization, naming the following officers: Eugene A. Livingston (St. Johns), President, Emil Lee (Laingsburg), Vice-president, Myron Ward (St. Johns), Secretary-treasurer. Board members were: Leslie G. Brown, A. J. Manly, and Chester Crosby, all of St. Johns, William T. Britten, Bennington, and Norman Gute of Owosso.[10]

The organization wasted little time in setting forth a program. At a massive meeting held on July 15 cooperative marketing was discussed and $10 shares were subscribed. Nearly $1,000 was collected. Speakers were Congressman Crawford and the state commissioner of agriculture, James F. Thomson, both of whom strongly endorsed a mint cooperative organization. Indiana was represented by S. J. Stewart and Louis Getz, both involved in the St. Joseph Valley cooperative attempt in that state a decade earlier.

In the meantime Livingston, who had serious reservations about cooperative marketing, resigned from the organization and was replaced by Leslie Brown. Opinion was divided on the marketing issue, many favoring an educational cooperative only. Organization continued, however, and a flyer was circulated by the Association on August 3 in which it was very clearly stated that the cooperative would not attempt to form an oil pool.[11]

> And remember, THIS IS NOT A POOL—Oil placed in the association warehouse will be tested, tagged and labeled for you and may be taken out and sold at any time you choose.

On August 8 interested growers met, set the capital stock limit of the new cooperative at $20,000, and named nine directors to head the organization.[12] Success was short lived. When the Association met in July of 1937 it had only 43 members, had sold only about $1,000 worth of shares, and had handled but five carloads of fertilizer which had produced $260 in revenue for the cooperative. The Association expected to hire a field man who would solicit new members, inspect crops, and contract for oil.[13] But too many growers remained outside the organization and it soon dropped its marketing function in favor of a broader program involving study and educational programming.

Albert M. Todd did not live to see the movement of the industry into central Michigan. He passed away in Kalamazoo on October 6, 1931. He had spent his later years actively studying municipal and public ownership of utilities in the United States and Europe, wrote several books on the subject, and aided in the organization of the Public Ownership League of America, serving as President from 1916 to 1922.

Collector of a magnificent library of books and works of art, his eighty-one year life ended during the sixty-second year of the company he had founded. His contribution to the American mint industry had been immense, fully worthy of the designation, "Peppermint King of America."

Developments in Indiana

The industry in Indiana followed an entirely different pattern during the 1930's than that in Michigan. With the exception of a small development on the Iroquois River mucklands in Jasper County no new acreages were brought under cultivation in the state and peppermint and spearmint continued to be grown in the same fields. In the middle of the decade the yields in the central Michigan district were better than double those of Indiana.[14]

As the central Michigan district expanded acreage in Indiana declined precipitously. Between 1929 and 1939 state acreage was reduced nearly 75 percent, from 40,600 acres to a meager 9,284[15] and over 1,300 mint growers in the state had abandoned the crop leaving only 709 farms left in mint production. Acreage had declined so rapidly that, by 1939, the central Michigan district itself produced more mint oil than the entire state of Indiana. The census figures make the comparison most distinct.

State	Number of Farms	Acres	Pounds of Oil
Indiana			
1929	1,980	40,600	508,848
1939	709	9,284	229,422
Michigan			
1929	707	11,141	226,134
1939	1,034	18,800	494,813
Oregon			
1929	160	2,285	84,333
1939	119	2,483	104,429
Washington			
1929	113	846	28,732
1939	100	957	45,051
Ohio			
1929	9	140	2,465
1939	7	213	2,513
California			
1939	1	800	32,400

By 1939 the two states had almost exactly reversed their 1929 production positions. It is significant, however, that Michigan farmers were producing about the same amount of oil on less than half the 1929 acreage in Indiana. The higher yields in the central Michigan district enabled growers there to weather the poor market. Indiana farmers had come too close to the slim margin of profit.

Yields and low prices were not, however, the only problem faced by Indiana mint growers during the decade. Indiana oil had come into some bad repute because of quality problems, and many growers were not weeding and cultivating properly. The resulting oil, discolored and off-flavor, did not command premium prices. At a special meeting of mint growers held in South Bend on December 20, 1935, experts at Purdue University were requested to investigate some of the major problems relative to the mint industry in the state. Stemming from this request, the University published a series of three bulletins, one covering cultivation practices,[16] one covering production costs,[17] and another dealing with oil handling and quality problems.[18]

Disease was not the problem in Indiana that it was in Michigan, although anthracnose was more widespread, being found to some extent in the majority of fields examined in 1939.[19] Control measures were soon developed that made the disease of much less significance.

By 1939 American peppermint was still found in Indiana, but only in fields where it was mixed with the Black Mitcham variety. Scotch spearmint the same year made up nearly 75 percent of the Indiana acreage.[20]

Cooperative marketing in Indiana still attracted some attention. An attempt to organize in 1930 with help from the Federal Farm Board failed to materialize (Figure 48). At the special meeting held in South Bend in 1935, a report concerning cooperative marketing in Indiana was presented by Myron H. Smith of LaPorte. The general tone at the meeting regarding such marketing was negative, but it was suggested that an additional meeting be held at South Bend on January 20, 1937, to further discuss the possibility. At the January meeting a resolution to form a marketing cooperative in Indiana in conjunction with that in Michigan was unanimously adopted and the following flyer was circulated to the growers:

> Mint Growers' Cooperative
> (to be incorporated)
> Temporary Address—La Porte, Indiana
>
> Dear Fellow Mint Growers:
>
> As many of you have attended one or more of the three meetings of mint growers in South Bend and East Lansing, you know of the strong opinion prevailing in favor of taking advantage of the new facilities offered for marketing peppermint oil through a cooperative organization of growers. That opinion is about to be crystallized into action—if a substantial number of growers desire it.
>
> A special committee of Indiana and Michigan growers of mint after a thorough investigation and discussion made this report to the general meet-

ing held in South Bend on January 20th: "This committee recommends to the mint growers of Michigan and Indiana that a legally incorporated marketing association be organized immediately to be ready to function during the coming marketing season." The report was adopted at the general meeting without a dissenting vote.

At the same meeting a board of temporary directors was elected as follows:

Leslie G. Brown, St. Johns, Mich.
Emmet Scott, LaPorte, Ind.
Earl McNamara, Mentha, Mich.
Charles Werker, Albion, Ind.
Leslie Haefner, Decatur, Mich.
George Dodd, South Bend, Ind.
Alois DeBeck, New Carlisle, Ind.
H. Myron Smith, LaPorte, Ind.

This group was instructed to take the necessary steps to complete the organization. The writer was elected Chairman of the Board.

Mr. John E. Brown, President of the Louisville Bank for Cooperatives was invited to meet with the Board. After an all day conference with him at South Bend on February 28th, the Board is even more convinced that it is entirely reasonable and logical to organize for the purpose of selling our mint oil cooperatively. After Directing many searching questions at members of the Board, and after a visit to a chemists laboratory, Mr. Brown expressed himself that it would appear as if mint oil lent itself admirably to a cooperative selling organization such as growers now contemplate and because among other things:

1. The product is valuable and capable of storage in small space.
2. When properly stored it does not depreciate in quality.
3. That it can be graded for buying and selling by chemical analysis reinforced by inspection as to color and odor, and
4. That the territory producing mint and the number of individual producers was not as large as in the case of many other products, which are successfully marketed cooperatively.

He further stated that with proper organization and efficient management, he felt his bank would make conservation loans to the organization with the oil as collateral at a very low rate of interest. This would enable the cooperative to make advances to the grower members when the oil is stored. With this type of financing, the sale of stock to members will not be necessary, in fact the only investment a member need make is a small membership fee of One Dollar.

Following the meeting with Mr. Brown, the Board decided on the following probable steps in organization:

March 1st—until completed, campaign for members.
May 1st—incorporation of company.
June 1st—opening of main office and warehouse in South Bend.

So we're on our way. You and the other mint growers in Michigan and Indiana hold the answer as to whether we continue to sell our oil as in the past or whether we join hands and market our own oil. Think of this for a minute, men: In 1929 in the United States there was produced 1,073,000 pounds of peppermint oil, the price per pound was $3.19 per pound. In 1932, production dropped to 421,000 pounds—less than one half of 1929— and the price instead of going up with such a decrease in supply actually went DOWN to $1.42 per pound. Now 1934 was not such a good year but the production was a little more than 1932—653,000 pounds to be exact, but in spite of the increased supply the price was up too, the average being

$2.35 per pound. And now last year: Production about the same as 1929—remember it was a poor year in 1934. In 1935 there was exported 338,238 pounds or nearly 100,000 pounds greater than in any one year in history—and what did we get for oil? AVERAGE PRICE $1.71. Is there any rhyme, reason or logic to such figures? Can we be blamed for feeling that the law of supply and demand which SHOULD have some influence on what we get is being tampered with by somebody, somewhere? (The above figures by the way are from the Bureau of Agricultural Economics of the Crop Reporting Board, Washington, D.C.) Oh, if I could take the space here, I could give you a lot more figures and facts that would make you wonder like it does me—Why have we stood it so long? If there ever was a need for farmers to join together to protect their own interests—it is in the marketing of mint oil. The time has arrived for you and me to back up this generally accepted opinion with appropriate action. You are being given the opportunity right now to put your shoulder to the wheel.

Here are some of the additional objectives our cooperative will strive for—others have accomplished them, so can we:

1. Prevent dumping huge quantities of oil on the market during the distilling season and make possible its being sold to the consumers over a reasonable period of time throughout the year. The oil stored with the Cooperative would be in strong hands and not pressing for sale. In order to be profitable to all of us, it should constitute a substantial volume of the country's total production.

2. Secure for the grower members the additional profit in marketing their oil, now going to private firms and individuals. Remember you and I are "small potatoes" in our present dealings with powerful and wealthy buyers, but by joining together, we not only become a factor to be respected, but could increase our combined and individual incomes considerably.

3. Supply to grower members periodically, data on acres in production, pounds produced and sold, prospective production and such other information which will enable our members to plan their own production based on supply and demand.

4. Arrange for a new and more accurate method of testing and grading oil.

5. Seek new uses and new outlets for oil in an effort to increase demand. There are many outstanding examples of success among producers' cooperatives in this respect. California Orange Growers quadrupled the consumption of their products and at the same time increased the net profit to the producer. Examples such as this is one of the best reasons for us going ahead.

Just a word about organization and management: To merit the support of the Louisville Bank for Cooperatives, our bylaws and methods of operation must have their approval. In a way therefore our cooperative will be supervised by this organization which is a part of the Farm Credit Association (Federal) set up. Responsible officers must be bonded; accounts audited by C.P.A. accountants; officers and directors are prohibited from employing relatives or from having any personal interest in the transactions other than the marketing of their own mint oil the same as other members. These are but a few of the safeguards. These and many other provisions in the bylaws will insure a square deal for every member making his association cooperative IN FACT as well as in name.

There are nearly 12,000 successfully operated cooperatives for farmers in the United States. With your supporting membership along with hundreds of others, ours will be another profitable one. I believe all the more progressive growers will welcome an opportunity to improve their own income and to lend a hand in improving the whole industry.

You will find enclosed your membership agreement—two copies. Sign the white copy, enclose with your remittance (dollar bill, check, draft or money order). Mail it in the enclosed envelope which is addressed and needs no postage.

We must know before we proceed further how many of you are for this and how many want to be charter members. Much remains to be done to be ready for business in time for the new crop of oil, as well as to sell the growers' carry over of last year's crop which some of you may still be holding. You will be notified of a general meeting for the adoption of by-laws and election of permanent directors to be called as soon as we have sufficient members. Let's get going on this now—this year 1936—this month, March—or "forever hold our peace" about prices and methods of selling our oil. Why not try at least to "distill" a half million dollars out of this business for your own pocketbook and those of your fellow growers. Right now while the information in this letter is fresh in your mind, is the time to act.

Yours for a brighter mint future,
H. MYRON SMITH
For Board of Directors

P.S. Should any of your neighbors growing mint fail to receive a copy of this letter with enclosures, do him and yourself a favor by dropping us a card giving his name and address.

But the memory of the debacle of 1926 was still too vivid among Indiana growers. The proposed cooperative did not solicit enough members to implement its program and it died on the vine, although the involvement of Michigan growers continued for some time.

Oregon and Washington

Production in the Pacific coast states remained relatively stable during the 1930's. Although the acrege in both Washington and Oregon increased slightly over 1929, the number of growers decreased. There was a slight trend toward larger acreages.

In Washington 70 of the 100 mint farms were located in the irrigated lands of the central portion of the state. Acreage in this section expanded from 156 in 1929 to 447 in 1939 and the increased yields are evident in the state totals. During the same period irrigated acreage in Oregon declined from 481 to 396. On the whole, however, there were no radical developments during the decade and no new production areas were developed. As the decade closed the two states commanded only 15 percent of the total national mint production. Indiana and Michigan had not yet been challenged.

Conclusion

The troubled 1930's ended on about the same note as they had begun. Oil prices were still quite low, supplies adequate, consumption limited. Cooperative marketing had once again failed. Michigan and

Indiana exchanged production positions while relative stability prevailed in Oregon and Washington. The export market continued to increase. Disease had reared its ugly head and, in the case of Verticillium wilt in Michigan, remained unchecked. Farmers in the state responded by abandoning the older areas and developing new sections. The central district of Michigan had become the most important mint producing region in the nation. The depression was coming to a close and developments in Germany and Japan would soon launch the mint industry into one of its most perplexing periods.

REFERENCES

[1]R. Nelson, "Some Important Diseases of Muck Crops," *Report of the Proceedings of the Seventeenth Annual Convention of the Michigan Muck Farmers Association,* pp. 32-36, 1935; R. Nelson, "Peppermint Diseases and Their Control," *Ibid.,* eighteenth annual convention, pp. 44-54, 1936; R. Nelson, *Verticillium Wilt of Peppermint,* Technical Bulletin 221, Michigan State College, Agricultural Experiment Station, June, 1950.

[2]R. Nelson, 1936, *op. cit.,* p. 52.

[3]U.S. Census of Agriculture, 1939.

[4]R. Nelson, 1936, *op. cit.,* p. 44.

[5]*The Laingsburg Press,* centennial issue, Laingsburg, Michigan, September 15, 1938.

[6]*Ibid.*

[7]J. F. Collier, "Charges Mint Oil Prices Manipulated," *Decatur Republican,* October 17, 1935, Decatur, Michigan.

[8]"Hold Peppermint Growers Meeting," *The State Journal,* Lansing, April 30, 1936.

[9]*Ibid.*

[10]"Mint Growers Organize Here," *Clinton County Republican-News,* St. Johns, Michigan, May 7, 1936.

[11]Flyer, Michigan Peppermint Growers Association, August 3, 1936.

[12]*The Owosso-Argus Press,* Owosso, Michigan, August 8, 1936.

[13]"Mint Growers Meet July 20," *Clinton County Republican-News,* July 22, 1937.

[14]R. Nelson, 1950, *op. cit.,* p. 33.

[15]U.S. Census of Agriculture, 1939; 1929 figures from *Indiana Crops and Livestock,* Purdue University.

[16]N. K. Ellis, *Mint Culture in Northern Indiana,* Circular No. 227, Purdue University, Agricultural Experiment Station, February, 1937.

[17]M. G. Smith and L. Robertson, *An Economic Analysis of the Production of Peppermint and Spearmint Oils in Indiana,* Bulletin No. 459, Purdue University, Agricultural Experiment Station, March, 1941.

[18]N. K. Ellis, K. I. Fawcett, F. C. Gaylord, and L. H. Baldinger, *A Study of Some Factors Affecting the Yield and Market Value of Peppermint Oil,* Purdue University, Agricultural Experiment Station, June, 1941.

[19]M. G. Smith and L. Robertson. *op. cit.,* p. 22.

[20]*Ibid.,* pp. 16, 27.

Note: the A. M. Todd Company, Kalamazoo, Michigan, has a lengthy film documentary of the total mint production process, from spring planting to harvesting and distilling. The film was made at the Mentha Plantation in Van Buren County, Michigan, about 1935.

Chapter 12.

Peppermint and Spearmint Go to War

The War Approaches

New times create new problems. As the activities of Nazi Germany made it increasingly apparent that a conflict of major proportions was in the making several problems emerged that acted to create new concerns for American growers. The first, and most significant, was a slight trend toward increased import shipments of peppermint oil. Japanese mint oil continued to come into the country but its major use, as a source of menthol, was no longer a competitive factor because of the labelling required by the Pure Food·and Drug laws. Other shipments, however, were of oil distilled from true peppermint plants in various countries and represented actual competition.

The Soviet Union was the major exporter and the Russian oil could be shipped in, duty paid, for about 35 cents a pound less than the American product. In 1941 imports represented nearly 10 percent of domestic production. Having just passed through a decade of extremely low prices American growers looked upon such competition with a great deal of dissatisfaction and there was considerable interest in obtaining an increase in the tariff rates. Before such action could be implemented, however, German troops invaded the Soviet Union and eliminated this problem for the duration. On June 30 the *Oil, Paint, and Drug Reporter* commented:

> competition by Russian peppermint oil in the United States stopped June 23.
> On that day, the shadow of the Russian Bear lifted from the American

134

peppermint farmer when the German fighter planes, Stuka bombers, Panzer divisions, and shock-troops knifed into Russia in an all-out war against the Soviet Union.

The prize coveted by Germany is this rich Russian Ukraine—where Russian peppermint oil is produced. Should Germany win, the shadow of the German swastika in all likelihood will hang over the American producer of peppermint oil. Meanwhile, he gets a respite.

The war on the continent had disrupted normal export channels as well. All shipments to Germany, a good customer for American oils, were discontinued in 1940 and those to France and the Netherlands the following year. The United Kingdom, until recently the major export outlet, received substantially reduced amounts in 1941. The combination of reduced exports and increased imports acted to maintain the depressed price situation of the preceding decade.

In the meantime, by 1941, domestic supplies of Japanese mint oil had become virtually non-existent as no shipments were received for over a year.[1] Menthol users, despite the high costs, began to turn to natural peppermint oil for a supply source and the prices of oil steadily climbed. From $2 a pound in 1939 peppermint oil increased in value until, by the autumn of 1943, it was selling for $4.85. Despite all indications of an improving market American growers responded only sluggishly and the 1939 peppermint acreage was increased by 1941 only a meager 540 acres. This slow response, so uncharacteristic of mint cultivators in the past, laid the foundation for many of the problems that soon developed.

Some New Studies

Two significant studies involving the mint industry were published in 1941 and, had it not been for the chaotic conditions in the world at the time, both might have had much greater impact at the moment.

The first was the result of experiments conducted on peppermint plants in relation to the length of the photoperiod or daylight length requirement.[2] It was discovered that peppermint is a long-day plant and produces optimum oil yields in a geographical zone with a photoperiod of from 16 to 18 hours, considerably higher than either northern Indiana or southern Michigan. It was not until after the war, however, that the important implications of this finding were fully realized.

The second study involved a federal government release in which the cooperative marketing of peppermint oil was strongly recommended.[3] The study, in fact, was unsympathetic to the country dealers and their important function of taking diverse oils from many producing districts and blending these according to the demands of customer specifications. As usual, the major grower dissatisfaction was the price factor but the study failed to analyze the supply-demand situation in any detail that would illuminate the problem. Another limitation of the study was the failure to examine the numerous attempts at cooperative marketing which had been made in the previous 15 years and come to some conclusion as to why they had all been failures. The full impact of the study, however, was negated by the slow improvement of mint oil prices. As the market gained strength there was little continued interest evidenced for any form of cooperative marketing.

The ABC Agencies Enter the Scene

During 1941 two important government agencies came into being that would be closely involved with the mint industry for some time; the Office of Price Administration and Civilian Supply (OPA) and the Supply Priorities and Allocation Board, later renamed the War Production Board (WPB). As early as January, 1942, rumors were spread that the OPA was considering price ceilings on mint oils,[4] an action that did not come until considerably later.

In the meantime the war had disrupted all imports, leaving the United States as the only significant mint oil supplier. Production of peppermint oil in 1941 was 34,000 pounds less than the preceding year. Thus, Pearl Harbor came at a time of reduced supply. At the same time large amounts of oil were being diverted to new uses, especially as a source for menthol; increasing demands were being placed on the industry resulting from the war in Europe; and prices were steadily climbing. But the industry had not yet adjusted to the pressures of the market and the added demands occasioned by Pearl Harbor came at a time domestic acreage was growing very little.

The Aftermath of Pearl Harbor

The possibility of any shipments of Japanese mint oil was completely eliminated by Pearl Harbor. Menthol users, led by the Vick Chemical Company,[5] began placing large orders for domestic peppermint oil. To forestall the evidence of inflationary trends, and eliminate the necessity of price ceilings, Michigan mint growers suggested a voluntary ceiling price of $5.00 per pound for peppermint oil,[6] a figure rejected by industry representatives at a meeting in Washington on the basis that dealers were not allowed a fair margin of profit.[7]

One of the most significant pieces of wartime legislation, the General Maximum Price Regulation (GMPR), administered by OPA, became effective April 28, 1942.[8] This act froze prices at their March, 1942, levels. Mint oils were not specifically listed in the GMPR but it was understood that a "voluntary" maximum, based on current New York quotations of $5.10 a pound for peppermint oil for growers and $5.60 a pound for dealers, would be adhered to. Michigan growers again expressed their opinion against rigid price ceilings[9] and, with a new harvest season approaching, it looked as if such a move by the government would not be necessary.

Mint growers were given distinct benefits in 1942 when the OPA exempted them from adherence to the voluntary price maximum and established price ceilings on custom distilling of the oil (oil processed for one grower by another).[10] This move, probably occasioned by a desire to stimulate increased production, also made it necessary for the OPA to permit the Todd and Leman companies to adjust their prices upward.[11] The OPA, however, gave the industry a stern warning that the situation was being carefully watched.[12]

The 1942 harvest was a successful one. Peppermint acreage expanded 11,000 acres over 1941, yields were high, and the 1941 production was exceeded by half a million pounds of oil. Spearmint production increased nearly 40 percent. The market adjustment had taken place and the increased supply eased the necessity of any firm governmental action.

During the following winter the demand for chewing gum and candy for service personnel had increased to such an extent that both peppermint and spearmint were placed on a list of "essential war crops,"[13] and the War Manpower Commission (WMC) termed medicinal and flavoring agriculture necessary for the war effort and recommended draft deferments for mint growers,[14] specifying a minimum of 16 units for deferment with a unit equivalent to 3 acres of mint.

The Price Margin Dilemma

By this time grower asking prices for mint oils had moved into line with prices of dealers, who were not exempt from the voluntary maximum. Faced with the possibility of buying oil, processing it, then selling it with no margin for profit, dealers removed themselves from the market and the movement of mint oil came to a virtual standstill,[15] although some users bought oil directly from the farm. Some evidence of black market activity was heard[16] and this, coupled with a rumor that the British had requested a large shipment of peppermint oil under Lend-Lease, caused OPA investigators to move into the fields to determine acreages and examine the price dilemma.[17] There was increased talk that price ceilings could no longer be avoided.

The Department of Agriculture, in an effort to guide OPA regarding possible price ceilings on mint oils, issued a list of "comparable prices" and quoted peppermint and spearmint oil at $3.10 and $2.28 a pound, respectively. This list, in effect, was a form of grower parity, and the price quotation established a minimum, a floor, beneath which growers were not required to sell. Spot quotations by this time, however, were considerably in excess of the comparable prices.

During the summer of 1943 the price margin dilemma remained unresolved and little of the oil moved into the hands of dealers. Hopes that 1943 production would alleviate the situation were shattered for two reasons: faced with labor supply problems, replacement of distillery parts which could not be obtained, and dissatisfied with the marketing situation, growers had planted 5,000 acres less peppermint than in 1942; the weather was so bad that 1943 yields fell precipitously and production dropped 43 percent. This decrease of nearly 600,000 pounds of mint oil at such a crucial time proved to be the most critical factor in World War II mint history.

The Stage is Set

Michigan growers appealed to the OPA for ceiling prices, apparently now feeling that government control was better than potential bankruptcy, and suggested $7.50 a pound for peppermint and $5.00 for spearmint (dealer maximum for peppermint at the time was $5.85), but the OPA countered with a recommendation of $5 and $3.[18] Meanwhile the rumors of the British request were confirmed and it was announced that they desired 200,000 pounds of peppermint oil compared to 72,664 received in 1942. The War Food Administration (WFA) requested the British to reduce their request to 125,000 pounds and suspended all shipments pending a review of domestic needs. WFA advertisements for 110,000 pounds of peppermint oil for the country's Lend-Lease commitment met practically no response.

With national supplies of mint oil already short, 1943 production off 43 percent, an increasing share of peppermint oil being diverted into the manufacture of menthol, danger of not meeting Lend-Lease commitments, and the market completely static, the stage was set for some sort of action.

Meeting the Crisis

It came swiftly. On September 10, 1943, the WFA issued Food Distribution Order 81 (FDO 81) which froze the entire national supply of peppermint oil (Figure 49).[19] All persons and dealers with quantities of oil in excess of 25 pounds were directed to place 100 percent of their supply at the disposal of the WFA for sale and file a statement of inventory before September 28. Consumers of peppermint oil were allowed to use 30 percent of the oil they had used in the final quarter of 1942 in the corresponding quarter of 1943. A press release from the WFA stated:[20]

> the War Food Administration has acted to assure an equitable distribution of oil of peppermint—an essential oil now limited in supply but important in both food preparations and pharmaceutical uses—by reserving all such oil for Government action . . . Since the war, American farmers have attempted to increase the production of oil of peppermint to meet increased civilian, military, and Lend-Lease requirements for this essential oil. Due to unfavorable weather conditions this year, domestic production is very short, and control over the limited supply is necessary to assure that it will be distributed equitably.

OPA action followed immediately and rigid price ceilings were established on mint oils effective September 30,[21] as follows:

	Growers	Dealers
Natural Peppermint Oil	$5.50	$6.00
Natural Spearmint Oil	3.50	4.00
USP Redistilled Peppermint Oil		6.35

Commissions for brokers and dealers were limited to 1942 levels, and their complaint that the margin of profit was too slim continued to be voiced. Growers were also unhappy with the price ceilings, and some threatened to "take a vacation" for the duration. An October 7 editorial in the *Clinton County Republican-News* (Michigan) mirrored the sentiments of many growers.

> The price of peppermint oil has been frozen at $5.50 per pound to the growers. The government, through OPA, is dictating the price. We are not surprised. In a measure, we think, some peppermint growers asked for it. It was about two years ago, if we remember rightly, that a group went to Washington. They argued for a higher price before some men who had no more idea of what the growers' problems and the growers' costs were than the Man in the Moon.
> Our point is the peppermint growers, by this action, convinced OPA or WFA, that mint oil was something that should be controlled. Now they are controlling it.
> Likely most people in this community will live if peppermint oil is not raised. That's beside the point. What we regret is that an industry which brought many thousands of dollars into this community is being badly, if not irreparably, damaged. We have talked with a large number of growers who frankly say that they will not attempt to produce oil next year with labor and price conditions as they are. Anyone who knows anything about this business knows that men do not jump into it and out again as price and labor conditions fluctuate. Peppermint culture—and that is what it is—demands knowledge and experience that is not gained in a year.
> Growers know this. We strongly doubt if OPA or WFA have any adequate appreciation of the business—although they pretend they do.

About this time a clamor arose regarding a conflict in statements issued by various agencies. Peppermint and spearmint had been placed on a list of critically needed and essential war commodities. The National Research Council, however, circulated a statement to the effect that the oils were not essential war commodities. This caused many of the users of mint oils to take strong exception to the WFA food order and they requested the Murray Small Business Committee of the U.S. Senate to conduct an investigation into executive interference with a non-essential industry.[22]

The confusion created by the disagreement of various agencies was further compounded in a jurisdictional dispute between the WPB and the WFA. The WPB claimed authority over all chemical products of agriculture. The WFA, on the other hand, held that anything that grew came under its jurisdiction. As the two agencies vacillated, the national supply of mint oil continued to sit, immobilized, under the freeze order.

In an effort to bring the situation to some form of satisfactory conclusion the Food and Drug Administration, under the Essential Oils and Flavors Section of the Special Commodities Branch, headed by A. L. Kalish, appointed an Oil of Peppermint Advisory Committee and called the group to a meeting in Washington on October 15, 1943.[23] The Committee requested self-autonomy in the matter of equitable allocation of supplies, but the jurisdictional disputes prevented any such action. One of the results of the Washington meeting, however, was a clearer picture of the national inventory. It was reported that approximately 1,250,000 pounds of peppermint oil was in the hands of users and dealers, of which nearly 1,000,000 pounds would be required by menthol manufacturers. After all the calculations were completed, it was discovered that an additional 800,000 pounds was needed but only 500,000 pounds was available.[24]

The uncertainty over sources of supply continued to plague users. Many feared that growers would remove a large portion of their mint acreage because of the confusion over marketing and prices, and banks were encouraged to allow generous loans on oil production to keep production stimulated. A great battle waged behind the scenes regarding eventual authority over allocation and, in the meantime, the entire industry was in a muddle.

Finally, the critical situation was resolved on New Year's Day, 1944, when the WFA, taking the bull by the horns, issued amendment 1 to FDO 81, leaving no doubt that it would oversee equitable distribution and get the oil moving.[25] A WFA press release stated:

the War Food Administration has increased the quotas on the use of peppermint oil—an essential oil now limited in supply . . . Increased quotas are now possible as a result of more favorable inventories compared with requirements for peppermint and the cooperation of the industry.

Among the salient points of the new order were the following: WFA would have complete control over all peppermint allocation; the 30 percent clause was set aside in favor of a more lenient schedule which allowed confectionery and chewing gum manufacturers to utilize 70 percent of any 1941 quarter use, dentifrice manufacturers 75 percent, and pharmaceutical companies 100 percent; users of less than 10 pounds of oil in any 1941 quarter were exempt during the correspond- ing 1944 quarter; no users were to have more oil on inventory than legally allowed; and companies manufacturing products for delivery to the armed forces were allowed a 90 day supply in addition to their normal quota.

The net result of the order was to resolve the uncertainty of users over their supply by placing allocation control in specific hands. Al- though the peppermint industry was denied the self autonomy which it had requested the order was looked upon with general favor by both dealers and users.[26] Slowly the mint oil supply began to move into the needed hands.

Unfortunately, the order could not resolve the price differential be- tween growers and dealers. The OPA was requested to raise ceilings and, since no action was taken, dealer activity continued minimal.[27] Charges were hurled that the OPA was openly encouraging socialism by attempting to spread the margin of profits by manipulating the mar- ket.[28] The beleagered organization finally responded and, in April, established a new price schedule.[29]

	Growers	Dealers
Natural peppermint oil	$7.00	$7.50
Natural spearmint oil	3.50	4.00
USP redistilled peppermint oil		8.05

Although prices were increased, the grower-dealer differential was unchanged and dealers continued to maintain that the margin of profit was entirely inadequate for the expense involved in their work. The new price schedule, however, did have a most ironic effect. Menthol users, already hard hit by the rigid allocation, now found themselves priced out of the peppermint market, the cost making the oil prohibitive to use as a source of natural menthol. Thus, the menthol users, one of the chief groups responsible for the emergency of 1943, were forced to look elsewhere for a source of supply and were eased out of a market that the original government controls were designed to protect. Fortunately, newly developed Japanese mint fields in Latin America helped supply the menthol users.[30]

The harvest season of 1944 was a successful one for peppermint, acreage and oil production closely approximating 1942 levels. The increased supply eased the emergency situation on peppermint but attention was now shifted to spearmint. Because of the more favorable market for peppermint, grower expansion had been almost entirely of that crop, and 1944 spearmint acreage was down 300 from 1941; yields were down considerably and production was 18,000 pounds less. Because of the increased demand dealers requested a reduction in grower price ceilings. The OPA responded by sending investigators into the field, reporting that production was down because of price dissatisfaction. Growers blamed "drought" for the shortage.[31] No specific action was taken, however, and the shortage continued until the following season when Indiana acreage and production expanded considerably.

The Crisis is Terminated

As a result of more favorable inventory the WFA increased the quotas for users of peppermint oil, twice in 1944 and finally on July 23, 1945.[32] Before the final order could be fully implemented, however, the WFA was liquidated. By the end of 1945, of all the agencies that had been involved in the peppermint crisis, only the OPA remained in existence. But it continued active. In 1945 the agency raised ceiling prices on peppermint oil, placed ceiling prices on custom stilling in Oregon and Washington, and released mint herb and flakes from all controls. In 1946 an additional increase was made on mint oil ceilings and, on November 19, all controls were terminated. The war was over, the crisis was past, and the American mint industry returned to a free market.

Developments in Producing Areas

On the whole, American mint growers, considering the problems they faced, could be proud of their wartime production. Lacking adequate labor supplies, forced to patch distilleries with non-existent parts, and facing, for much of the time, a controlled market, little fault could be found with their efforts.

Indiana. The wartime response was especially vigorous in Indiana. Peppermint acreage went from 12,200 in 1941 to 18,000 in 1944 and 1945. Spearmint, during the same period, increased from 4,600 to 7,800.[33] From 1941 on Indiana was once again the leading state in mint acreage. It was this increased production in Indiana that aided immeasurably in easing the critical shortage of the mid-war period.

Michigan. The wartime response in Michigan was considerably subdued. Acreage of both peppermint and spearmint in 1946 was almost identical to 1941 levels. Clinton and Shiawassee counties in the central district continued to be the main producing centers, but the older areas did not return much land to mint during the war. By 1946 the combined acreage of Oregon and Washington almost equalled that of Michigan. In the meantime, Verticillium wilt was spreading rapidly throughout the central district.

Oregon. Peppermint acreage in Oregon expanded nearly 300 percent between 1941 and 1946, reaching 8,000 acres during the latter year. The major centers were the Jefferson area in the Willamette Valley and the Clatskanie area along the lower Columbia River. These two regions alone accounted for nearly 75 percent of the total state acreage, in approximately equal proportions. In the latter area, in 1943, the Clatskanie Mint Growers Association was formed, but performed primarily an educational function and did not become involved in cooperative marketing.[34] Forerunners of difficulty were found in Oregon in 1944 when Verticillium wilt was discovered in a field near Lake Labish,[35] and mint rust of peppermint was reported from the Clatskanie area in 1946. Both soon proved to be considerable problems.

Washington. Peppermint acreage also expanded considerably in Washington but not to the same extent as in Oregon. Between 1941 and 1946 acreage went from 1,800 to 4,200 and the irrigated lands of the Yakima Valley now accounted for nearly 75 percent of the plantings (Map 15).

Growers in the Richland area had their land preempted by the federal government during the war, harvesting their last crop in 1944. Although everyone believed, at the time, that the land was being taken over for use by the Army, it was revealed following the war that the construction that actually took place was related to the development of atomic energy, and a huge plant was built on the Columbia River. The Richland growers dispersed, some moving east toward Kennewick, and others moving west into the Yakima Valley.

On August 16, 1944, the Washington State Mint Growers, Inc., was incorporated with offices in Kennewick and Henry J. York as President. Organized to promote cooperative marketing of peppermint oil in the Yakima Valley and Kennewick area, the attempt gained little grower response and became defunct within a year.[36]

It was during the war that the first effort was made by a western firm

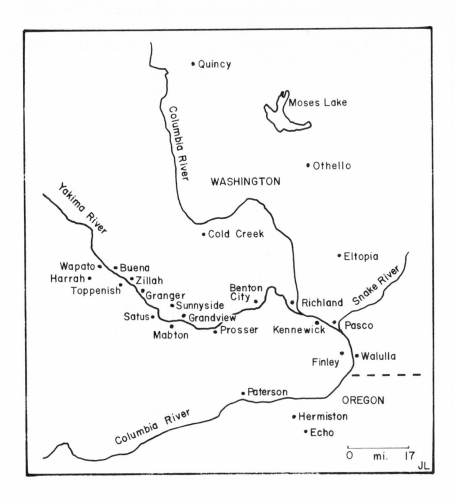

Map 15. The Lower Yakima Valley, Kennewick, and Columbia Basin districts of Washington and the Hermiston district of Oregon, showing the towns associated with commercial mint oil production since 1925.

to enter the mint industry as an active buyer and dealer. I. P. Callison was a schoolteacher in Chehalis, Washington, who forsook education in favor of editing and publishing a weekly newspaper. Early in the twentieth century Callison entered into partnership with a gentleman in an enterprise to supply Parke, Davis and Company with several loads of cascara bark. This venture proving successful, Callison abandoned the newspaper business and began developing a network of collecting agents and stations to handle crude drugs and wild plants gathered in the Pacific northwest.

In 1941 the firm purchased W. J. Lake and Company, a drug supplier dealing in a small way with western mint oils. At this time the western mint acreage was still fairly small and most buyers preferred the peppermint and spearmint oils from the Middle West. The peppermint oil produced in the Yakima and Kennewick areas of Washington was especially difficult to market due to peculiarities in taste and odor.

By 1943 the Callison firm had extended its buying operations enough to enter the market as a supplier of mint oils. Adopting the slogan "The finest peppermint oil comes from the Pacific Northwest" the company conducted a national advertising campaign designed to acquaint users with the properties of the western oils and promote their sales. It was largely through the efforts of the Callison company that the western oils, particularly peppermint oil from eastern Washington, found increasing acceptance in the world's markets.

Ohio. Ohio continued as a very minor producer of both peppermint and spearmint during the war, mainly in Wayne, Richland, and Hardin counties, but no great expansion took place and peak acreage was 240 in 1945.

California. Peppermint was produced in California throughout the war, primarily in the Stockton area, and also small acreages of spearmint until 1943. There were 1,120 acres of peppermint in 1944 but spearmint acreage never exceeded 165.

New Regions. There was a notable dearth of new producing centers during the war. Some peppermint was grown near Galveston, Texas, and it was suggested that the lower Rio Grande sections of Texas would be desirable; experiments were conducted at the University of Texas during 1945.[37] Only in Wisconsin did any permanent acreage become established. Ten acres of peppermint were planted in the southern portion of the state in 1945,[38] and increased to 80 the following year in addition to 9 acres of spearmint.[39]

Some Market Developments

As the war drew to a close the possibility of renewed shipments of peppermint oil from the Soviet Union again attracted attention. The mint farmers of Indiana, through the Northern Indiana Muck Crops Association, filed a brief with the Committee for Reciprocity Information in anticipation that the tariff on imported oils might be reduced. In part, the brief stated:[40]

your petitioners respectfully hold that they represent the oil of peppermint producers and farmers of Indiana. That there are approximately 1100 individual and partnership concerns separately producing such oil in the state. Our importance in the matter of producing oil of peppermint is that we originate the product itself and are therefore the first and most important factor in all of the various phases and activities of the industry. We produce this critical raw material which can not be duplicated or produced synthetically.

As producers of this oil in Indiana we employ approximately 5200 people; of that number approximately 2316 are skilled workers and laborers and the balance unskilled workers and laborers. This oil is used by and affects the American industry in its various phases in the probable total sum of $250,000,000.

We respectfully submit that the approximate cost of producing a pound of peppermint oil in the State of Indiana is $5.16 per pound. This cost is more particularly and definitely itemized as follows:
(per acre)

Man labor for 88 hours	$59.84
Tractor power for 8.5 hours	10.63
Supervision of growing and distilling	10.00
Fertilizer and insecticides	14.62
Distilling (using the state average of 25 pounds to the acre at a cost of 40¢ per pound)	10.00
Average tax rate	2.25
Depreciation on equipment	10.00
Interest on the investment	11.60
Total cost of one acre	$128.94

These petitioners respectfully submit that oil of peppermint will be imported from Russia even though the present rate of duty is maintained, or even increased, because we believe production costs involving farm labor in Russia are very definitely less than production costs in the United States of America. We further submit that the American farmer has in the past, and will in the future, be able to meet any quantity demand for the production of oil of peppermint at a normal price level providing the price paid provides a small margin of profit above the actual cost of production.

We therefore respectfully request that the present protective tariff be maintained.

A similar brief was filed by the essential oil growers in Michigan. But the anticipated Russian shipments never materialized and the tariff rates were unchanged until the successful implementation of the Kennedy Round in 1968. As a result of this agreement, the peppermint oil tariff will be reduced to 12.5 percent of value by 1972.

Some good signs for the American industry were seen in 1946 when the chewing gum industry announced plans for at least $15,000,000 of capital expansion.[41] Spearmint gum shipments had tripled over 1941 levels, and total gum sales were expected to increase over 10 percent of 1945 records. By this time, the chewing gum industry accounted for better than 50 percent of the domestic consumption of peppermint oil and more than 40 percent of spearmint oil. Dentifrice manufacturers consumed about 40 percent of the spearmint and 15 percent of the peppermint, and candy and confectionery concerns utilized approximately 5 percent of the peppermint and 3 percent of the spearmint. Only 1 percent of both oils moved into the drug trade. The remaining production was exported or used in sundry small items.

This consumption pattern was a matter that brought some attention to the mint oils. The only specified standards, other than those in the trade itself, for mint oils were those of the *United States Pharmacopeia* and were established for drug use. This resulted in the peculiarity that the entire domestic consumption of natural mint oils was based on standards existing for less than 1 percent of the usage. This was a distinct advantage, however, for growers and dealers since the standards protected the industry from much use of synthetics and substitutes, especially dementholized Japanese mint oil or corn mint oil.

Conclusion

The mint industry weathered the storm of allocation and price controls of the World War II period and by 1946 was once again operating in a free market condition. The nation remained the leading producer of mint oils and, as the post-war period began, the only important producer in the free world.

Definite changes had taken place in the producing districts. Michigan production had remained essentially static, and Indiana once again led the nation in mint acreage. A considerable expansion had taken place in Oregon and Washington and, by 1946, the two states combined commanded nearly one-third of the national acreage of peppermint and were producing nearly 40 percent of the oil supply. Clearly, the Pacific states had become powerful factors in the mint industry. As the industry moved into the post-war period, amidst many signs of a strengthening market, all indications pointed to even more significant production and consumption changes involving peppermint and spearmint.

REFERENCES

[1]*American Perfumer and Essential Oil Review,* vol. 42, p. 81, February, 1941.

[2]H. A. Allard, "Further Studies of the Photoperiodic Behavior of Some Mints (*Labiatae*)," *Journal of Agricultural Research,* vol. 63, pp. 55-64, 1941.

[3]F. M. Hyre, *Factors Influencing the Development of A Cooperative Marketing Program for Peppermint Oil,* U.S. Dept. of Agriculture, Farm Credit Administration, Cooperative Research and Service Division, Special Report No. 82, April, 1941.

[4]*American Perfumer* etc., vol. 44, p. 71, January, 1942.

[5]"Peppermint Crisis," *Business Week,* no. 734, pp. 34, 37, September 25, 1943.

[6]*American Perfumer* etc., vol. 44, p. 75, February, 1942.

[7]*Ibid.*

[8]General Maximum Price Regulation, 7 *Federal Register,* pp. 3153-3157.

[9]*American Perfumer* etc., vol. 44, p. 75, May, 1942.

[10]General Maximum Price Regulation-Amendment 4, 7 *Federal Register,* p. 4339; Maximum Price Regulation 165, as Amended, *Ibid.,* pp. 6429-6436; *Oil, Paint and Drug Reporter,* vol. 142, p. 59, August 24, 1942.

[11]OPA, Order 24 and Order 25, 7 *Federal Register,* pp. 6682-6683.

[12]*American Perfumer* etc., vol. 44, p. 71, September, 1942.

[13]*Ibid.,* vol. 45, p. 83, March, 1943; *Oil, Paint and Drug Reporter,* vol. 143, pp. 3, 57, May 3, 1943.

[14]War Manpower Commission, Regulation No. 4, 8 *Federal Register,* pp. 5136-5138.

[15]*American Perfumer* etc., vol. 45, p. 79, May, 1943; *Oil, Paint and Drug Reporter,* vol. 142, p. 61, November 30, 1942.

[16]*Ibid.*

[17]*Ibid.*

[18]*Ibid.,* vol. 45, p. 85, August, 1943.

[19]WFA, Food Distribution Order 81, Oil of Peppermint, 8 *Federal Register,* pp. 1525, 1527; *Oil, Paint and Drug Reporter,* vol. 144, p. 5, August 30, 1943.

[20]The press release, appended to the original order, did not appear in the *Federal Register.* Copies are available from the library of the USDA.

[21]OPA, Maximum Price Regulation 472, 8 *Federal Register,* pp. 13126-13127.

[22]*American Perfumer* etc., vol. 45, p. 69, November, 1943; p. 81, December, 1943.

[23]*Ibid.,* p. 69, November, 1943.

[24]*Ibid.*

[25]WFA, Food Distribution Order 81, Amendment 1, 9 *Federal Register,* pp. 152-154.

[26]*American Perfumer* etc., vol. 46, p. 63, January, 1944; *Confectionery-Ice Cream World Weekly,* vol. 31, no. 1, pp. 1, 29, January 7, 1944.

[27]*American Perfumer* etc., vol. 46, p. 95, March 1944.

[28]*Ibid.*

[29]OPA, Maximum Price Regulation 472, Amendment 1, 9 *Federal Register,* pp. 3426-3427.

[30]S. C. Saunders, "Menthol Situation: Perplexities and Expedients," *Foreign Commerce Weekly,* vol. 15, no. 9, pp. 14-15, 35, May 27, 1944.

[31]*American Perfumer* etc., vol. 46, p. 71, September, 1944.

[32]WFA, War Food Order 81, Amendment 6, 10 *Federal Register,* p. 9258.

[33]Annual figures from *Agricultural Statistics,* USDA.

[34]*Oregon Farmer,* November 18, 1948.

[35]L. W. Boyle, "Verticillium Wilt of Mint in Oregon," *Plant Disease Reporter,* vol. 28, p. 1095, 1944.

[36]W. A. Paulson, *The Mint Industry in the State of Washington,* pp. 9-10, Pacific Coast Banking School, research paper, University of Washington, April, 1966.

[37]"Peppermint Growing in Texas Studied," *Oil, Paint and Drug Reporter,* vol. 143, p. 56, October 25, 1943; G. M. Hocking and L. D. Edwards, "Cultivation of Peppermint in Florida," *Economic Botany,* vol. 9, p. 81, 1955.

[38]From the files of the A. M. Todd Company.

[39]*Ibid.*

[40]Brief of the Northern Indiana Muck Crops Association in Support of the Retention of the Present Protective Tariff Upon Oil of Peppermint from *Mentha piperita* L., Committee for Reciprocity Information, December 18, 1946.

[41]*Confectionery-Ice Cream World,* March 29, 1946.

Chapter 13.

The Opening of the West

The Immediate Postwar Years

As the battles with the wartime government agencies faded into history the American mint industry returned to a free marketing economy and resumed the much older battle of adjusting supply with demand. The rise of personal income, coupled with the extraordinary wartime demands, had kept domestic consumption of mint flavored products relatively high and the American public continued to favor peppermint and spearmint chewing gum, candy, and toothpaste.[1]

But production always exceeded domestic consumption, and the export market continued to play an important role in the industry. Bulwarked with Marshall Plan funds exports of peppermint oil, primarily to western European nations, exceeded a half million pounds in both 1949 and 1950. An expected drop in exports took place the two following years, since no further Marshall Plan funds were available. But the European economy was strengthening and exports returned to the half million pound level in 1953 and continued to grow. This took place despite the availability of dementholized Japanese mint oil, increasing production of mint oil in various European nations, and the higher cost of the American product. There was some concern that Americans might price themselves out of the European market,[2] but increasing production in the United States acted as a constant price stabilizer. Since World War II, peppermint oil prices have ranged between $5 and $9 per pound at the extremes, and spearmint oil between $3 and $10, generally being nearer the middle level.

149

The development of chlorophyll toothpastes in 1947, in which spearmint oil is used as the flavoring ingredient,[3] offered a new market for mint growers. As expected, demand increased, prices rose, and spearmint acreage, in 1948, reached 22,200, an all-time high for the crop. The resulting production of over a half million pounds of the oil so far exceeded the demand that the depressed prices caused spearmint acreage to be halved in just three years. An identical cycle was repeated between 1954 and 1958. The demand-supply battle was a long way from being solved.

The major concern facing the industry was the problem of Verticillium wilt in Indiana and Michigan. By 1950 wilt had become severe in the central Michigan district and was increasing in Indiana. As it became apparent that the problem was not being solved, and the amount of new muckland suitable for mint culture in the two states was running out, dealers and users began to focus increased attention on the Pacific coast states. By 1948 peppermint oil production in Oregon exceeded that of Indiana, although the latter state had considerably greater acreage. The higher yields in the west, resulting from the more favorable geographic environment and the lessened incidence of wilt, slowly turned the tables. As early as 1952 Oregon growers requested an embargo on mint roots from the Middlewest to keep disease from further spreading and threatening what was becoming an extremely important western crop.[4]

The West Emerges Dominant

The year 1950 proved to be a significant one. Plagued by bad weather, disease, inflation, national overproduction and reduced prices, Middlewestern farmers found their margin of profits barely exceeding production costs.[5] This dilemma was met in Indiana and Michigan in two ways: gradual abandonment of peppermint acreage in favor of more lucrative crops, especially corn and soybeans; and by substitution of the more disease resistant spearmint. In 1953 and 1954 spearmint acreage in Indiana greatly exceeded that of peppermint, an unusual situation since the total national acreage of spearmint seldom exceeds one-third of that of peppermint for which there is a much greater demand. Between 1949 and 1959 the number of mint farms in Indiana and Michigan decreased from 1,681 to 473.[6] Such a wholesale abandonment of cultivation, even though confined mainly to marginal producers and growers of small acreages, enabled the western states to assume the commanding position in the industry, one which has since become even more deeply entrenched.

Besides the widespread infestation of the middlewestern fields with Verticillium wilt there were a number of other reasons for the sudden rise of the Pacific coast states to this important status. Generated by the firm market of the war years, and favored by much higher yields than in the Middlewest, western growers found in mint an excellent cash crop which provided a considerable source of spendable revenue. In 1947, many Washington growers were enjoying the luxury of selling mint oil and banking more than 50 percent of their income as profit.[7] Although costs were generally higher than in the Middlewest, the increased yields more than offset the added expense involved. Michigan and Indiana farmers simply could not compete.

The development of portable irrigation equipment in western Oregon was a significant technological innovation. The light-weight, easily moved, overhead sprinkler apparatus enabled growers to maintain critical water supply levels, which not only favored plant growth but also lessened the effects of disease. In 1959 supplemental irrigation was being utilized by all except a handful of the 280 mint farms in Oregon.[8] The same year, in Indiana, only nine of 304 mint growers employed such a technique.

The industry having emerged at a much later date, the mint growers in the western states generally developed an almost total mechanical operation. Digging and planting roots by machine (Figure 54), harvesting the hay directly into portable distilling tubs (Figures 55 and 56), and distilling with relatively new and very efficient automated plants (Figure 57), the western growers avoided a good deal of the expensive and unavailable hand labor required in the Middlewest (Figure 52). Such a change in Indiana and Michigan was generally made on only the larger farms. The smaller growers continued to plant roots by hand, haul the hay in wagons to stationary distilling tubs, and process the oil in old and outmoded distilleries. Indiana lost the peppermint production lead to Oregon in 1948 and was relegated to second place in spearmint production by Washington in 1955.

Developments in the Western States

Oregon. Although peppermint cultivation in Oregon became extremely important the success was not achieved without obstacles and formidable problems. The consequences varied in the different producing districts.

1. *Lower Columbia River District.* Cultivation of peppermint along the Columbia River in Oregon was especially important in the Rainier, Clatskanie, and Quincy areas of Columbia County, and of less impor-

tance on the river flats near Portland and at the mouth of the river near Astoria. The Astoria plantings, during the great price rise and again in 1945, never proved successful and the lands near Portland gradually gave way to urbanization.

The Columbia County area was the first to suffer the full effects of disease. Mint rust, first reported in 1946, spread quickly and was especially severe between 1948 and 1953, reaching its most damaging extent in the latter year.[9] On May 30, 1948, the Columbia River flooded, wiping out the great majority of mint fields. Although many were replanted, the increased supply of water created conditions which promoted the spread of the disease, since mint rust flourishes directly with the extent and frequency of water supply and rainfall. The disease became so severe that, between 1950 and 1954, peppermint acreage in the Clatskanie area declined from 2,681 to 424. In 1947 there were more than 15 peppermint growers cultivating nearly 500 acres in the Rainier area (Figure 53). By 1957 only a single farm was left. Some growers established new plantings further west, in the vicinity of Brownsmead, Westport, and Woodson, and considerable acreage was maintained for several years in the early 1950's. But rust also attacked the new sections and the fields were removed from production. The entire district, for all practical purposes, ceased to be a mint oil producer.

In 1963 James Morton purchased land near Quincy and established new peppermint plantings with disease-free roots brought from Longview, Washington. The entire county is now under quarantine and only certified rootstock may be planted. Whether the area will ever again be an important mint producing region is uncertain, but there are nearly 13,000 cultivable acres in the seven drainage districts serving the Clatskanie and Quincy area.

Spearmint production was introduced in 1956 near Quincy by Henry Embast but spearmint, even more susceptible to rust than peppermint, has never proved successful in Oregon west of the Cascades. In 1949 Knippel and Held planted 65 acres of peppermint on Sauvie Island near Scapoose in the deltaic mudflats between the Willamette and Columbia rivers and production was maintained until 1958.

Since the late 1930's the Pusey Manufacturing Company at Clatskanie, owned and operated by Jerry Pusey, has been an important manufacturer of mint tubs and distillery equipment and, in 1967, an entirely new distillation plant, radically different from any known, was designed, built, and placed in experimental operation by Walt Thomas of Quincy (Figure 51). The tub is portable and consists of a 60 foot long circular tube through which the hay is conveyed by an auger at various adjustable speeds.

2. *The Willamette Valley.* The Willamette Valley producing district includes the alluvial flats and bench lands adjacent to the Willamette, McKenzie, Calapooia, Pudding, Tualatin, Yamhill, North Santiam, and South Santiam rivers. In general, the district extends north from Eugene over 100 miles to Portland and includes the counties of Clackamas, Yamhill, Polk, Marion, Benton, Linn, and Lane. Mint acreages in Washington and Multnomah counties, also in this district, were located mainly near Portland and have been lost to urban developments.

The major producing centers within the Willamette district are Coburg, just north of Eugene, and Jefferson, located near the fork of the Santiam rivers. Nearly 200 of the state's 280 mint farms in 1959 were located in these two areas. The flavor of the oil is quite comparable to that of the Middlewest and is generally in high demand.[10]

In this beautiful valley, situated at about 300 feet of altitude between the towering Cascades on the east and the low Coast Range to the west, amidst a bewildering diversity of agricultural products, the major peppermint acreage of the state has always been located. Characterized by extensive networks of overhead irrigation sprinklers, mint fields are set and generally not removed for periods of 10 to 25 years or until disease renders the fields unprofitable (Map 16). Mint rust was also severe in the Valley during the early 1950's and, in 1953, accounted for nearly a 20 percent crop loss.[11] Control measures were perfected, however, that lessened the severity of the disease.

Verticillium wilt began to be widespread in the Jefferson area about 1951 and, within 6 years, was responsible for the withdrawl of nearly 10,000 acres of land from mint cultivation. Since that time, an additional 4,000 acres have been removed.[12] By 1968, however, using new control measures, a considerable portion of the lost acreage was being returned to peppermint cultivation with every indication of success.

Spearmint production in the Valley has never been extensively developed but there have been small acreages. About 1946 Leon Funke obtained spearmint roots from Michigan and set them out on his farm near Coburg. Since that time other growers in the Jefferson and Coburg areas have maintained plantings of from 3 to 20 acres.

The small town of Jefferson is an important hub of the Valley mint industry. The town's Lions Club annually sponsors a Mint Festival and the local newspaper, *The Jefferson Review,* periodically publishes editions in a beautiful mint green color complete with a small scenting of peppermint oil.[13] The town is also the headquarters of the Cobb

Map 16. Field pattern of a 225 acre general farm, on which peppermint is grown, located in the Willamette Valley, Linn County, Oregon, just east of Corvallis. Water for overhead sprinkler irrigation is supplied from 4 thirty foot wells. (Modified from R. C. Brown, *The Agricultural Geography of Peppermint in the Pacific Northwest*, p. 37, M.S. thesis, Oregon State University, 1962.)

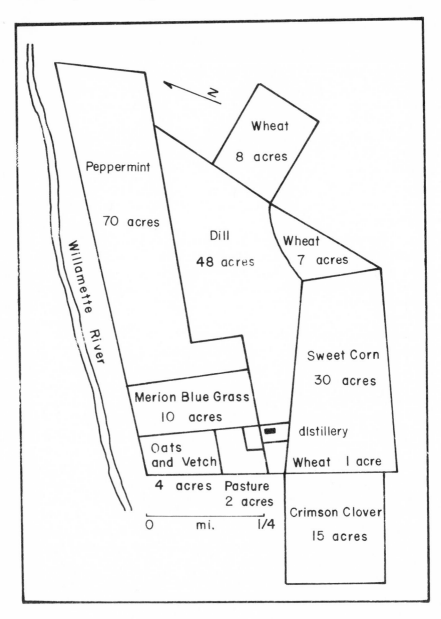

Manufacturing Company, the leading distillery and equipment manufacturer in the western states (Figure 50).

Although developments in other sections of Oregon are beginning to challenge the Valley as a mint producing area, if the necessary disease control measures prove successful, there seems no reason why the district should not continue as one of the major mint centers in the country. In 1967 the Valley peppermint acreage accounted for nearly 20 percent of the national total and nearly equalled the acreage of Indiana, Michigan, and Wisconsin combined. Nearly 130 growers are located in the Valley, distributed as follows: 65 in the Jefferson area located near such colorful towns as Buena Vista, Independence, Corvallis, Crabtree, Scio, Greens Bridge, Dever, Marion, Talbot, Salem, and Lake Labish (the heaviest concentrations being at Dever, Talbot and Buena Vista); the remaining in the Coburg area located near Harrisburg, Springfield, Junction City, and Monroe (the largest number being near Coburg and Junction City). The largest single peppermint farm in the Valley is that of Gorden Turnidge near Salem, where annual acreage may exceed 700.

3. *Southwestern Oregon.* South of Eugene the Coast Range gradually widens and merges with the Cascades in the massive Klamath Knot. Interstate highway 5 has considerably eased the tortuous journey across this mountainous section, locale of Crater Lake, Oregon Caves, and Klamath Wildlife Refuge. In scattered vales of this highland, between Eugene and Roseburg, Sievers had found several hundred acres of peppermint in 1927 which had been set out in response to the great price rise. The fields were located near Yoncalla, Camas Valley, Sutherlin, Dillard, and further west at Coquille.[14] Production never flourished due to the extreme winter cold, most of the roots died, and the area went out of production for some time. Since the war several mint farms have operated in the Yoncalla and Cottage Grove areas.

Between 1949 and 1953 Dan Fry of Salem, long time representative of the Todd Company in the Willamette Valley and a pioneer in developing overhead sprinkling in Oregon, attempted several growing experiments with peppermint and spearmint in this area. Plantings were made at Grants Pass and at Midland just south of Klamath Falls. The Kalamath Falls plants froze out, spearmint plants did not thrive, but peppermint did quite well at Grants Pass. In 1955 Fry acquired property in the Grants Pass area and now runs the largest peppermint farm in the state of Oregon. Here, the irrigation crews, fully equipped with Yamaha motorcycles, move about dutifully changing the irrigation pipes the required distance of 60 feet every four to six hours.

4. *Eastern Oregon.* The early plantings of peppermint on flood ir-

rigated land in Morrow and Umatilla counties in the vicinity of Hermiston during the great price rise did not long survive, but numerous attempts have been made to establish plantings in various irrigation districts since. Peppermint was successfully reintroduced into the Hermiston area in 1942 by Norbert Mueller and several growers, including some in the nearby town of Echo, are annually raising about 500 acres. Spearmint has also been produced in the past near Echo.

Peppermint plantings were made at Weston in 1949 and in the John Day Valley in 1947. The Weston acreage disappeared but production by a single grower at John Day continued for some time. The most successful development in eastern Oregon began in 1946 when two growers from the Willamette Valley, Leo Scott and Joe Martin, began peppermint production near Vale in Malheur County (Map 14). The plantings proved successful, yields were very high, and acreage expanded from 110 to 483 between 1954 and 1959. Today, nearly 1,300 acres and a dozen growers can be found in the district, which extends between Vale and Ontario, the largest single farm being located along Bully Creek.

In 1967 peppermint plantings on irrigated land were made near Keating in Baker County and at Lakeview in Lake County. Other plantings near Halfway, LaGrande, and Grand Ronde have also been made.

5. *Central Oregon.* In 1946 irrigation water from the Deschutes River was made available in Jefferson County near the small town of Culver south of Madras. In 1948 Harry Dinkel, who had come from the Willamette Valley, planted three-fourths of an acre of peppermint and gradually extended his acreage. Having no still, he sent the mint hay to the Talbot area of the Valley for processing.

As a result of research on the light and temperature requirements of peppermint the Todd Company officials had concluded that central Oregon would be an especially desirable locality for optimum production and was primarily responsible for initiating, in 1955, a large-scale expansion in the Madras area under the leadership of Herman Kieper. Fifteen growers, including Dinkel, Kieper, Paul Jasa, Clyde Kunze, Art Stevens, John McDaniels, B. Northrup, Wm. Cooley, W. Nichols, Art Yungun, Sid Elliott, Don Ferguson, Wm. McPheeters, Carl Anderson, and Hennigson-Ayers, planted 561 acres of peppermint with roots obtained from the Yakima Valley. Kieper and Kunze constructed stills to handle the crop,[15] and yields exceeding 40 pounds of oil to the acre were obtained.

A more unlikely mint producing district can not be imagined. Situated on a high western tableland, covered with a layer of volcanic, ashy soil, half barren, half sagebrush, and the remainder pure desert, the towering peaks of Mt. Adams and Mt. Jefferson overlook the town of Madras, only recently carved into the parched hillsides once devoted primarily to cattle and dryland wheat farming. But water has made the difference, and the meticulously weeded fields of peppermint cover the area, primarily under overhead sprinkler irrigation systems (Figure 54), although some furrow irrigation is utilized on the more level areas (Map 17).

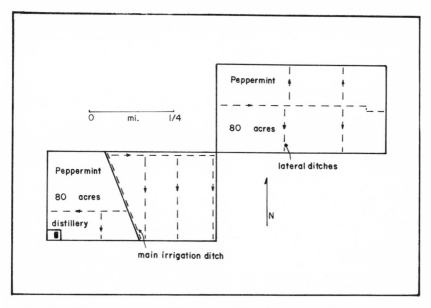

Map 17. Field pattern of a 160 acre specialized peppermint farm located just northwest of Madras, Oregon. The land has been levelled for gravity flow irrigation with water supplied from the Deschutes River. (Modified from R. C. Brown, *The Agricultural Geography of Peppermint in the Pacific Northwest,* p. 56, M.S. thesis, Oregon State University, 1962.)

Madras farmers wasted no time in organizing to protect their new area. Under the leadership of Jasa the Central Oregon Mint Growers Association was formed in 1955 and immediately requested the state government to quarantine the area from root shipments to keep out diseases, weeds, and insects.[16] Despite the quarantine, Verticillium wilt appeared simultaneously in eight fields in 1961.[17] Fumigation was successful in controlling some of the spread, but nearly 1,500 acres in the area have been lost to the disease.

The year 1956 was a troubled one in the Madras area. Many growers had applied Karmex as a weed killer and this, coupled with a hard winter and heavy spring and summer rains, combined to kill off nearly 500 of the 1,391 acres that had been planted.[18] Yields dropped to 20 pounds, and several growers threatened the manufacturer of Karmex with lawsuits.

In the following years growth and expansion were fairly steady and today nearly 100 mint growers are caring for some 14,000 acres of peppermint in the Madras area and there has been expansion to the south into the Redmond and Prineville areas and to the north near Wamic. Some of the largest acreages are those of William Towery, Paul Jasa, and Marola Farms, Inc. The central Oregon district is one of the most productive and important in the nation, and ranks second in Oregon only to that of the Willamette Valley (Map 18).

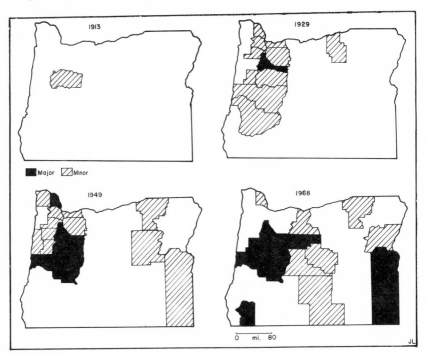

Map 18. The spread of commercial peppermint oil production in Oregon, by counties, for selected years since 1913. Major producing counties are those in which 500 acres or more were reported under cultivation.

Madras is home to two distillery equipment manufacturers, both having originated from the work of Keith Foster. In 1952 Foster had manufactured a still for use in the Yakima Valley of Washington and supplied a number more during the following years. When mint cultivation was introduced into the Madras area Foster built the first stills in the district and has constructed most located in that vicinity. In 1964, he withdrew from the partnership of the Foster Manufacturing Company and established an independent metal working shop. The original firm now continues production under the name of Tompsett-Shortline Manufacturing Company.

Washington. Unlike Oregon, the major mint producing sections of Washington have definitely switched into the irrigated lands east of the Cascades. Less than 2,000 acres are now planted in western Washington, in the Puget Sound Lowland and along the lower Columbia River and nearby lowland sections of organic soils.

1. *The Puget Sound Lowland.* Although there have been numerous mint farms located in various sections of the Puget Sound Lowland, the area has never been an important producing district. Farms near the Canadian border, in Whatcom, Skagit, and nearby Okanogan counties have been abandoned, as have the plantings near McKenna in Pierce County. Attempts to raise peppermint near Suquamish, in the vicinity of the grave of Chief Seattle, by J. W. Lawler lasted from 1956 to 1959, and several growers had mint near Chehalis between 1948 and 1952. The only mint production in the Lowland at this time is by the Berry Valley Farms at Lake Stevens near Everett, and by the Olympic Mint Association at Sequim on the western shore of the Sound.

2. *The Lower Columbia River.* Mint cultivation has become quite limited in the lower Columbia River district, the original mint producing center of Washington. The alluvial flats between Kelso and Skamokawa, and Puget Island and other nearby islands near Cathlamet, have all gone out of production because of mint rust problems. This area lies directly across the Columbia River from the Rainier-Clatskanie district of Oregon, and both have had a similar history. The only mint farm in the area today is Fry Farms located near the aluminum plant at Longview.

Several drained marshes in small vales north of Vancouver have been mint producing areas for some years, especially Fargher Lake located near Lafayette Center. The area was drained in the early part of the century, Chinese labor being employed to dig the ditches, subsidized by the Reed Garden Tracts company of Portland, Oregon. For many years Fargher Lake was an important daffodil bulb center. Mint was brought in during the great price rise in 1926 by Craig and Hartley, two hop growers from the Willamette Valley. It has been grown continuously since, between 400 and 600 acres annually now being cultivated.

Rust is a problem in the Lake during very wet years, and Verticillium wilt first appeared in 1962 after a load of roots had been shipped in from the Yakima Valley. There are three peppermint distilleries, owned by the Seely, Kunze, and Erickson families, and one 35 acre tract of peppermint owned by the Seeleys has been in mint continuously since 1929.

There are also several peppermint farms near Orchards, just outside Vancouver, but attempts to raise mint on the Chelatchie Prairie north of Fargher Lake, between 1955 and 1958, were abandoned because of low yields.

3. *The Lower Yakima Valley.* The rise of Washington to a position of dominance in the mint industry has been due to the tremendous expansion east of the Cascades, especially in the Yakima Valley and the area south of Moses Lake.

The Yakima Valley production is actually centered in two distinct areas; on opposite sides of the Columbia River near its confluence with the Snake River in the vicinities of Kennewick and Pasco, and in the Lower Yakima Valley on both sides of the Yakima River between Union Gap and Benton City. The bulk of the production is confined to the Valley itself.

The mint development is by no means an anomaly in the Yakima area. Yakima County leads the nation in the total number of fruit trees, apples, and hops. It is an extremely diversified agricultural section, and specialized crops in both the fruit and vegetable line are numerous. In the entire district, both the upper and lower valleys, mint production is exceeded as a crop revenue source only by apples, hops, sugar beets, and asparagus.[19] In 1965 Yakima farmers sold nearly $5.2 million dollars worth of mint oil.

The lower Valley, neatly sandwiched between the Yakima and Rattlesnake ridges on the north and Toppenish, Horse Heaven, and Ahtanum ridges on the south, appears as an emerald in a massive pile of dust. Sagebrush and barren desert border directly on lush, neat fields supplied with water from the two main irrigation projects, Roza and Sunnyside, which curl across the parched landscape like twinkling blue snakes.

Expansion of the mint industry was occasioned by a number of factors besides the wartime price interest. The Roza Canal, supplying water to the lands at a much higher elevation, began operation in 1944 and brought an additional 72,000 acres of the lower Valley into cultivation.[20] Mint farmers took full advantage of the new possibilities. By

1949 over 300 of the state's 349 mint farms were located in the Yakima and Kennewick areas.

This early expansion was occasioned by extremely high yields, some farmers obtaining as much as 150 pounds of oil from each acre, although 70 pounds was more average. The high yields were essential since dealers and users noticed that the oil from the area was quite different from that produced elsewhere.

> During the first years of production the quality of the Yakima oil was found to be inferior, owing to abnormal physicochemical properties (optical rotation considerably below the U.S.P. limits) and to an inferior odor which in many cases prohibited the use of this type of oil in chewing gum flavours. Research work on the chemical composition of the Yakima oil showed that it had an exceptionally high content of menthofuran . . . It was found that this compound is present mainly in the oil derived exclusively from flowers; in the entire plant it reaches a maximum during the blooming period and decreases as the menthol content increases . . . the peppermint plants in the Yakima region bear an abundance of flowers, blooming more profusely than for example in the Willamette Valley. Any layman walking through a peppermint field in full bloom has only to pick a blossom, squeeze it between his fingers, and he will immediately notice that the blossom oil has a rather disagreeable cloying odor, quite different from the refreshing delightful aroma of the leaf oil . . . To reduce the content of methofuran the plants are now cut after the maximum bloom of the first growth (from the end of August to the end of September), and before the second growth starts to blossom.[21]

Despite this knowledge, and improved methods of redistilling the Yakima oil, it is still regarded as the least desirable oil, finding its major outlet through export and in commodities where the peppermint taste and aroma need not be too sensitive. This is an extremely interesting predicament, since the area is the most important producing region in the United States, yet in periods of active sale Yakima growers receive a reduced price. The high yields are a most essential factor in the local mint economy.

Mint in the Yakima area is cultivated by means of furrow irrigation (Map 19). Since the furrows must be moved each year, only first year planting techniques are utilized and there are no fields of meadow mint. Weeds, especially water grass, have always been a problem and observers new in the area are frequently startled to see a harvested field of mint about ready for second cutting to be more composed of grass than mint. The development of a new weed killer, Sinbar, tested extensively in Washington and Oregon, and first applied to commercial fields in 1967, looks to afford growers substantial control of this perplexing problem. It creates crop rotation problems, however, and few crops will survive in a Sinbar treated field until two years following the last

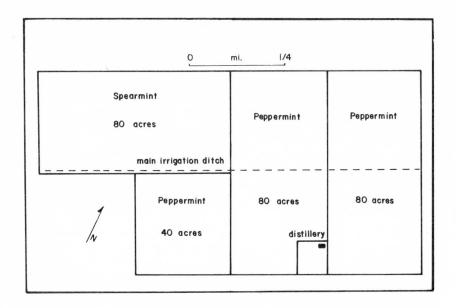

Map 19. Field pattern of a 280 acre specialized peppermint and spearmint farm located just west of Wapato, Washington, in the Lower Yakima Valley. Water for furrow irrigation is supplied through ditches from the Yakima River. (Modified from R. C. Brown, *The Agricultural Geography of Peppermint in the Pacific Northwest*, p. 48, M.S. thesis, Oregon State University, 1962.

application. Fortunately, mint has an extremely high tolerance to the new chemical.

In 1955 Verticillium wilt was observed in several fields near Mabton in the Valley, shortly after a shipment of roots had been received from Indiana. Within a few years the disease had become so severe that spearmint began to replace peppermint in that general area. But even the spearmint yields were reduced and this, coupled with a tremendous overproduction of spearmint oil in the nation in 1961, caused many growers in the area between Mabton and Satus to move into the production of other crops. By 1960 wilt had spread into the Kennewick area and was gradually spreading westward in the lower Valley. This caused many growers to abandon mint cultivation, switch to spearmint, or move their operations to new areas.

The development of the Yakima Valley as the nation's chief spearmint producing region began in 1946 when the I. P. Callison Co. leased land near Sunnyside and had two train car loads of Scotch spearmint roots shipped in from the Middlewest. One car arrived with the roots in bad condition so additional stock was obtained from an area near Coburg, Oregon. An experimental 160 acres planting was established, the first harvest coming in 1947. Other growers, Herman, Mosebar, and Williams, obtained roots and began plantings the following year, but the subsequent decline of the market due to surplus production in the Middlewest put a damper on the experiment. By 1951, spearmint acreage barely exceeded 50.

In the fall of that year, Henry Callison, formerly general manager of the I. P. Callison Company, left the employ of the firm, moved to the Yakima Valley, and took over the operation of the Broadview Farming Company just north of Sunnyside. He bought up all the spearmint roots that could be obtained in the area and immediately expanded his acreage. By this time the spearmint market had somewhat rebounded but, even more fortunately, within several years growers in the wilt infested areas near Mabton and Satus fell on spearmint as a substitute for peppermint. As the latter declined, the former prospered. Acreage and production of spearmint expanded rapidly and, by 1955, Washington was the nation's leading producer. In 1961 an all-time high production of American spearmint oil was recorded exceeding 1.1 million pounds, nearly 80 percent of which was produced in the Yakima Valley. The expanded production so glutted the market that dealers discontinued buying and many growers ruefully stored spearmint oil in their barns for several years. In the Middlewest spearmint oil could not even be sold at production costs. Washington farmers had stolen the spearmint market, beaten it to death, and now began to better realize the mysteries of supply and demand that had been such an interesting dilemma in the east for a century and a half. Such problems have revived interest in cooperative marketing and, in 1968, there were efforts to organize mint farmers in the Madras area of Oregon and in the Yakima Valley of Washington.

Henry Callison was also responsible for the introduction of Native spearmint into Yakima, planting 18 acres of Indiana roots in 1957. There had always been trade demands for both types of spearmint oil, and the Yakima Valley is the single most important producer of both. In 1967 nearly 15,000 acres of spearmint, of which 6,000 were the Native variety, were cultivated in the Valley.

Favored by a lengthy photoperiod and a relatively high degree of sunshine intensity, the Yakima Valley has become the most important and productive mint producing district in the history of the American industry. Over 200 growers are raising peppermint, and nearly an equal number spearmint. The chief concentration is in the area between Sunnyside and Toppenish, with a secondary nucleus near Prosser. In the

Toppenish area much of the irrigated land is leased from the Yakima Indians who derive a considerable source of revenue from the agriculture within the boundaries of their reservation.

Some of the largest peppermint operations in the area are those of Stanley Seely near Zillah, Sheldon Rumbolz at Toppenish, and Judd Cecil at Sunnyside. Large spearmint farms are those of Broadview, Herman Roskamp, Byrd and Hudnall, and Hull Farms, all near Sunnyside.

Because the acreages controlled by a single grower may be disconnected and some distance apart, the general practice is to mount distilling tubs on the back of large trucks so that the hay can be moved quickly to the distillery. Such an expensive method can be maintained only by continued high yields and a favorable market. So far, Yakima farmers have had the best of both these worlds.

4. *Columbia Basin.* As the wilt disease spread through the Valley, there was some relocation on the part of growers into newly irrigated lands farther north in the area adjacent to Moses Lake. This section, known locally as the Columbia Basin, is divided into three distinct producing areas; Quincy, northwest of Moses Lake; Othello, just south of Moses Lake; and Eltopia, between Pasco and Othello. There is also a planting by Walter George, irrigated from well water, in Cold Creek Canyon, just southwest of the toll bridge crossing the Columbia River near Vernita.

Plantings in the Columbia Basin were first made by Driggs and Son and Welch and Kandra in 1946, but expansion in the area was meager until after 1960, weeds being quite a problem in the cultivation. Today, there are several peppermint growers with nearly 400 aces near Quincy, but nearly 40 growers and more than 8,000 acres at Othello. Spearmint was planted in the Basin by Broadview Farms in 1955 and more than 1,000 acres are now annually cultivated in the area, being found at Quincy, Eltopia, and Othello. The Othello district ranks second in importance in the state to the Yakima Valley (Map 20). Some of the larger farms in the Basin are those of Wilfred Balch, Clarence Buck, Byrd and Hudnall, Morley Kerr, Jack Labbee, and Vic Yoshino.

There have been, since World War II, other mint plantings in eastern Washington. These include the areas of Paterson, Moxee City, Wiley City, Kittitas, near Springdale in Stevens County, and a recent planting has been made at Trout Lake on the White Salmon River.

Idaho. None of the pre-World War II attempts at mint cultivation in Idaho lasted, but there was an attempt to establish plantings in the Twin Falls area about 1941 with roots secured from the Yakima Valley.[22]

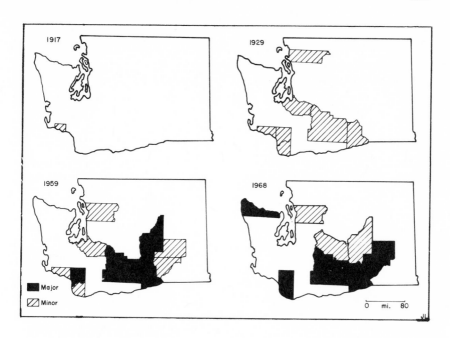

Map 20. The spread of commercial peppermint and spearmint oil production in Washington, by counties, for selected years since 1917. Major producing counties are those in which 500 acres or more of mint were reported under cultivation.

In 1946 small acreages of peppermint were planted along the Snake River in the vicinity of Payette and the industry has gradually spread southward from that point. Nearly 5,000 acres are now being raised near the communities of Wilder, Greenleaf, Eagle, Caldwell, and Nampa, by more than 40 growers (Map 21). Large acreages are maintained by the Batt, Eldred, and Obendorf families. Scotch spearmint was introduced into the Caldwell area about 1963 and nearly 1,000 acres are presently cultivated. Several growers initiated plantings of Native spearmint in 1968.

In 1953 spearmint culture was begun by Donald Diehl and others along the Kootenai River near Bonners Ferry in the Idaho panhandle country. Weed problems coupled with a falling peppermint market resulted in cessation in 1959. The 1957 acreage exceeded 300 when both peppermint and spearmint were grown.

Peppermint was also grown for a time at Roberts about 17 miles north of Idaho Falls, but the only farm in that area at present is located several miles east of Idaho Falls.

Map 21. Idaho, showing the towns associated with commercial peppermint and spearmint oil production since 1905.

Montana. Peppermint growing began in Montana in 1964 with a large 600 acre planting on the Bob Stonebrook farm at Plains just west of Missoula, and 5 acres were planted on the Koyoma farm at Harding in north-central Montana in 1967. Both farms are still in production. The Stonebrook planting resulted from successful experiments which had started in 1961 with spearmint roots imported from the Yakima Valley.

Wisconsin. Not all the successful expansion of the mint industry since World War II has taken place in the Pacific northwest. From experimental plantings in 1945 the peppermint industry in Wisconsin expanded so successfully that the state now ranks third in acreage, behind Washington and Oregon. This development came about largely as a result of Michigan and Indiana farmers moving into the southeastern section of the state and establishing plantings on newly drained mucklands.

The Wisconsin industry began in 1945 when two Michigan farmers, Max Haviland and the late Don Dellamater, each planted 5 acres of peppermint, Dellamater on the Bird Marsh just west of Jefferson in Jefferson County and Haviland at Bancroft on the Buena Vista Marsh in Portage County (Map 22).[23]

Dellamater, the twenty year old son of a mint grower near St. Johns, Michigan, had spotted the Bird Marsh as a potential mint area in 1944 when, with his father, he had scouted Wisconsin for a possible farming site. The Marsh, at that time, was largely undrained, but ditch digging was begun in 1947 to carry the water to Crawfish River and over 1,000 acres was reclaimed.

Dellamater harvested his first crop and had the hay hauled to Bancroft where Haviland had constructed a distillery. Yields were promising enough that he expanded his acreage in 1946 to 40, but, due to excessive winterkill, new roots had to be imported from Michigan. Nine acres of spearmint were also planted in 1946 and Dellamater constructed his own distillery to handle the crop. The spearmint was not too successful but, by 1948, Dellamater had increased his peppermint acreage to better than 80. During 1949 several other Michigan growers came into the Jefferson area and more than 400 acres, including 5 of spearmint, were planted, and this was increased to 900 the following year. Mint production soon spread into the Lake Mills area, also in Jefferson County.

With the success of mint culture established it was not long before other areas were brought into use. A 6 acre peppermint planting in 1946 west of Pound in Oconto County did not survive, but peppermint was successfully introduced into Walworth County near Delavan (Figure 54), Columbia County in the section near Columbus, and in Sauk

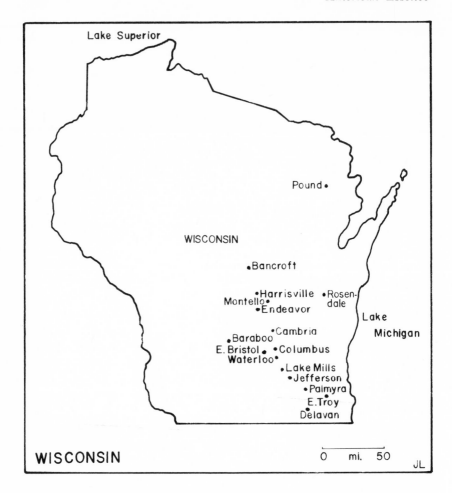

Map 22. Wisconsin, showing the towns associated with the commercial production of peppermint and spearmint oil since 1945.

County near Baraboo, all in 1950. Since that time mint has also been grown in Marquette, Waukesha, Dane, Dodge, Green Lake, Kenosha, Monroe, Oconto, and Fond du Lac counties.

Verticillium wilt eventually appeared in the peppermint being grown on the Bird Marsh and at Lake Mills and the reduced yields have caused the area to become one largely planted to spearmint. As a result the major peppermint producing districts have been switched to newer locations. At the present time the most important sections are in Marquette County between Endeavor and Harrisville on the Montello

Marsh, Walworth County at Delavan and East Troy, and along the Columbia and Dane counties boundary.

Jefferson County peppermint production is still important, but the major centers are now located near Palmyra and Waterloo. By 1968 more than 8,000 acres of peppermint were found in the state and more than 40 growers were established in the industry. About 1,000 acres of spearmint are being raised in Wisconsin, equally divided between Scotch and Native, principally at Jefferson and near East Bristol (Map 23).

Michigan and Indiana. As the fortunes of the mint industry in the western states continued to wax Indiana and Michigan were relegated to secondary positions in the industry. Census and other figures clearly indicate the steady decline in both states.[24]

	1949	1954	1959	1967
Michigan				
Number of farms	662	408	169	82
Acres	15,344	13,340	6,241	4,659
Indiana				
Number of farms	1,019	597	304	107
Acres	28,272	18,157	9,491	8,537

Although acreages varied somewhat over the years depending on weather, market prices, and the vagaries of the wilt disease, the net trend since the war in both states has been a steady decline in total acreage and the gradual replacement of peppermint by spearmint in many of the producing districts (Map 24).

In Michigan the wilt disease continued to increase in severity in the central district. This, coupled with wartime demands, encouraged the

Map 23. The spread of commercial peppermint and spearmint oil production in Wisconsin, by counties, for selected years since 1945. Major producing counties are those in which 500 acres or more of mint were reported under cultivation.

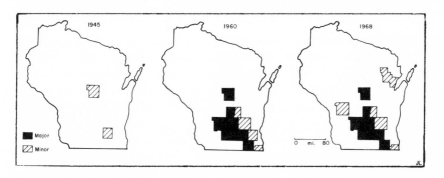

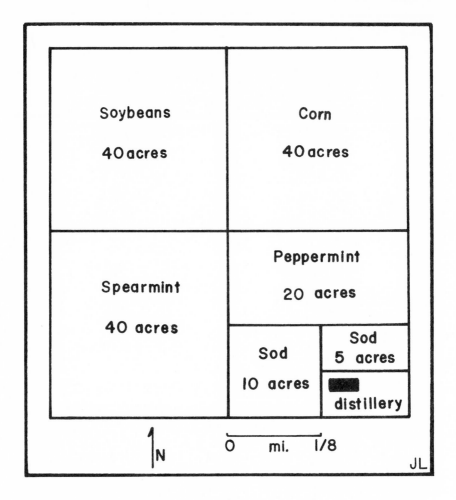

Map 24. Field pattern of a 160 acre rotation muckland farm, on which pepper-mint and spearmint are grown, typical of many found in central and south-western Michigan and northern Indiana.

development of a considerable acreage in the Thumb section of the state, especially in Sanilac, St. Clair, Tuscola, and Lapeer counties (Map 25). Only Sanilac County production remains. The central district, once the most important mint producing region in the nation, is now devoted largely to cultivation of spearmint, with Clinton, Shiawassee, Jackson, and Ingham counties containing the most extensive plantings. For many years spearmint acreage has exceeded that of peppermint in the state and in only a single county, Newaygo, can more than 250 acres of

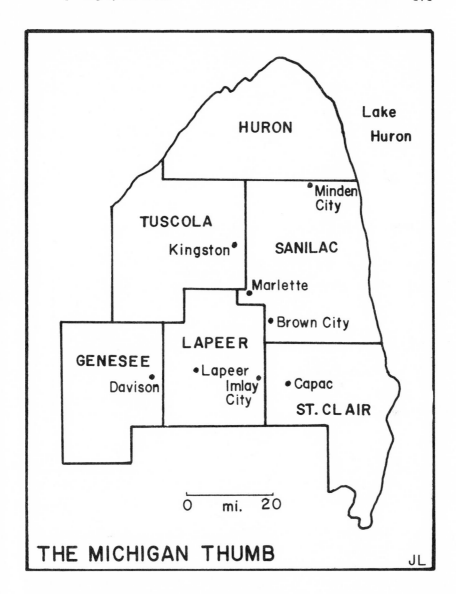

Map 25. Counties of the thumb area of Michigan, showing the towns associated with commercial peppermint and spearmint oil production since 1936.

peppermint be found. Counties in which peppermint acreage exceeds 100 are Clinton, Ingham, Jackson, Mason, Muskegon, and Van Buren (Map 26).

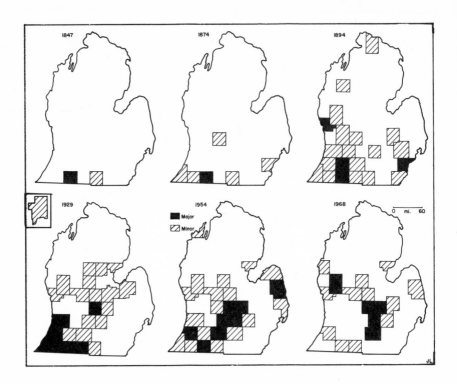

Map 26. The spread of commercial peppermint and spearmint oil production in the lower peninsula of Michigan, by counties, for selected years since 1847. In 1929, following the great price rise, 78 acres were cultivated in Schoolcraft County in the upper peninsula. Major producing counties are those in which 500 acres or more of mint were reported under cultivation.

In 1947 the Michigan Peppermint Growers Association was replaced by the United Mint Growers which continued to function for some time as a service organization for growers.

The eastern section of the state of Indiana was gradually replaced in importance by counties to the west. Jasper and Pulaski counties are now the most important for the production of peppermint with St. Joseph and Starke counties also containing large acreages. The same four counties also lead in spearmint production, but Lagrange and Kosciusko counties still have considerable acreage (Map 27). Indiana spearmint is approximately 80 percent of the Scotch variety. Among the larger mint farms in Indiana at the present time are those of William Gehring at Newland in Jasper County (Figure 58), Richard Gumz in the North Judson area, and Elmer Gumz near North Liberty.

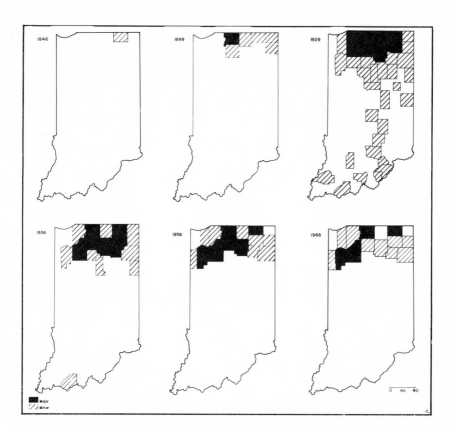

Map 27. The spread of commercial peppermint and spearmint oil cultivation in Indiana, by counties, for selected years since 1846. Major producing counties are those in which 500 acres or more of mint were reported under cultivation.

Because of the increased dependence on spearmint, both states were hard hit in 1961 by the tremendous production of oil resulting from the great expansion in the Yakima Valley of Washington. Mint growers, unable to obtain satisfactory yields of peppermint and unable to market spearmint at a profitable price, turned their interest to other crops. Numerous abandoned mint distilleries now dot the Indiana and Michigan landscape, mute testimony to their once important position as well as to the power of change.

The only mint distillery manufacturer left in the Middlewest is the Honeyville Metal Works, owned and operated by an Amishman, C. M. Hochstetler, in Lagrange County, Indiana. Hochstetler took over the interests of the Star Tank Company of Goshen in 1952.

Other States. No other states have developed a mint industry since the war, but a small number of farmers have attempted cultivation in various localities. In addition, older producing states like California and Ohio have abandoned the crop entirely.

Much of the mint oil produced during World War II in California came from the J. O. Hayes farm and other farms near Stockton. As recently as 1949 the Hayes farm had 835 acres in peppermint,[25] but production was discontinued shortly afterward. The same year there was a 26 acre planting in Kern County. By 1959 only a single acre, in Orange County, was grown in the state. Small plantings established later at Modesto and Patterson were discontinued in 1965.

Following the war mint production was continued in Ohio by the Huston family and the Scioto Land Company in Hardin County and by Lingle and Sons at Edon in Williams County. In 1948 M. W. Henry attempted a planting near Ottoville but the effort was discontinued. Lingle gave up production in 1951 and the Scioto Land Company in 1954. The following year Victor Huston shifted production entirely to spearmint and maintained acreage until 1964. Since that time there has been no mint oil produced in Ohio.

Peppermint was introduced in Minnesota on the Reynen Brothers farm in northern Freeborn County about 1954, and the acreage maintained until 1966. There have been several plantings attempted in Nevada, 10 acres in Humboldt County about 1959,[26] 2 acres by Dan Fry, Jr. near Reno in 1961, and 40 acres by Ray Wilcox in the Las Vegas area in 1966. The latter acreage was expanded to 150 the following year.

Agriculture census figures since the war have also revealed some small mint farms in various localities.[27]

Census Year	Location	No. of Farms	Acres
1954	New York	1	1
	Richland Co.		
1959	Maryland	1	1
	Baltimore Co.		
1959	Texas	1	10
	Hale Co.		

The location of the New York farm is uncertain since there is no Richland County in the state. Although the outcome of attempts is unknown, peppermint roots have been shipped to various localities in Arizona, Alabama, and Nebraska,[28] and there were reports of production in Kentucky in 1962.

Conclusion

Following World War II the major centers of the American mint industry shifted into the producing districts of the Pacific northwest, especially the Willamette Valley of Oregon and the Yakima Valley of Washington. Favored by a more compatible geographic environment, the higher yields of mint oil obtained in the western states enabled growers to so outproduce Middlewestern farmers in Indiana and Michigan that the latter two states have become secondary producers of both peppermint and spearmint oil.

More recently Wisconsin and Idaho have become important peppermint states, and the acreage of the former exceeds that of Indiana and Michigan combined. Today nearly 80 percent of the nation's peppermint acreage and 65 percent of that of spearmint is found in the Pacific coast states.

Behind the story of the west coast success, however, lies an interesting trail of research and service on the part of many persons and organizations whose contributions have benefitted not only the American mint industry but other agricultural and scientific enterprises as well.

REFERENCES

[1]M. D. Thomas, "The Economic Outlook for Peppermint Oil," *Proceedings of the Oregon Essential Oil Growers League,* 2nd annual meeting, p. 36, 1951.

[2]W. Todd, "The Export Situation," *Ibid.,* p. 22.

[3]E. Guenther, "Recent Developments in the Field of Essential Oils," *Journal of the Society of Cosmetic Chemists,* vol. 7, p. 322, 1956.

[4]*Proceedings of the Oregon Essential Oil Growers League,* 3rd annual meeting, p. 28, 1952.

[5]J. E. Landing, *Analysis of the Decline of the Commercial Mint Industry in Indiana Since World War II,* p. 45, MS thesis, Pennsylvania State University, 1963.

[6]U.S. Census of Agriculture, 1949, 1959.

[7]L. N. Liebel, *Peppermint Oil: An Economic Study,* p. 15, Popular Bulletin No. 199, Agricultural Experiment Stations, State College of Washington, August, 1950.

[8]U.S Census of Agriculture, 1959.

[9]C. E. Horner, "Progress Report on Mint Disease Control," *Proceedings of the Oregon Essential Oil Growers League,* 5th annual meeting, p. 8, 1954.

[10]E. Guenther, "The Peppermint Oil Industry in Oregon and Washington States," *Perfumery and Essential Oil Record,* vol. 52, p. 640, October, 1961.

[11]C. E. Horner, *op. cit.*

[12]C. E. Horner, personal communication, August, 1967.

[13]One example is the issue of September 2, 1949.

[14]A. F. Sievers, *Travel Report,* p. 12, USDA, 1927.

[15]*The Madras Pioneer,* Madras, Oregon, September 1, 1955.

[16]*Ibid.,* August 18, 1955.

[17]A. W. Bierly, *Mint Production in Central Oregon,* (p. 2), Jefferson County Extension Service, 1963.

[18]*Ibid.,* (p. 1). The identity of Karmex was revealed to the writer by numerous growers.

[19]*Facts About Yakima, Washington and the Yakima Valley,* Greater Yakima Chamber of Commerce, 1967.

[20]R. Sheller, *Sunnyside at 60,* published by the author, p. 27, not dated, Sunnyside, Washington.

[21]E. Guenther, 1961, *op. cit.,* pp. 641-642.

[22]The roots were shipped by Francis Wetherell from Mabton, Washington.

[23]The development of the mint industry in Wisconsin is covered briefly in: G. E. Ewald, *Wisconsin Peppermint Production and Marketing, S*pecial Bulletin No. 9, Wisconsin State Dept. of Agriculture, 1952, and the revision by the same name, Special Bulletin No. 59, 1956. The Dellamater farm was described in an article in *The Wisconsin State Journal,* Madison, Wisconsin, August 28, 1949.

[24]Census figures for 1949, 1954, and 1959. The 1967 figures from the files of the A. M. Todd Company.

[25]Census of Agriculture, 1949.

[26]Census of Agriculture, 1959.

[27]Census of Agriculture, 1954 and 1959.

[28]Francis Wetherell of Mabton, Washington, shipped peppermint roots to a farmer in Nebraska about 1946; the Arizona and Alabama reference is from N. K. Ellis, "Peppermint and Spearmint Production," *Economic Botany,* vol. 14, no. 4, p. 285, 1960.

Chapter 14.

Mint Industry Research and Service

The Growers Receive Aid

Any successful enterprise involves considerable research and evaluation. Before World War II there was no semblance of a comprehensive program of research devoted to the problems of the mint industry, although the agricultural experiment stations in Indiana and Michigan had initiated small programs as a response to grower concern. The buyers and users of mint oils carried on their individual programs, but dissemination of information was virtually non-existent. Periodical reports in technical literature, many completely unknown to peppermint and spearmint growers, were largely related to the mysteries of botany and oil chemistry, and contributed little of significance to the industry as an integrated system of production, processing, utilization, and consumption.

As early as 1922 the Todd Company had forwarded funds to the University of Wisconsin for use by Edward Kremers in problems dealing with mint oil analysis. There were undoubtedly similar sporadic efforts over the years. But it was the spread of the Verticillium wilt disease throughout Michigan and Indiana and the development of the industry on such a large scale in the western states that finally prompted the development of a comprehensive research program. The movement began in 1946 when the Beech-Nut Packing Company expended funds to make a survey of the industry in the various producing districts and hold a series of meetings during which common problems involving growers, buyers, and users could be discussed. Accordingly, during

177

1946 and 1947, N. Kent Ellis and E. C. Stevenson of Purdue University, Ray Nelson of Michigan State University, and Paul Tornow, Chief Chemist of I. P. Callison, toured the mint fields of Indiana, Michigan, Oregon, and Washington, and presented their recommendations on major research problems at two Mint Research Conferences, the first held in Canajoharie, New York, in December of 1947, and the second a year later at Purdue University.[1] Other reports were given on important problems of the industry, a *Proceedings* published which included an extensive bibliography of mint literature,[2] and the semblance of a program was devised.

A major outgrowth of the Mint Research Conferences was the establishment by the Beech-Nut, Wrigley, and Todd companies of a program of assistantships and fellowships devoted to mint research and to be conducted by the staff members of Purdue, Michigan State, Oregon State, Washington State, the University of Washington, and the University of Rochester.[3] In time, this beginning of industry sponsored research spread to other interested organizations and, in 1956, a mint industry research fund was established involving contributions from growers, dealers, and users.[4] In the next ten years it was estimated that the research fund expended nearly $400,000 on various projects in the different mint producing states. Funding sources were indicated as follows:[5]

Users	(Wm. Wrigley Jr. Co., Beech-Nut Inc., Colgate-Palmolive Co., American Chicle, Procter and Gamble)	71 percent
Dealers	(A. M. Todd Co., M. Brown & Sons, I. P. Callison, Wm. Leman Inc.)	9
Growers		18
Chemical companies, banks, etc.		2

It is difficult to assess in any quantitative way the results of the money expended on research, but the contribution has been a significant one and the fund is annually being increased as the scope of research activity becomes more diverse. At the present time the research funds are being primarily focused on Verticillium wilt projects at Oregon State and Purdue, and insecticide problems, mint oil residue analysis, and weed control studies at Oregon State.[6]

Botanical Research

The mint plants have been extensively used in various phases of botanical research. As early as 1699 the English botanist John Woodward utilized mints in experiments on water culture, and both Joseph Priestly and De Saussure used mints in their famous studies on photosynthesis.[7] As peppermint and spearmint became important commercial crops they attracted even greater attention, and many years of great debate regarding their origins, true identity, and nomenclature involved the time of a number of interested workers. Much of this story has been summarized in excellent detail in the comprehensive studies of Mabel Ruttle and George Hocking.[8] Although much of the taxonomic work was done by European botanists, such American scholars as Edward Kremers and G. C. Jenison of the University of Wisconsin did important botanical studies on mint by analyzing the constituents of the oils. One of their students, F. J. Bacon, later did extensive research on the mints at Western Reserve University.[9]

Studies on the physiological mechanisms of peppermint and spearmint have been limited but important contributions have been made, especially the series of studies supervised by F. C. Steward, first at the University of Rochester and later at Cornell.[10] It was largely the work of Steward, in which he suggested that cool night temperatures acted as a stimulus to increased oil development in peppermint, that set off the search by the Todd Company resulting in the development of the Madras area in central Oregon as an important producing district. A series of studies supervised by Ruble Langston at Purdue University was designed to assess the manner in which various mineral elements are distributed throughout peppermint plants,[11] and findings indicated characteristic concentrations which could have great potential in the future use of systemic chemicals in controlling disease and insects.

Correct Harvesting Time

An extremely important aspect of mint research has been that devoted to determining the best time of mint harvesting for maximum yield of oil. Throughout most of the history of the industry growers simply pinched off a few leaves, rubbed them vigorously, and smelled the aroma. Such empirical techniques left much to be desired and a good deal of oil was lost as a result of cutting too early or too late. In 1944 a method of determining the best harvest time was devised at Purdue University and was based on two important facts: oil yield is highest when the free menthol content of the oil approaches 45 percent; and the viscosity of the oil increases as the free menthol content increases.[12] Accordingly, a method of determining the free menthol content with a viscometer, designed for use by growers, was published and made available. But the technique was time consuming as sample hay had to be cut, distilled, and tested chemically. Growers were not generally ready to employ such devices and the search continued.

Significant answers were obtained in Oregon as a result of studies headed by D. E. Bullis.[13] The findings of this important work, now taken for granted by those in the industry, laid the foundation for scientific mint harvesting, and can be summarized as follows:

1. the number and size of oil producing cells in the plants increased rapidly until full-bloom stage, then increased only slowly in size and remained about constant in number;

2. maximum oil yields were obtained at about full bloom stage;

3. 99 percent of the oil producing glands were located on the leaves and only 1 percent on the stems;

4. oil yields of cut and weathered hay did not differ significantly from freshly cut hay providing no leaves were lost.

The association of oil production with the leaves and the harvesting time with full-bloom stage were significant advancements in an industry centered around the best judgments of the growers, but indicated some peculiar biological paradoxes. The conditions which create maximum leaf growth may not be the same as those that result in maximum stolon or root growth and may be quite different from those that aid in making the plants taller or stemmier. These paradoxes remain yet unsolved. The method also has a severe limitation in those regions, like the Middlewest, where a full-bloom stage which is based on a mimimum daylight requirement is seldom found.

The Oregon findings were verified by later studies in eastern Washington,[14] where it was discovered that growers were cutting mint at a much later stage of development than in other producing districts. Peppermint in the Kennewick area blossomed about a month earlier than the plants in the lower Columbia River area and was cut at a time when blossoming was much heavier and more extensive than in other areas. This fact was of extreme significance in unravelling the mysteries of the peculiar nature of the peppermint oil produced in eastern Washington.

In a study conducted on western peppermint oils during the years 1944 through 1945 it was discovered that the eastern Washington product deviated significantly from the *United States Pharmacopeia* standards in regard to optical rotation, specific gravity, and refractive index.[15] It was already well known that the aroma and taste of the oil did not meet most consumer demands, especially for chewing gum. The reasons for this peculiarity began to be understood in 1948 when Paul Bedoukian was successful in establishing the fact that the complex compound known as methofuran was especially prevalent in the flowering heads of peppermint.[16] Later studies in Washington by V. K. Watson and J. W. Elliott established the relationship between menthofuran and the peculiar odor and flavor of the eastern Washington oils.[17] Even a small quantity of blossom oil, high in menthofuran, was enough to produce the characteristics that made the oil undesirable.

Continued work on menthofuran in peppermint oil has resulted in a number of findings that have wide import for the future of the industry in the Yakima Valley. It was discovered by J. A. Lemli that menthofuran is especially prevalent in the stolons and young tissues of peppermint but ceases to be secreted at a certain age in the leaf and stem tissue.[18] This led C. E. Horner of Oregon State to speculate further on the oil of eastern Washington.

> The peppermint plant exhibits apical dominance; for example, pinching out the terminal bud stimulates new growth from nodal buds below. Flowering also results in termination of apical dominance. Flowering in Yakima is earlier and is more profuse than in Willamette Valley and in the Madras area. Early, profuse flowering results in high menthofuran content which originates partly from the flowers and partly from the young growth; the latter becomes profuse after flowering of the terminal shoots has destroyed apical dominance.[19]

Field techniques have now been developed which aid in controlling the content of menthofuran. Cutting before full bloom is now an accepted technique. To stimulate profuse new growth in such quantity that the menthofuran content will be diluted, fields are now dragged and excessively sprinkled which causes the plants to lodge and originate new growth. Such research on menthofuran will merit much future attention.

Sunlight and Photoperiod

As early as 1916 Frank Rabak had shown that climatic effects materially influenced the quality of peppermint oil.[20] Later studies on peppermint plants in relation to the length of the daylight period, photoperiod, were carried on simultaneously by Ray Nelson at Michigan State University and H. A. Allard of the Department of Agriculture but were initially reported by the latter in 1941.[21] Because of their early date and significance Allard's findings regarding peppermint are worthy of reprinting.[22]

Photoperiod	Date When Budded	Flowered	Stolons, Number	Longest
10 hours	None	None	Many	29 inches
12	None	None	Many	29
13	None	None	Fewer	29
14	July 13	July 29	Fewer	23
18	July 12	July 29	Very few	16
Full day	July 9	July 29	Few	17

The results clearly indicated that peppermint flowered in response to a lengthened photoperiod characteristic of the higher middle latitudes,

Figure 50. Schematic diagram of a portable tank (tub) mint distillery manufactured in Oregon.

Figure 51. A circular, auger-fed mint distillery, designed and tested experimentally in 1967 at Longview, Washington.

Figure 52. Tamping long mint hay into a stationary distilling tub on a farm in Indiana. Packing the hay insures more even distribution of steam during distillation.

Figure 53. A custom-built mint chopper near Rainier, Oregon, in 1948. Chopping the mint hay allows more to be placed in the tub and lessens the distillation time. The chopper has a blowing device for conducting the hay into the portable distilling tub which is hooked behind.

Figure 54. Field operations in various mint producing districts.

A : A mint planter laying roots in muckland near Delavan, Wisconsin.

B : Geese weeding a peppermint field in Indiana. Geese are most commonly used for weeding in the irrigated fields of Washington and Oregon.

C : Portable wheel irrigation system in a peppermint field near Madras, Oregon. Following a setting of from 8 to 12 hours, the entire sprinkler line can be wheeled to the next position by a single man. Power is supplied by the gasoline engine which can be seen in the center. The pipe itself serves as the axle for the wheels.

D : A propane burner flaming peppermint stubble in the Willamette Valley of Oregon. The application of intense heat aids in the control of rust and Verticillium wilt by destroying the disease spores.

E. Dusting peppermint for insect control on a farm in Indiana. Large farms are now commonly dusted by airplane.

Figure 55: Field operations in various mint producing districts.

A : Mowing Scotch spearmint with a swather in Idaho. The machine cuts the mint at ground level and deposits the hay in windrows at the center of the mowing reel.

B : Self-propelled mint chopper delivering hay from the windrows to a truck-mounted distilling tank which is run alongside. The men in the tank are tamping the hay to insure more even distillation. Truck-mounted tanks are commonly employed where mint fields are located at a considerable distance from the distillery.

C : Truck-mounted distilling tanks in position at a large mint distillery in the Yakima Valley of Washington.

D : Dumping pumy (mint hay after distillation) from a portable tank following distillation. The pumy is frequently returned to the fields to serve as organic fertilizer.

Figure 56. Field operations in various mint producing districts.

Upper Left: Self-propelled mint mower and chopper blowing the hay into a trailing distilling tank. Such tanks require no labor for tamping. Windrow of long hay can be seen in the foreground.

Lower Left: Connecting a portable tank at a distillery in Idaho. The girl on the catwalk is adjusting the pipe which conveys the distilled vapor to the rectangular water-cooled condensing tank. The man is connecting the steam pipe from the boiler. Oil receiving cans (separators) and shipping drum can be seen in the right foreground.

Right: Sequence showing the manner by which the large portable tubs filled with mint hay are moved from the fields to the distillery.

Figure 57. Distillery scenes near Caldwell, Idaho.

A and B : Moving the portable distilling tanks into position at the distillery; these large tanks hold more than twice the quantity of mint hay than the conventional truck-mounted tanks.

C : Clamping the lid on the distilling tank; aluminum water-cooled multitubular condensers can be seen on the platform in center.

D. Drawing off the mint oil from the distilling tank; the mint oil level in the separator cans (right foreground) is raised by closing off the water overflow (operator's right hand) and the oil is drained into a shipping drum shown suspended from the scale in the foreground.

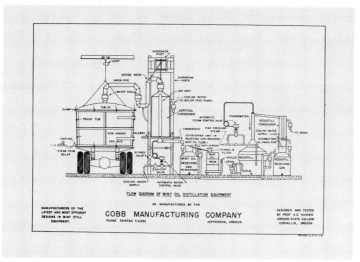

Figure 50

Figure 51

Figure 52

Figure 53

Figure 54

A

B

C

D

E

A

Figure 55

D

C

B

Figure 56

A

B

Figure 57

C

D

A

B

C

Figure 58

D

F

E

G

H

Figure 59

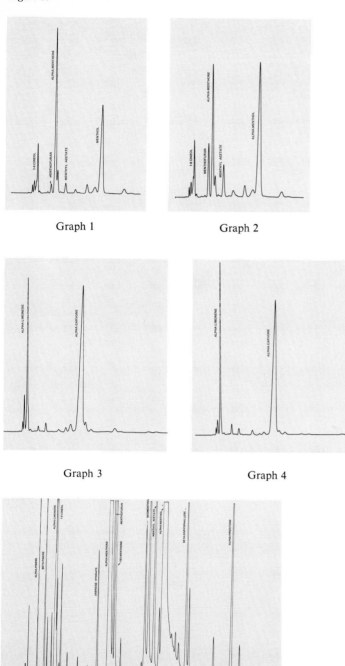

Graph 1

Graph 2

Graph 3

Graph 4

Graph 5

Figure 60

A

B

C

D

E

F

Figure 58. Research has become increasingly significant to the modern American mint industry and is based on the scientific skills of capable personnel and the utilization of sophisticated technical equipment.

A: Ralph J. Green, Jr., Purdue University.

B: N. Kent Ellis, Purdue University.

C: Ray Nelson (1893-1967), Michigan State University.

D: M. J. Murray, A. M. Todd Company.

E: William Gehring and William Gehring, Jr. standing in a field of Scotch spearmint on their farm at Newland, Indiana; the Gehring farm has been the locale for extensive field-scale research.

F: Chemist in a dealer's laboratory checking data on the recorder of a Beckman GC-5 gas chromatograph used to analyze the chemical components of mint oils.

G: C. E. Horner, Oregon State University.

H. Oliver H. Todd (1847-1930), whose pioneer peppermint plantings in the Willamette Valley of Oregon beginning in 1909 led directly to the extensive mint cultivation now found in Oregon, Washington, and Idaho.

Figure 59. Graphs showing the major terpene constituents in natural American peppermint and spearmint oils done by gas chromatographic analysis. Graphs 1 through 4 were run on a Beckman GC-5 with a 20' x ⅛" packed column. Graph 5 is a high sensitivity run from a Beckman GC-4 with a 200' x 0.01" open tubular column.

Graph 1: Middlewestern Black Mitcham peppermint oil;

Graph 2: Yakima Valley (Washington) Black Mitcham peppermint oil;

Graph 3: Native spearmint oil from Washington;

Graph 4: Scotch spearmint oil from Washington;

Graph 5: Middlewestern Black Mitcham peppermint oil..

Figure 60. The major mint oil dealers perform many important functions related to their task of moving the oils from the farms to the primary users.

A: Wm. Leman and the head office of Wm. Leman, Inc., of Bremen, Indiana.

B: Benjamin Brown (left), founder and President, and Irvin Brown (right), Vice-President, in front of their office in Bremen, Indiana.

C: The main processing plant of the Callison firm at Chehalis, Washington.

D: I. P. Callison (1871-1961), founder of the firm of I.P. Callison and Sons, Inc.

E: Albert J. Todd (1881-1960), who succeeded his father, Albert M. Todd, as President of the Todd Company and served until 1956.

F: The head office of the A. M. Todd Company at Kalamazoo, Michigan.

as well as pointing out the interesting inverse relationship between plant and root development. Such evidence largely explains why quality and quantity mint oil production has never been satisfactorily achieved in the southern United States as well as in other subtropical and tropical areas with a reduced photoperiod. Nelson's findings were consistent with those of Allard and led him to comment:[23]

> peppermint flowers earlier and more profusely in Oregon and Washington than in Michigan. This is a response to the more favorable conditions for flowering, including a longer photoperiod and a greater total of sunshine hours during the growing season. As a native of northern Europe it is attuned to longer and brighter days than occur in Michigan where the maximum day length is barely sufficient to stimulate bud formation in some seasons.

Further controlled research on photoperiod by F. A. Crane at Cornell University and Ruble Langston and A. C. Leopold at Purdue University definitely established the long day characteristics of peppermint with a critical daylength response between 16 and 18 hours, with maximum oil production being obtained nearer the upper limits.[24] This led directly to experiments on the effects of temperature on peppermint conducted by R. H. Biggs and A. C. Leopold,[25] in which it was discovered that high day temperatures and low night temperatures (80 degrees and 60 degrees) promoted the maximum yield of oil, a verification of the earlier suggestion of Steward. This work was also important because it lent support to studies on the critical nature of night temperature in enhancing the aromatic properties of certain plants done by F. W. Went who noticed that strawberries grown at a low temperature had a higher content of aromatic compounds than those grown under hot conditions.[26]

Part of the mystery of Yakima was now unravelled. Favored with a long photoperiod, high day temperatures, and a great amount of sunlight, mint produced in the Valley bloomed quickly and fully and gave high oil yields. The penalty, however, was an increased content of menthofuran. The Valley, lacking a night time cooling as found in the Madras area of Oregon which is set at a higher elevation, was denied optimum yields even though the present yields are as high or higher than in any known district.

All of this work on photoperiod and temperatures laid the foundation for several important studies of W. David Loomis at Oregon State University, which are all the more interesting because they involved techniques developed to remove and analyze oil from sections as small as only part of a mint leaf. In one study he found that cool or short nights depressed the formation of menthofuran,[27] another advantage of

Madras over Yakima. The other study, based on the synthesis of terpenes, demonstrated the possible chemical development of menthofuran in mint plants.[28]

The mystery of menthofuran and Yakima is now known in its broad outline. The peculiarity of eastern Washington peppermint oil set off a chain reaction of scientific endeavors which will, undoubtedly, result in even further work to the benefit of the industry as a whole and to all related activities to which the various findings will be applicable.

Plant Breeding Work.

Most experts agree that both peppermint and spearmint are complex hybrids developed through centuries of natural crossing and mutation. No information exists on early attempts of Hiram G. Hotchkiss to produce hybrids in New York, but the hybrid work since has been fairly recent and largely the efforts of Mabel Ruttle, M. J. Murray, and Ray Nelson. The latter two were especially interested in developing strains of peppermint and spearmint that were resistant to Verticillium wilt, but no such plant has yet been produced by hybridization that can meet the trade demands for oil quality.

Developing hybrid mint plants is extremely complicated by the fact that commercial peppermint and spearmint are generally sterile and seldom set seeds. From one peppermint sample of 18,000 flower spikes containing approximately 2,888,000 ovules Nelson was able to recover only 55 seeds and, when planted, only 5 germinated.[29] This established sterility ratio is commonly cited as evidence for the hybrid nature of peppermint evidence, according to some experts, pointing to the original cross involving water mint and spearmint (*Mentha aquatica* and *Mentha spicata*). The hybrids are generally unstable and mutations are common. A hairy mutation observed on the Mentha Plantation in Michigan, and named "Gray" Mitcham peppermint, was once increased to seven acres and yielded a good quality oil.[30] Hairy mutations, however, are generally low oil yielders and the quality is most frequently undesirable.

During the early history of the American industry it was not uncommon for accounts of mint culture to include references to planting with seed. Stearns, in his account of the industry in Michigan during the 1850's, makes the following interesting statement:[31]

> some few Mint-farmers raise the plant from the seed, carefully cultivating the ground, and protecting the young shoots from the early frosts, the Mint not being cut until the second year of its growth. Those who operate in this manner, usually re-set their fields every two years, planting them with new Mint, raised in a nursery, from the seed.

This account so varies with the present known seed producing capacity of peppermint that it lends considerable credence to the idea that some of the commercial mint plants of that day may not actually have been peppermint or spearmint. The American and Black Mitcham peppermints contain from 70 to 72 chromosomes, but some varieties with as few as 36 have been reported.[32]

A large number of hybrids were developed by both Nelson and Murray and an interesting sidelight of the work of the latter, plant breeder since 1947 for the Todd Company, has been the production of strains having oils of very delicate aromas and scents. The possibility of hybrid mint oils being used extensively in the aromatic trade, as contrasted with their most common usage as a flavoring, opens up many new vistas for the industry.

Field Distillery Research

Although the distillation process is one of the most important aspects of mint cultivation it has attracted very little professional interest. Some early research in Indiana concentrated on problems of dirty distillery equipment and storage cans,[33] but the bulk of the work has been that of A. D. Hughes of Oregon State whose inventions and improvements have been incorporated into the distilleries marketed by the Cobb Manufacturing Company of Jefferson, Oregon.[34] A study of distillery efficiency has also been conducted at Michigan State University.[35]

Weeds and Insect Control

A wide variety of insects, nematodes, and symphylans are known to attack various parts of the peppermint and spearmint plants (Figure 54). For convenience, they can be categorized as follows:

beetles and wireworms	loopers and caterpillars
leafminers	grasshoppers
leafhoppers and aphids	thrips
stink bugs	mites
nematodes	symphylids
root weevils	scarab beetles

Growers, of course, are basically interested in control, but control consists of understanding the habits of the various pests in order that techniques and insecticides will have greatest impact.

Since the growing conditions, soil, and water supply measures in the various producing districts differ considerably, the pest problems also differ from one region to another. The mint flea beetle was especially destructive in Indiana and Michigan and its life cycle extensively studied by L. G. Gentner.[36] Indiana research on pest problems was carried on by George E. Gould,[37] in Washington by Kenneth Frick, L. F. Faulkner, and E. C. Klostermeyer,[38] and in Oregon by Harold Jensen and H. E. Morrison.[39]

Control measures for the major pests have been fairly well worked out and a wide variety of bulletins and circulars is available from the various state agricultural stations regarding the utilization of insecticides and cultivation control measures.

Despite the fact that various weeds and grasses in the mint hay when harvested will give the distilled oil a bad color or taste, extensive research on weed control has been contemporary with the rise of chemical herbicides. Until this time growers had to expend considerable labor weeding the fields, either by hand or cultivator, generally the most expensive item in the growing process. In an effort to cut costs, sheep, cows, goats, and geese have been employed as weeders, and geese raising for weeding purposes has become an important industry in the Yakima Valley of Washington (Figure 54). A goose grower's brochure provides the following information.[40]

> Weeder geese are used with great success to control and eradicate troublesome grass and certain weeds in a variety of crops and plantings. The geese consume grass and young weeds as quickly as they appear but do not touch the cultivated plants. Why do geese eat certain plants with relish while showing no interest whatsoever for certain others? Perhaps only a goose knows the answer, but nevertheless, it is a long established fact which is being taken advantage of by farmers and growers throughout the country. . . .
>
> It has been estimated that twelve young weeder geese, properly managed, will replace the work of one man and hoe. Substitute your cost for hand labor ($150 is probably low for most sections of the country) to obtain an idea of how much you can save. Cost of $36 for twelve geese includes costs of purchasing goslings, brooding, supplemental feeding, etc., for an average cost of $3.00 per goose per season. The returns from marketing the geese should be deducted which will make the actual cost far less than this figure.

Goose hatchers generally deliver the young birds in the spring and pick them up in the fall months for marketing. Several years ago an earthquake in Washington shattered most of the brood eggs and the goose supply was quite limited, resulting in a considerable quantity of weedy oil being produced and sold off various farms who were not able to "hire" weeders.

Not all weeds can be controlled chemically, but a great deal of work on the problem has been conducted at Oregon State by W. R. Furtick and D. O. Chilcote and more recently by A. P. Appleby on terbacil, marketed by DuPont under the trade name Sinbar.[41] A comprehensive weed control program is now in operation in Washington supervised by Dean Brown, agricultural agent in Yakima County.[42]

Sinbar, first used on a great scale in 1967, appears to be the most successful herbicide yet developed for use in mint cultivation. Although some weeds resist the chemical the outlook at present is for decided reduction in weeding expenses on most mint farms.

Disease

With the appearance of mint anthracnose and Verticillium wilt in Indiana and Michigan, disease became, and still remains, the single most important problem facing the industry. Adequate control measures for anthracnose were quickly developed and, although significant strides have been made on stemming other diseases, the problems are far from solved. Verticillium wilt, primarily on peppermint, remains the most destructive disease in all producing regions, but peppermint rust in western Oregon and Washington, and spearmint rust in the Middlewest, are also very troublesome.

For over a quarter century Ray Nelson at Michigan State University conducted research on the wilt disease, having been associated with its presence since the first reports in Michigan in 1924 (Figure 58). He discovered optimum incidence during seasons of high temperatures and low water supply and concluded that supplemental irrigation by which adequate water levels could be maintained would reduce the interference with growth and oil yield.[43] But such methods were not generally practical on the small Middlewestern farms and the disease continued to spread.

Further research in Indiana conducted by Ralph J. Green, Jr. (Figure 58) demonstrated that limited control of wilt could be obtained through two different methods: deep plowing with a 36 inch moldboard plow;[44] and rotation cropping involving following mint with five years of corn or canary reed grass.[45] The plowing technique was based on the fact that the wilt pathogen was absent in muck soils below a depth of 12 to 18 inches and that inverting the topsoil and the subsoil provided temporary, but limited, control.

Wilt research in Oregon developed from earlier studies begun on the peppermint rust epidemic that became so destructive in the western portion of the state in the late 1940's. Rust control studies were begun in Oregon in 1949 by A. P. Steenland and, in 1951, as a result of funds from the Beech-Nut company, the problem was transferred to an interested doctoral student, C. E. Horner (Figure 58). Horner was successful in working out the life cycle of the rust disease,[46] and obtaining effective controls through clean plowing and applications of Phygon.[47] Continued research has resulted in more effective measures involving applications of DNBP as well as propane flaming of the mint fields,[48] techniques now commonly employed in western Oregon (Figure 54).

With the rust problem successfully dealt with, Horner then turned his attention to the Verticillium wilt problem and, with the assistance of H. L. Dooley, discovered that the propane flaming technique was also effective in providing temporary controls on wilt.[49] Soil fumigation experiments demonstrated that wilt could also be alleviated with applications of Dow 2467 and Vorlex, the latter also having proved successful on Indiana muck soils and in Washington.[50]

The wilt disease problem is by no means solved. There is still no known method of eliminating the fungus from the soil, and developed control measures are temporary ones. But the work of Horner and Green has amply demonstrated that the day may not be too far off when Verticillium wilt will join the list of destructive crop diseases that have been eliminated. If not, there is hope that disease resistance can be effected through mutation by irradiation of the rootstock. M. J. Murray of the Todd Company had a large number of peppermint roots irradiated at the Brookhaven Laboratories in New York and, after several years of extensive field research, has selected several disease-resistant strains with oil quality very similar to that of Black Mitcham. These plants are now being grown on a commercial scale and the results should be available in a short time.

With the increased attention to growing spearmint in the Middlewest, diseases of that crop now attract more interest. Early studies on spearmint rust were carried out under greenhouse conditions at Cornell,[51] and later in the field by Nelson in Michigan.[52] Extensive studies are now conducted at Purdue University[53] and by M. J. Murray of the Todd Company (Figure 58).[54]

Certified Rootstock

The possibility of spreading disease through transportation of diseased mint roots led to a statewide quarantine in Washington in 1961 forbidding the shipment of rootstock from the Middlewest and severely restricting the movement of roots within the state. Both Washington and Oregon agencies initiated certified, disease-free plantings in 1962 and an extensive acreage is now available so that growers may draw upon the certified plants for expansion in new areas. Disease-free roots, however, become immediately contaminated when placed in soil with a history of wilt, so the certification program offers little to growers in areas where the disease has been present.

In Washington, at the present time, the state is divided into three types of districts: quarantine areas, restricted areas, and regulated areas.[55] Originally, only movement of roots from quarantine areas was prohibited, primarily the Yakima and Kennewick sections, but in 1967 the movement of machinery and weeding fowl was also restricted.[56]

Chemical Residues

Increased use of pesticides, herbicides, and fungicides in mint cultivation eventually resulted in concerns about the chemical residues occurring in the oils. The nature of the problem, in general, was brought forcibly to the attention of the American public with the famous cranberry incident, which temporarily stunned that industry, and with the publications of Rachel Carson. Miss Carson's work caused the Shell Corporation to remove, temporarily, from the market Aldrin and Dieldrin, two of the more effective insecticides.

The utilization of various chemicals on the farm is controlled by the U.S. Department of Agriculture, but the marketing of goods which may contain residues is supervised by the Food and Drug Administration. Although the latter establishes residue tolerances it is the responsibility of the marketing firm to demonstrate that the tolerances have not been exceeded in their product. This has led to great improvement in analytical techniques on mint oils since the problem of analyzing residues which may occur in such limited quantity as 50 parts per billion is readily apparent. The improvement of gas chromatographic analysis within the past few years has been a great aid to dealers and users of mint oil, since it offers not only a more effective way of analyzing residues but other components of the oils as well.

A related problem is the gradual development of immunity on the part of many oganisms to chemical controls. This means that new compounds must be perfected, new tolerances established, and continuous residue studies made, *ad infinitum*. Mint industry research has supported residue studies by G. E. Gould at Purdue University, R. R. Legault at Washington State University, and L. D. Terriere at Oregon State University.

Chemistry of Mint Oils

The present marketing of peppermint and spearmint oils is a judicious blend of sophisticated chemical analysis coupled with delicate and subjective tests of aroma and taste. Chemical research has not greatly aided in the latter, but has been of great significance in better understanding the composition of the oils, removing desirable and undesirable fractions, and blending oils to meet certain specifications.

The chemical work related to the mint industry is so voluminous that it would require a special edition of its own, but there have been milestones worthy of record. Certainly, two were the publication of the work of Ernest J. Parry on the essential oils in London in 1899,[57] and the translation into English by Edward Kremers of the German work on volatile oils by Gildemeister and Hoffman.[58] Although not restricted to mint oils, the works set forth in considerable detail techniques for analyzing various substances and pulled together a wide variety of published information of some importance. The comprehensive six volume work of the American authority Ernest Guenther appeared between 1948 and 1952,[59] and extensive studies of the synthesis of terpenes, utilizing mint plants and oils, have been carried out by Robert Reitsema and Fred Cramer of the Todd Company.

Experiments on gas-liquid partition chromatography (GLPC) analysis of peppermint oils began as early as 1958 at Purdue University under the supervision of N. K. Ellis (Figure 58),[60] and has now become the accepted methodology in the industry, as well as in all phases of industry requiring chemical analysis (Figures 58 and 59).

Economic Studies

Production cost studies for mint have not been made in Michigan, Indiana, or Oregon since World War II, but two have been made in the irrigated sections of Washington. In 1947 Lester N. Liebel compiled data from 51 farms in the Kennewick and Yakima areas reporting an average net income per acre of $217.15.[61] Six years later, A. L. Walker collected cost data from 28 farms in the same area and reported a net income of $14.65,[62] a distinct reflection of the depression of oil prices since the earlier study, and a convincing argument which might stay new growers from entering the business unless they wish to make a long term commitment and prepare to weather the bad years as well as the good ones.

Organizations and Societies

A small number of dedicated organizations have served various phases of the mint industry over the years and have contributed much to better dissemination of information and understanding of various problems.

The Michigan Muck Farmers Association was founded in 1919 and, acting in cooperation with Michigan State University, has held annual conferences, field days, demonstrations, and exhibits for muck farmers in general. One of the Vice-Presidents of the organization is elected to represent the mint and other essential oil producers of the state, and the oil growers frequently conduct separate sessions as well. The Association was served for many years as Secretary-Treasurer by Paul M. Harmer, muck crop specialist at Michigan State University, who conducted numerous experiments on peppermint plants with special emphasis on disease and fertilizer requirements. An annual *Proceedings* is issued which contains a wide variety of articles on the mint industry as well as muck crop cultivation in general.

The Northern Indiana Muck Crop Farmers Association serves a similar function in that state and holds an annual muck crop clinic at which new techniques in agriculture are demonstrated.

The Oregon Essential Oil Growers League was incorporated on February 10, 1950, at Corvallis,[63] and has become an especially significant representative of the growers. Devoted to service to mint farmers the League holds an annual meeting in January during which a wide variety of pertinent topics are discussed, not only by growers, but by representatives of all phases of the industry from farm to consumer. The annual *Proceedings* provides a neat capsulization of the significant production and research developments in Oregon over the years as well as acquainting the state's growers with general developments in the industry as a whole.

The League sponsors its own research fund and financing is maintained by a voluntary contribution from the growers of one cent per pound of oil produced. In 1967 nearly half the League membership contributed to the research fund and this, coupled with support from other companies and organizations, exceeded $10,000.[64] The major beneficiary over the years has been Oregon State University where present research is concentrated on wilt disease, resistant hybrids, weed and insect control, and new systemic chemical fungicides, especially DuPont 1991, which offers promise as a Verticillium wilt control.

The League is governed by a Board of Directors of nine growers representing the Coburg-Springfield, Jefferson-Salem, Madras, Ontario-Nyssa, and the remainder-of-Oregon areas. Men who have served as Secretary since the founding have been A. P. Steenland, H. J. O'Reilly, C. E. Horner, and Iain MacSwan.

The Washington State Mint Growers, Inc., which had become defunct right after the war, was reorganized on February 26, 1949, with Henry J. York as President but, after three years of continued efforts to promote cooperative marketing, the group disbanded. It was succeeded in August, 1954, by the Washington State Mint Growers League with offices in Kelso. "It was organized as an all service organization and provided all kinds of information on fertilizers, insect and weed control, irrigation and other aspects of mint farming."[65] This group also became inactive and was dissolved.

The current organization, Washington Mint Growers Association, was incorporated on June 27, 1961, with offices at Sunnyside, and continued the functions of its predecessor. On February 21, 1963, the Association published the first number of its current periodical, *Mint Drops,* devoted to general dissemination of material important to growers. The office was moved to Pasco in 1964 and Kenley Mourer hired to serve as Executive Secretary. Since 1962 the Association has held an annual meeting at Sunnyside devoted to talks concerning various aspects of growing and marketing mint oils.

The Association initiated its own research program in 1965 with experiments on wilt and rust control and was primarily responsible for the organization, on February 1, 1967, of the Washington Mint Commission with the purpose of promoting "research and dissemination of information."[66] The Commission now coordinates all phases of research activity through compulsory contributions of one cent per pound of oil sold from the farm. The dealers and buyers of Washington mint oils act as agents of the state in deducting the assessment from grower payments and forwarding the funds to the Mint Commission.

Research currently under way through Association and Commission contracts involve weed and insect control, hybrids, irradiation, and the use of fertilizers. The Commission publishes its own periodical under the title *Washington Mint Research* and conducts its own meetings. The present Chairman is Haynes Gearhart of Othello and research-coordinator is Harold Wagner of Grandview.

Federal and State Contributions

For many years experiments on various phases of mint cultivation were carried out at the U.S. Department of Agriculture experimental farms at Beltsville, Maryland, and Arlington, Virginia, and reports issued periodically.[67] The Department bulletin on mint farming has been revised and reissued four times since 1948,[68] the latest in 1963.

The state and federal research contribution has been especially significant through utilization of staff members and facilities of the agricultural schools and experiment stations, especially in Michigan, Indiana, Oregon, and Washington. The results of staff expertise far exceed the monetary contribution involved in carrying on such programs.

Conclusion

The research and service effort of the American mint industry has been a most commendable one. The switch from empirical cultivating techniques to those solidly based on modern researched technology has been especially pronounced since World War II. This has been accomplished primarily through research funds made available from growers in Oregon and Washington through their respective organizations.

No aspect of the industry has escaped the scathing eye of science, and the history of disease and insect control, plant breeding work, mint botany, and chemical analysis, offer considerable testimony to the significant achievements of the researchers as well as demonstration of the exceedingly complex problems involved. Extremely interesting examples of scientific endeavor have been the developments in Verticillium wilt control, capped by the achievements of C. E. Horner, Ralph J. Green, Jr., and M. J. Murray, and the relationships between sunlight, temperature, blossoming, and the content of that once mysterious ingredient menthofuran.

Backed by a solid subsidy from users, dealers, growers, and interested banks and chemical companies, the mint research program, conducted by the various agricultural schools, will undoubtedly continue to illuminate the many problems that still face the industry at all levels.

REFERENCES

[1] N. K. Ellis (ed.), *Mint Research, 1947-1948: Proceedings of the First and Second Mint Research Conferences*, Purdue University, mimeo, 1949.

[2] *Ibid.*

[3] L. G. Cox, "Current Progress in Peppermint Research," *Proceedings of the Oregon Essential Oil Growers League*, 2nd annual meeting, p. 13, 1951.

[4] W. Todd, "Report on Mint Industry Research Program," *Ibid.*, 17th annual meeting, pp. 47-50, 1966.

[5] *Ibid.*, p. 47.

[6] *Ibid.*

[7] F. C. Steward, "Mentha as a Plant for Physiological Investigations," *Growth, Nutrition, and Metabolism of Mentha piperita L.*, pp. 1-2, Memoir 379, Cornell University Agricultural Experiment Station, August, 1962.

[8] M. L. Ruttle, "Some Common Mints and Their Hybrids," *The Herbarist*, pp. 17-29, 1938; G. M. Hocking, "Scotch Mint and Spearmint. A Comparative Study of Cultural, Morphological, and Histological Characteristics of Species of *Mentha* Growing in Florida," *Journal of the American Pharmaceutical Association*, vol. 38, pp. 394-402, 1949; G. M. Hocking and L. D. Edwards, "Nomenclature of Peppermint and Its Varieties," *Ibid.*, vol. 33, pp. 333-342, 1944.

[9]See, for example: F. J. Bacon, G. C. Jenison, and R. E. Kremers, "Studies in the Genus *Mentha,*" *Journal of the American Pharmaceutical Association,* vol. 12, pp. 1075-1077, December, 1923.

[10]*Growth, Nutrition, and Metabolism of Mentha piperita L.,* Memoir 379, Cornell University Agricultural Experiment Station, August, 1962.

[11]R. Langston, "Distribution Patterns of Radioisotopes in Plants," *Proceedings of the American Society for Horticultural Science,* pp. 370-376, 1956; R. W. Rinne and R. Langston, "Effect of Growth on Redistribution of Some Mineral Elements in Peppermint," *Plant Physiology,* vol. 35, pp. 210-215, March, 1960; R. W. Rinne and R. Langston, "Studies on Lateral Movement of Phosphorus 32 in Peppermint," *Ibid.,* pp. 216-219.

[12]N. K. Ellis, L. J. Swift, and M. H. Thornton, *A Method for Telling the Time of Cutting Peppermint for Highest Oil Yield,* Mimeo No. 3, Dept. of Horticulture, Purdue University, June, 1944.

[13]D. E. Bullis, F. E. Price, and D. E. Kirk, *Relationship of Maturing and Weathering to Yield and Quality of Peppermint Oil,* Station Bulletin 458, Agricultural Experiment Station, Oregon State College, August, 1948.

[14]V. K. Watson and J. L. St. John, "Relation of Maturity and Curing of Peppermint Hay to Yield and Composition of Oil," *Journal of Agricultural and Food Chemistry,* pp. 1033-1038, vol. 3, December, 1955.

[15]P. A. Tornow and L. Fischer, "A Study of the Physical and Chemical Properties of Natural Washington and Oregon Peppermint Oils," *Journal of the American Pharmaceutical Association,* vol. 27, pp. 76-78, February, 1948.

[16]P. Z. Bedoukian, "Occurrence of Menthofuran in Oil of Peppermint," *Journal of the American Chemical Society,* vol. 70, pp. 621-622, February, 1948.

[17]V. K. Watson and J. L. St. John, *op. cit.,* p. 1038.

[18]J. A. J. M. Lemli, "The Occurrence of Menthofuran in Peppermint Oil," *Journal of Pharmacy and Pharmacology,* vol. 9, pp. 120-127, 1957.

[19]E. Guenther, "The Peppermint Oil Industry in Oregon and Washington States," *Perfumery and Essential Oil Record,* pp. 641-642, October, 1961.

[20]F. Rabak, *The Effect of Cultural and Climatic Conditions on the Yield and Quality of Peppermint Oil,* Professional Paper, Bulletin No. 454, USDA, Dec. 9, 1916.

[21]H. A. Allard, "Further Studies of the Photoperiodic Behavior of Some Mints," *Journal of Agricultural Research,* vol. 63, pp. 55-64, July, 1941.

[22]*Ibid.,* p. 57.

[23]R. Nelson, *Verticillium Wilt of Peppermint,* p. 202, Technical Bulletin 221, Agricultural Experiment Station, Michigan State College, June, 1950.

[24]R. Langston and A. C. Leopold, "Photoperiodic Responses of Peppermint," *Proceedings of the American Society for Horticultural Science,* vol. 63, pp. 347-352, 1954. Much of the work of Crane is reported in *Growth, Nutrition, and Metabolism of Mentha piperita L., op. cit.*

[25]R. H. Biggs and A. C. Leopold, "The Effects of Temperature on Peppermint," *Proceedings of the American Society for Horticultural Science,* vol. 66, pp. 315-321, 1955.

[26]F. W. Went, "The Effect of Temperature on Plant Growth," *Annual Review of Plant Physiology,* vol. 4, pp. 347-362, 1953.

[27]A. J. Burbott and W. D. Loomis, "Effects of Light and Temperature on the Monoterpenes of Peppermint," *Plant Physiology,* vol. 42, pp. 20-28, January, 1967.

[28]J. Battaile and W. D. Loomis, "The Site and Sequence of Terpene Formation in Peppermint," *Biochimica et Biophysica Acta,* vol. 51, pp. 545-552, 1961.

[29]R. Nelson, *op. cit.,* p. 194.

[30]*Ibid.,* p. 12.

[31]F. Stearns, "The Peppermint Plantations of Michigan," *American Journal of Pharmacy,* vol. 31, p. 37, 1859.

[32]R. Nelson, *op. cit.,* p. 13.

[33]N. K. Ellis, K. I. Fawcett, F. C. Gaylord, and L. H. Baldinger, *A Study of Some Factors Affecting the Yield and Market Value of Peppermint Oil,* Bulletin No. 461, pp. 16-20, Agricultural Experiment Station, Purdue University, June, 1941.

[34]A. D. Hughes, *Improvements in the Field Distillation of Peppermint Oil,* Station Bulletin 525, Agricultural Experiment Station, Oregon State College, August, 1952. Also published as Bulletin No. 31, Engineering Experiment Station.

[35]W. H. Kahl, C. W. Hall, L. N. Shepherd, and D. M. Jerrim, "An Investigation of Some Factors Affecting the Distillation of Peppermint Oil," *Quarterly Bulletin,* vol. 38, pp. 570-579, Michigan Agricultural Experiment Station, May, 1956.

[36]L. G. Gentner, *The Mint Flea-beetle (Longitarsus waterhousei Kutschera): Its Habits and Measures for Control,* Circular 125, Michigan Agricultural Experiment Station, 1929.

[37]G. E. Gould, "Problems in the Control of Mint Insects," *Journal of Economic Entomology,* vol. 53, pp. 526-531, 1960.

[38]K. E. Frick, "Control of Insects and Mites Attacking Mint in Central Washington," *Ibid.,* vol. 54, pp. 644-649, August, 1961; L. R. Faulkner, "Pathogenicity and Population Dynamics of Paratylenchus hamatus on *Mentha* spp.," *Phytopathology,* vol. 54, pp. 344-348, March, 1964; E. C. Klostermeyer, *1966 Progress Report: Mite and Insect Control on Peppermint,* mimeo, Irrigation Experiment Station, Washington State University, 1966.

[39]H. J. Jensen, *Nematodes Affecting Oregon Agriculture,* Station Bulletin 579, Agricultural Experiment Station, Oregon State University, May, 1961; H. E. Morrison and R. F. Koontz, *1966 Studies for Control of Mint Pests, Hop Pests and Soil Arthropods,* Oregon State University, ditto, 1966.

[40]Richards Goose Hatchery, Outlook, Washington.

[41]W. R. Furtick and D. O. Chilcote, *Chemical Weed Control in Mint,* Circular of Information 559, Agricultural Experiment Station, Oregon State College, revised, February, 1957; A. P. Appleby, "Progress Report on Sinbar for Peppermint Weed Control," *Proceedings of the Oregon Essential Oil Growers League,* 18th annual meeting, pp. 14-15, 1967.

[42]"Weed Research Being Explored," *Washington Mint Research,* May, 1967.

[43]R. Nelson, *op. cit.,* p. 253.

[44]R. J. Green, Jr., "Deep Plowing for Controlling Verticillium Wilt of Mint in Muck Soils," *Phytopathology,* vol. 48, pp. 575-577, October, 1958.

[45]*Idem,* "Control of Verticillium Wilt of Peppermint by Crop Rotation Sequences," *Plant Disease Reporter,* vol. 51, pp. 449-453, June 1967.

[46]C. E. Horner, "Field Disease Cycle of Peppermint Rust," *Phytopathology,* vol. 53, pp. 1063-1067, September, 1963.

[47]*Idem, Control Peppermint Disease,* Station Bulletin 547, Agricultural Experiment Station, Oregon State College, February, 1955.

[48]*Idem,* "Control of Mint Rust by Propane Gas Flaming and Contact Herbicide," *Plant Disease Reporter,* vol. 49, pp. 393-395, May, 1965.

[49]C. E. Horner and H. L. Dooley, "Propane Flaming Kills Verticillium Dahliae in Peppermint Stubble," *Ibid.,* vol. 49, pp. 581-582, July, 1965.

[50]*Idem,* "Control of Verticillium Wilt of Peppermint by Soil Fumigation," *Ibid.,* vol. 50, pp. 97-99, February, 1966; R. J. Green, Jr., "Control of Verticillium Wilt of Peppermint by Soil Fumigation in Muck Soils," *Ibid.,* vol. 48, pp. 960-963, August, 1964; L. R. Faulkner and C. B. Skotland, "Control of Verticillium Wilt of Mint and Plant Parasitic Nematodes Associated with Mint by Soil Fumigation," *Ibid.,* vol. 47, pp. 662-665, July, 1963.

[51]J. S. Niederhauser, *The Rust of Greenhouse Grown Spearmint, and Its Control,* Memoir 263, Cornell University Agricultural Experiment Station, 1945.

[52]R. Nelson, "Mint Rust and Its Control," *Quarterly Bulletin,* Michigan Agricultural Experiment Station, pp. 436-455, vol. 34, 1952.

[53]W. J. H. Stone, "The Epiphytology of Spearmint Rust in Indiana," *Mycopathologia et Mycologia Applicata,* vol. 31, pp. 17-26, 1967.

[54]M. J. Murray, "Spearmint Rust Resistance and Immunity in the Genus *Mentha,*" *Crop Science,* vol. 1, pp. 175-179.

[55]Mint Wilt Quarantine, Quarantine Order No. 1001, Department of Agriculture, Olympia, Washington, Feb. 28, 1966.

[56]*Ibid.,* Quarantine Order No. 1054, July 5, 1967.

[57]E. J. Parry, *The Chemistry of Essential Oils and Artificial Perfumes,* Scott, Greenwood and Son, London, 1899.

[58]E. Gildemeister and F. Hoffman, *The Volatile Oils,* 2nd edition by E. Gildemeister, English translation by E. Kremers; vol. 1, 1913; vol. 2, 1916; vol. 3, 1922; John Wiley and Sons, Inc., New York.

[59]E. Guenther, *The Essential Oils;* vol. 1, 1948; vol. 2, 1949; vol. 3, 1949; vol. 4, 1950; vol. 5, 1952; vol. 6, 1952; D. Van Nostrand Co., Inc., New York.

[60]G. Papathanassiou, N. K. Ellis, and R. E. Henze, *Gas-Liquid Partition Chromatography in the Qualitative Analysis of Essential Oils,* Journal Paper No. 1298, Agricultural Experiment Station, Purdue University, 1958.

[61]L. N. Liebel, *Peppermint Oil: An Economic Study,* p. 17, Popular Bulletin No. 199, Agricultural Experiment Stations, State College of Washington, August, 1950.

[62]A. L. Walker, *Peppermint Oil Production in South Central Washington, 1953,* p. 8, Stations Circular 253, Agricultural Experiment Stations, State College of Washington, May, 1954.

[63]*Proceedings of the Oregon Essential Oil Growers League,* 2nd annual meeting, p. 2, 1951.

[64]*Ibid.,* 19th annual meeting, p. 50, 1968.

[65]W. A. Paulson, *The Mint Industry in the State of Washington,* p. 10, Pacific Coast Banking School, University of Washington, April, 1966.

[66]"Mint-A History of Research," *Washington Mint Research,* (p. 4), Washington Mint Commission, May, 1967.

[67]e.g., "Breeding for Verticillium-wilt Resistant Mint," pp. 47-48, USDA, *Report of the Chief of the Bureau of Plant Industry, Soils, and Agricultural Engineering: 1947.*

[68]A. F. Sievers and E. C. Stevenson, *Mint Farming,* Farmers' Bulletin No. 1988, April, 1948; L. M. Pultz, *Mint Farming,* Farmers' Bulletin No. 1988, revised, February, 1954; R. J. Green, Jr. and H. T. Erickson, *Mint Farming,* Agriculture Information Bulletin No. 212, February, 1960; R. J. Green, Jr., *Mint Farming,* Agriculture Information Bulletin No. 212, revised, February, 1963.

Chapter 15.

From Grower to Consumer

On the Farm

In the middle of July the mint harvesting and distillation season in the United States begins. Because of the differing conditions in the various producing districts there is a considerable harvesting overlap, spearmint and peppermint in the Middlewest and in the sections west of the Cascades reaching harvest stage about the first of August, Washington spearmint even earlier. In the Yakima Valley and the Columbia Basin districts peppermint, due to the menthofuran problem, is generally cut near the end of August although some growers are now cutting twice, first time before peak blooming and second time again before second blooming stage. The practice of second cutting requires an exceptionally healthy field since it saps the vitality of the roots. The second cutting oil is also less desirable in quality, thus the practice is not widespread.

The length of the harvest season is dependent upon the acreage involved and the capacity of the distillery, but extends well into September in the Far West. Not all growers have mint stills so their hay must be trucked to that of a neighbor for custom stilling. The distilleries commonly run around the clock until the entire crop has been processed.

For nearly two months, then, the fresh supply of peppermint and spearmint oil is being obtained from the nation's farms. Over 700 peppermint and nearly 360 spearmint farms annually process nearly 100,000 acres of mint and produce in excess of 6 million pounds of oil. Since the cultivation and distillation techniques of both crops are practically identical they are commonly grown by the same farmer. Because of disease, however, some areas have become devoted primarily to spearmint raising (central Michigan, northeastern Indiana, Jefferson County, Wisconsin, and the Mabton area of the Yakima Valley). Production figures for 1967, one of the most productive harvest seasons in the history of the American industry, are shown in Table 1 and Table 2. At a representative value of $5 per pound this production represented a gross farm income of nearly $34,000,000.[1] When the oil has been distilled it is stored by the grower in 225 or 400 pound galvanized drums peppermint oil, of course, being kept separate from spearmint oil. The drums are furnished free of charge to the growers by the dealers who have contracted for the purchase of the oil. The business of advance contracts from the dealers is not guaranteed, being based on amount of oil needed and estimated production. When contracts are let, however, they generally specify oil type, quality, amount, and price. The latter is dependent entirely on the quality of the oil.

Table 1
Spearmint Oil Production in the United States: 1967

Producing District	Number of Farms	Acres	Pounds of Oil	Average Yields (Pounds Per Acre)
Middle West	144	6,545	222,100	34
Scotch spearmint	91	3,808	135,000	35
Native spearmint	56	2,737	87,100	32
Indiana	71	2,748	106,600	39
Scotch	60	2,209	85,400	39
Native	15	539	21,100	39
Michigan	58	2,682	89,100	33
Scotch	25	1,029	35,900	35
Native	33	1,653	53,300	32
Wisconsin	15	1,115	26,400	24
Scotch	6	570	13,700	24
Native	8	545	12,700	23
Far West	209	16,612	1,628,200	92
Scotch	139	10,338	1,015,000	98
Native	133	6,274	613,200	98
Washington	202	16,279	1,608,300	99
Scotch	132	10,005	995,100	99
Native	133	6,274	613,200	98
Idaho (all Scotch)	7	333	19,900	60
Total U.S.	353	23,157	1,850,300	80
Scotch	230	14,146	1,150,000	81
Native	189	9,011	700,300	78

Source: various reports from dealers and government publications.

During the fall and winter months the dealers send trucks into the producing districts to pick up the drums of oil, or the individual growers haul the oil to a nearby receiving station. All major mint oil dealers

Table 2
Peppermint Oil Production in the United States: 1967

Producing District	Number of Farms	Acres	Pounds of Oil	Average Yields (Pounds Per Acre)
Middle West	176	15,707	579,500	37
Wisconsin	49	7,941	328,100	41
Indiana	74	5,789	201,400	35
Michigan	53	1,977	50,000	25
Far West	543	50,872	3,859,300	76
Washington	263	22,498	2,015,200	90
Yakima Valley and Columbia Basin	254	20,620	1,904,900	92
Lower Columbia River	9	1,878	110,300	59
Oregon	236	24,170	1,616,800	67
Willamette Valley	130	13,357	825,800	62
Lower Columbia River	2	150	8,700	58
Madras	89	9,342	703,900	75
Eastern Oregon	15	1,321	78,900	60
Idaho	42	3,589	203,000	57
Montana	2	605	24,100	40
Total U.S.	719	66,579	4,438,800	67

Source: various reports from dealers and government publications.

maintain receiving stations in one or more of the various producing districts. It is the accepted practice in the industry that the grower is paid immediately upon delivery of the oil. If the market is weak, or the oil has not been contracted for, the dealers will store the supply, making payment at the time of usage.

Once the harvest has been completed the business of moving the better than 15,000 drums of mint oil from the farm and preparing the oil for marketing becomes the responsibility of the country dealers.

Into the Hands of the Dealers

The natural peppermint and spearmint oils continue their journey from the farms into the receiving stations of the dealers then to the main processing plants for final disposition. Although there are a number of small buyers of oils in the country, the bulk of the American product moves into the hands of the four major dealers, A. M. Todd Company, I. P. Callison and Sons, Inc., Wm. Leman Inc., and M. Brown and Sons, Inc.

A. M. Todd Company

The head office and main processing plant of the Todd Company are located at Kalamazoo, Michigan, having been moved from Nottawa,

Michigan, in 1891 (Figure 60). Conveniently located between the major producing districts of the west and the dominant market outlets of the east, the natural oil arrives by truck and by train from all the various districts.

The company is now in its third generation of management. A. M. Todd was succeeded as President by his son, Albert J. Todd, who served until 1956 (Figure 60). Since then, A. J. Todd, Jr. has headed the company. Vice-Presidents are Winship A. Todd, A. A. Todd, Jr., and Walter Phillips who supervises buying operations in the western states.

The company has more diversified interests than just handling mint oils. Great interest has been shown in the development of new production regions for citrus oils with special emphasis on lemon and lime. As a result of the extensive hybrid research carried out by M. J. Murray, Todd plant breeder since 1947, the company is also developing new types of essential oils of special interest to the fragrance industry.

I. P. Callison and Sons, Inc.

The Callison company has head offices in Seattle and its major processing plant at Chehalis, Washington (Figure 60). Especially active in buying peppermint and spearmint oils in the western states, the company also maintains its position as the major supplier of cascara. Other botanical drugs handled by the company include digitalis, fenugreek, aloin, and podophyllin.

I. P. Callison served as President until his retirement in 1933 (Figure 60). Succeeding heads of the company have been: H. A. Callison (1933-1942); Cecil Callison (1942-1961); and Larry Givens (1961-). I. P. Callison passed away in 1961 in his ninetieth year.

The Callison company constructed, in 1949, the first continuous peppermint oil fractionating plant, later adding a column to process spearmint oil. The new process, as opposed to the previous rectification in batches, made it possible to secure better control of the chemical analysis and preparation of the oils for marketing.

Wm. Leman Inc.

The Leman company has head offices and its processing plant in Bremen, Indiana (Figure 60). William Leman, Sr., the founder, serves as Chairman with John Leman as President. Vice-Presidents are Sam Leman and Wm. Leman, Jr. Founded originally as Leman-Gerber, the company was incorporated in 1941 under its present name.

M. Brown and Sons, Inc.

The head office and processing plant of the Brown company is also located in Bremen, Indiana (Figure 60). Named for the father, Morris, the company is still headed by the founder, Benjamin Brown. A son, Irvin Brown, serves as Vice-President and Treasurer, and a brother, Max Brown, serves as Vice-President in charge of buying operations. Another brother, Samuel Brown, passed 'away in 1962.

In addition to these four, there are a number of small, independent dealers, and the Hotchkiss Company continues its operations in Lyons, New York, under the direction of Anne D. Hotchkiss, the great-grand-daughter of the founder (Figure 20).

Functions of the Dealers

As mint oils from across the country arrive at dealer warehouses and collection points a sample is generally drawn from each drum as it is weighed. Experienced buyers give initial appraisal to the oil's odor and usually check the optical rotation to ascertain if it is within normal ranges for the grade. If all appears satisfactory the grower usually receives spot payment at the agreed price or a receipt for the oil if immediate purchase is not concluded. Buyers can, and do, purchase oil which on subsequent examination is found to be of less desirable quality but generally their intimate knowledge of the preharvest condition of each field and the general state of the crop tempers their judgment.

After the oil is taken into dealer hands, the samples of each drum or lot are more carefully evaluated in the laboratories of the major dealers. This evaluation may include both subjective organoleptic appraisal and objective scrutiny to determine physical constants. Elaborate and sophisticated apparatus is now in large part replacing the slower chemical assay methods traditional in the laboratory. Gas chromatography and computers are fast becoming required adjuncts to the dealer's nose. Yet, despite objective testing, each drum is almost certain to be given an aroma test, frequently consisting of placing a small quantity of oil in a smelling glass, whisking it around, heating in the hand and sniffing the fragrance. Experienced aroma testers, by this process, can detect undesirable qualities such as the presence of weed oil or other undesirable characteristics due to poor distilling or harvesting practices. Since fragrance and flavor are close kin in mint oil, these subjective appraisals reinforced by the analytical are all important in determining oil quality.

Based on the information of nose and laboratory, the dealer can attempt to blend his purchases to derive a uniform product typical of the grade and acceptable to the user—the ultimate arbiter of quality. The market for the various grades of mint oil depends on the price and quality considerations of the manufacturers end product. Oil which might not be perfectly suited to one product may well merit strong consideration in another.

Further processing then depends on the specifications of the dealer's customers. Both peppermint and spearmint are sold as natural oils, as natural blends of various producing districts or as redistilled or rectified oils depending on user requirements.

Peppermint is frequently specified to be U.S.P. standard. These minimums, set forth in the *United States Pharmacopeia*, demand the oil meet at least the following requirements.[2]

> Source: *Mentha piperita* L.
> Process: Rectified by steam distillation and neither partly or wholly dementholized
> Ester Content: Not less than 5%
> Total Menthol Content: Not less than 50%, free and as esters
> Color: Colorless or pale yellow
> Solubility in alcohol: 1 volume dissolves in 3 volumes of 70% alcohol
> Specific Gravity: Not less than 0.896 nor more than 0.908
> Angular Rotation: Not less than $-18°$ and not more than $-32°$ in a 100 mm. tube
> Refractive Index: Not less than 1.4590 nor more than 1.4650 at 20°

This specification was initially developed to ensure the removal of dimethyl sulfide from the oil, a process accomplished by steam or vacuum rectification. The specification, however, has gained wider acceptance as a nominal standard for peppermint oil, but most knowledgeable mint users consider the USP as only a minimum guide to quality.

Spearmint is described in *The National Formulary* and N.F. Spearmint must meet the following minimums.[3]

> Source: *Mentha piperita* L. or *Mentha cardiaca* G.
> Process: Distilled with steam
> Carvone Content: Not less than 55% by volume
> Color: Colorless, yellow or greenish yellow
> Solubility in Alcohol: Soluble in equal volumes of 80% alcohol
> Specific Gravity: Not less than 0.917 nor more than 0.934
> Optical Rotation: Not less than $-48°$ nor more than $-59°$ in a 100 mm. tube
> Refractive Index: Not less than 1.4840 nor more than 1.4910 at 20º

If a customer requests a fractionated oil from the dealer, it is processed thru either steam or vacuum stills and head fractions, tail fractions or even middle fractions can be efficiently removed. This processing results in a shrinkage of the natural oil which may typically range from 1% to 30%, depending on the product required. This shrinkage is reflected in the disparity of prices noted between those paid to the farmer and those in the trade press quotations.

The functions of the dealers are not confined to handling and marketing of the oils. They furnish the storage drums to the growers, supply storage space for many buyers, and advance considerable sums of money to enable growers to plant, cultivate, and harvest the mint crop. The latter is a distinctly important, but little discussed, service. Dealers also compile annual acreage censuses and oil production reports in the various producing districts, and make these materials available to their customers. Several of the dealers are involved in extensive, independent research programs involving practically every phase of the mint industry from farm to consumer, and generous contributions have been made to the Mint Industry Research Fund which supports activities at a number of agricultural colleges.

As the orders come in to the dealers the prepared oil is shipped in the 225 or 400 pound galvanized drums, costing about $15. The general practice is for the customer to place a full-cost deposit for the drum, although the cost is built in for oils shipped overseas. Some customers specify shipment in stainless steel or aluminum drums which cost from $65 to $100. For smaller orders mint oils are also shipped in cans ranging from 1 to 25 pounds in size.

The mint oils then move outward from the processing plants of the dealers into the two major channels; to the primary domestic users, and into the export trade.

The Primary Market

Literally hundreds of firms utilize mint oils in some phase of their manufacturing process. Although published information on the usage of the mint oils is not available an estimate, based on 1966 and 1967 usage (not production), would reveal the following approximate allocation of the oils.

Usage	Percentage of Peppermint Oil	Percentage of Spearmint Oil
Flavoring in chewing gum	43	34
Export trade	29	27
Flavoring in tooth paste and mouthwash	21	36
Confectionery flavoring	6	1
Other uses	1	2
	100	100

Available evidence indicates that the foreign usage of the mint oils is in nearly the same ratio as that in the United States.

The export trade is of considerable importance and is by no means static. Within recent years Japan has supplanted the United Kingdom as the major importer of American mint oils, receiving over 420,000 pounds in 1967. The most important receiving countries for peppermint oil are currently the United Kingdom, Japan, France, West Germany, Canada, and Mexico. For spearmint oil major importing countries are Japan, the United Kingdom, Canada, Mexico, and France.

The dominant use of mint oils is as a flavor, a very small amount being used for other purposes. An example of the popularity of the mints is well demonstrated in some recent research concerning odor preferences among British subjects.[4] Among the findings were the following:

1). peppermint aroma was exceeded in preference by only lemon and cinnamon;

2). out of 132 different odors, women placed peppermint 29th in preference while men ranked it 9th; men over 15, however, ranked peppermint 18th; spearmint was ranked 17th by women and 22nd by men, although men over 15 placed it 46th;

3). persons of introvertish temperament preferred the aroma of peppermint over spearmint, but the preference was reversed by extroverts;

4). the preference for spearmint odor is little changed after the age of five, although there is some increased favoritism by late teen agers.

The increasing popularity of chewing gum in the United States has been the great backbone of the twentieth century mint industry. Nearly 95 percent of the chewing gum sales, near $400,000,000 annually, are made by four companies: Wm. Wrigley Jr. Company of Chicago; American Chicle, a division of Warner Lambert Pharmaceutical Company since 1962; Beech-Nut Inc. of Canajoharie, New York; and Clark Gum, a subsidiary of Philip Morris Inc.

The American gums are recognized as high quality products and the primary users have exacting standards regarding the quality and source of the mint oils utilized in their products. The Wrigley Company is reported to account for nearly 50 percent of all gum sales,[5] with Spearmint being the top selling brand in the world. Doublemint (with peppermint flavor) outsells Spearmint in this country although Juicy Fruit is favored above both in certain sections.

American Chicle products (Dentyne, Clorets, Beemans, Chiclets, Trident, Adams), Beech-Nut (Beech-Nut and Frosty Mint), and Clark products (Clark, Di-et), together control about 45 percent of the market.

The flavoring in chewing gum is a major ingredient, accounting for nearly one percent of the total composition by weight. This compares with a range of 0.15 to 0.4 percent for most other types of confections and candies. The chewing gum flavor is expected to last for a considerable time, so it must have high strength and tenacity.

While chewing gum, as a market for mint, has been increasing in terms of absolute volume, there has been a phenomenal rise in the relative importance of the toothpaste industry which is now reckoned to have sales in excess of $300,000,000 annually. Mint figures prominently as a flavoring for many of the leading brands and usage of mint in toothpaste has spiralled upward since World War II when chlorophyll toothpastes, using spearmint oil as a flavoring base, were first marketed nationally in 1947. Subsequently these were to be largely supplanted by the decay preventative products containing fluoride compounds and using mint oils as a masking agent. Then in 1962, Beecham Products marketed Macleans Toothpaste which was advertised primarily as a tooth whitener. The whiteners as a group now account for nearly 12% of the total toothpaste market. Consumer preference shifts occur frequently in this highly competitive industry, but the leading whiteners, Ultra Brite and Macleans have been especially quick to carve their respective niches in the market share.

Of the numerous brand choices now marketed, the following comprise an estimated 92% of the toothpaste industry's domestic sales: Crest and Mint-flavored Crest, Gleem and Super Gleem (Procter & Gamble), Colgate Dental Cream and Ultra Brite (Colgate-Palmolive Company) and Macleans (Beecham Products). The remaining share of the market, some $24,000,000, is taken up with such brands as Pepsodent, Fact, Vote, Ipana Durenamel, Super Stripe, Mighty White, Plus White, and others.

The quality demands placed on the materials used in flavoring toothpaste are exacting and the fact that mint oils are used in the majority of the leading brands suggests the manufacturers' confidence in the mint industry.

Allied to toothpaste, as a mint user, is the growing mouthwash and mouth freshener market. Manufacturers now sell close to $125,000,000 worth of these preparations annually and mint flavored products are increasing their market share.

Peppermint is a much more popular flavor in candy and other confections than spearmint, although neither approach the levels as used in the chewing gum and toothpaste manufactures. Primary outlets are the popular Life Savers, Clorets, and Certs, and a number of mint flavored chocolate candies. A related item in this line would be mint flavoring extracts.

Mint oils are still staple items in the drug trade, but the annual consumption is quite limited. Other minor outlets include jellies, fine liqueurs, cigarettes and cigars, toothpick flavoring, and as a masking ingredient in such products as shoe polish. There are some indications that use of mint oils will increase in the soap and perfumery line.

The major asset of the mint oils as a flavoring ingredient, the strength of the taste and aroma, is also a considerable limiting factor since it requires so little of the oil. One part of mint oil may flavor as much as 300 parts of other materials, and some formulas include even less. The market is also limited in that mint oils have not successfully entered the beverage flavoring industry although small quantities are utilized in the manufacture of fine liqueurs.

The consideration of flavor materials for products in extremely competitive industries such as those of chewing gum, toothpaste and mouthwash, maximum emphasis is placed on quality and performance. On both counts, the cooperation of farmer, dealer and user alike has enabled mint oils to acquit themselves with demonstrated success.

New Horizons for the Industry

Developments within the mint industry indicate a number of promising new outlets for the oils. Hybrid plants are now available which produce oil with very delicate fragrances. If these products gain acceptance in the toiletry and cosmetic fields a whole new market will be opened which is, as yet, totally undeveloped.

The utilization of mint flavoring in a popular soft drink has been attempted, but no successful beverage has yet been marketed. If such a development could be achieved domestic outlet would be increased substantially.

There is little doubt that mint flavored products are gaining increasing acceptance among the world's population. Yet the bulk of the 4 billion residents of the earth consume very little. Increased demand, especially in such regions as Latin America, Africa, Southeast Asia, and the Middle East, would result in a tremendous expansion of the export trade with considerable benefit to American growers. And, of course, there is always the possibility that the world demand for peppermint and spearmint oils might reach such proportions in the future that American production might not prove adequate, even for domestic consumption. The possibility of the United States being a deficit producer appears unlikely at this time. There are considerable undeveloped acreages in the western states that could be brought into mint production, and the acceptance of disease-resistant varieties of plants may allow the Middlewest to re-enter the industry as a significantly important producing region.

Conclusion

Beginning in mid-July the mint harvest season in the United States begins. For several months over 700 peppermint farms and nearly 360 spearmint farms process the natural oil and deliver it into the hands of the country dealers. At present, the buying of the oil from the farm is concentrated in the hands of four major dealers: A. M. Todd Company of Kalamazoo, Michigan; I. P. Callison and Sons, Inc. of Seattle, Washington; and Wm. Leman, Inc. and M. Brown and Sons, Inc. of Bremen, Indiana. The dealers, in turn, prepare the oils to meet the wide variety of customer specifications and deliver the oil to the primary users and into the export trade.

The domestic consumption of American peppermint and spearmint oils is dominated by the chewing gum and tooth paste industries, with lesser amounts moving into the confectionery and drug trades. The limited outlets for mint oils could be considerably enhanced by the successful marketing of preparations in the cosmetic, toilet, and beverage line, but the most promising hope for expansion of the mint industry still lies in the realm of increasing consumer demand for mint flavored products, both in areas with well developed peppermint and spearmint tastes and those sections of the world where mint products are not yet too common.

REFERENCES

[1] Average U.S. values for 1967, per pound, were $5.55 for peppermint oil, and $5.48 for spearmint oil: *Vegetables-Fresh Market, 1967*, annual summary, p. 63, USDA, December 19, 1967.

[2] *The Pharmacopeia of the United States of America,* 17th revision, p. 445, United States Pharmacopeial Convention, Inc., New York, 1965.

[3] *The National Formulary,* 10th edition, p. 544, American Pharmaceutical Association, Washington, D.C., 1955.

[4] R. W. Moncrieff, *Odor Preferences,* Leonard Hall, London, 1966.

[5] Market figures and shares taken from various editions of *Advertising Age,* 1967 and 1968.

Chapter 16.

Perspective On An Industry

Nearly 180 years have passed since the first peppermint and spearmint oil in the United States was distilled in the hills of western Massachusetts. Within that time the American mint industry has grown from a small, very localized, largely experimental activity, based primarily on the European drug market, to an extensive, highly technical, strongly integrated, agricultural and marketing enterprise oriented toward domestic consumption.

This change was not accomplished without struggle. The first hundred years of the emerging industry were marked by the same problems faced by all developing commercial enterprises of that day; speculation, monopoly, fraudulent advertising, and intense corporate struggles. As the industry expanded, however, it eventually attracted the interests of men with a strong desire to promote the proper cultivation of high quality peppermint and spearmint oils. Among the early leaders in this effort were Hiram G. Hotchkiss of Lyons, New York, and Albert M. Todd of Nottawa, and later Kalamazoo, Michigan. Although their marketing strategies, at times, were intensely competitive, they were always conducted within the general bounds of the accepted American commercial practice of their day.

Of special significance during the first century were several developments in the mint industry that have influenced the production and marketing of mint oils to the present time. The application of steam power to the distillation process, by which the mint oil is separated from the fresh plants, made it possible for a farmer to process larger quantities of oil. This aided in the promotion of more extensive acreages, attracted the interests of growers who were desirous of making a return from a carefully cultivated product, and enabled the American industry to produce mint oil in such quantity that it quickly captured the largest share of the world market. This conquest was aided immeasurably by the development of muckland mint cultivation in Michigan and Indiana during the latter years of the nineteenth century. The higher yields of mint oil produced and the greater ease of cultivation on the flat, rich, organic muck soils, enabled the Middlewestern growers to dominate the industry in the same manner that the early growers of the Canandaigua Outlet of New York had outproduced and captured the industry from the mint farmers of western Massachusetts. By the end of the nineteenth century nearly the entire world supply of peppermint and spearmint oil was being produced on the mucklands of several counties in south-western Michigan and northern Indiana.

Another important development was the shift of production from the American peppermint plant to the variety known today as the Black Mitcham peppermint. A much hardier variety, the Black Mitcham produced more oil of a better quality and, within a few years, had completely replaced the earlier plant. This led to continued efforts to discover and develop mints with various growth and oil characteristics, involving hybridization, new cultivation techniques, and more effective and efficient processing. Although these efforts have produced numerous side benefits, the American commercial production of peppermint today is still centered around the Black Mitcham plant.

The cultivation and processing advancements of the nineteenth century paralleled the marketing developments, especially those promoted by Hotchkiss and Todd. In the early days it was the custom for field buyers to obtain the mint oils from the various growers and deliver it into the hands of brokers and shippers in the east coast cities who prepared the oils for the export trade. It was a common practice for the brokers to adulterate the oils with various substances, which not only enhanced their profit but rendered the American product a reputation for poor quality. Both Hotchkiss and Todd waged incessant battle against this pernicious practice, and it was overcome largely through their efforts. They bottled their own oils, sealed them with labels guaranteeing purity, and began to ship directly to users both in the domestic and export markets. In order to do this, however, both had to insure their source of supply. They were conveniently located in the major producing districts, Hotchkiss in Wayne County, New York, and Todd in St. Joseph County, and later in the muckland district at Kalamazoo, Michigan. Besides planting extensive acreages of their own, they began contracting with other growers to supply mint oil to their firms, and gradually began to control the source of supply. As Hotchkiss and Todd cemented their positions the activity of the east coast brokers declined and the American peppermint and spearmint oils slowly gained world-wide acceptance.

This basic marketing pattern, involving a middleman known as a country dealer, who purchases the mint oil from the growers and processes it for shipment to customers at home and abroad, serves the industry to this day.

As the nineteenth century came to a close, American mint production was strongly localized in the mucklands of the Middlewest. The once important fields in Massachusetts, New York, and Ohio, had all been removed from production. The great shift to the mucklands had enabled the farmers of Indiana and Michigan to dominate production and, as a result, the firm of Albert M. Todd emerged as the single most important force in the industry.

The second century of the American mint industry opened following a decade of increased production and falling oil prices, due to the considerable expansion of acreage in the Indiana and Michigan mucklands. The depressed market and strong localization of production enabled the Todd company to control almost the entire domestic supply of mint oil in 1902. Todd simply bought the oil and held it off the market, waiting for prices to advance to higher levels. This strategy, although effectively carried out, failed because mint oil users refused to pay the price. Many simply waited, using available reserves, and others turned to such substitutes as Japanese mint oil and various synthetic compounds. This marketing maneuver led directly to an attempt on the part of Middlewestern mint growers to form a cooperative marketing society in an effort to bypass the activities of the country dealers.

But developments were taking place that made it increasingly difficult for either growers or buyers to dominate the industry by monopoly. Both the domestic and export markets were increasing rapidly, occasioned by the widespread acceptance of peppermint and spearmint flavoring in chewing gum, candy, and toothpaste. As these products gained in popularity among the American public, the industry began to orient itself to a constantly increasing domestic market. The large industrial users of mint oils were desirous of a high quality product as well as a guaranteed source of supply. As the market improved more growers were attracted into cultivation and extensive new acreages were developed in Michigan and Indiana and production was originated in the Pacific northwest in western Oregon and Washington. Although the market outlets had increased substantially the new production continued to perpetuate a problem that had plagued the industry throughout most of its history, there was more or less continuous over-production. Not only did this act as a price depressant, but it made it difficult for efficient farmers producing high quality oil to reap the full benefits to which they were entitled, since there were abundant quantities of low grade mint oils available. This condition slowly began to change as the primary domestic users began to place a premium on quality. The dealers began to direct greater emphasis on desirable cultivation and distilling practices on the part of the growers, and rejected low grade production or paid considerably reduced prices. Slowly, careless and inefficient growers were forced to abandon cultivation due to the demands of the trade.

This trend was sharply reversed, however, when a serious shortage of mint oils resulted from two consecutive disastrous harvest seasons in Michigan and Indiana in 1924 and 1925. The shortage resulted in a great price rise with peppermint oil reaching all-time high levels of $32 a pound and spearmint oil $16 a pound. The great price rise attracted considerable attention and farmers from New York to California began to set out fields of peppermint and spearmint. Acreage in Michigan and Indiana increased sharply and production was originated in numerous agricultural sections in a number of states including irrigated lands in California, Washington, and Oregon. The resulting overproduction in 1926 brought prices tumbling and ended this vigorous response. Within several years much of the new acreage had been abandoned.

But the great price rise had stimulated the beginnings of organized research on the part of the various state agricultural colleges, especially in Michigan, Indiana, Oregon, and Washington. Since that time a steady stream of technical bulletins has been published concerning nearly every phase of mint oil production, distillation, and marketing. It also made users greatly conscious of the vulnerability of their source of supply concentrated in such a small district in the Middlewest. Greater attention began to be paid to the producing districts in Oregon and Washington as insurance against a repetition of the great price rise.

The American mint industry weathered the depression period in a reasonably sound manner, largely because consumer demand for mint flavored products continued to increase. The fact that the market for mint oil increases directly with the size of the American population has acted as a constant stimulant for new cultivation, but has not entirely eliminated the problems of overproduction.

As World War II approached the American mint industry had reached a stage of considerable stability. The cultivation was still strongly localized in the Middlewest, but the producing districts of the western states were increasing in importance. Both the marketing and usage patterns had become well established, the dealers handling the mint oil from the farms, processing them and shipping them to the primary users, the chewing gum, toothpaste, and candy manufacturers. The most significant problem facing the industry was the increasing severity of Verticillium wilt disease in Michigan.

The American mint industry successfully met one of its sternest challenges during World War II. With shipments of menthol and Japanese mint oil cut off following Pearl Harbor, American manufacturers began to turn to peppermint oil as a substitute source of supply. This increased and sudden demand created such a shortage of peppermint oil by 1943 that it became necessary for the federal government to assume absolute control over the allocation of the available supply and establish priorities for usage. Price ceilings were also set on peppermint and spearmint oils. With the development of Japanese mint fields in Latin America and an increased production of peppermint and spearmint oil in Indiana, Oregon, and Washington, the shortage was eased. The cooperation of dealers and users enabled all the allocation priorities to be met and the war ended as the mint industry returned to a free marketing economy.

The wartime conditions, however, had stimulated considerable interest in mint production in Oregon and Washington, and acreage continued to expand in both states. Middlewestern mint growers, faced with the perplexing problem of declining yields of oil as a result of the spread of Verticillium wilt, began to feel the effects of the increased supply of western oil. Prices stabilized, then began to decline, as production costs continued to increase. During the late 1940's and the entire decade of the 1950's there was wholesale abandonment of mint acreage in both Indiana and Michigan. Middlewestern growers could not compete against the high oil yields obtained in the western states and, by the end of the latter decade, Oregon and Washington had become the major producing states of peppermint and spearmint oil.

Western cultivation was also favored by the opening of successful new production districts in central Oregon near Madras, in the Snake River Valley of Idaho and eastern Oregon, and by the extension of the Yakima Valley industry into the Columbia Basin of Washington. During the same period, peppermint cultivation became established in southern Wisconsin and that state now ranks third in oil production behind Washington and Oregon.

The period following World War II was especially significant, not only in the geographic shift of cultivation to the western states, but for the great advancements made in applications of scientific knowledge to various phases of the industry. Backed by a generous subsidy from the dealers and major users of mint oils, extensive research had been carried out on such problems as disease, weed control, proper cutting, distillation, and chemical analysis of the oils. Since the major share of the domestic consumption of American mint oils is based on the utilization of a high quality product, continued research is necessary to insure a constant supply of the best possible mint oils.

A statement regarding quality, from a representative of one of the major mint oil users in the United States, provides an interesting insight into the nature of selection and utilization of the mint oils.

> Quality is an important variable in mint oils. Since the ultimate use is to impart appealing flavor to a host of confections, toiletries, pharmaceuticals, and other functional products, flavor characteristics are judged by experts in the flavor field. Variations due to cultivation in different geographical districts, utilization of various plant types, and unlike cultural practices, show up primarily in the commercial value of the oils. What is of even greater importance, however, is the fact that hundreds of consumer tests demonstrate the accuracy of the users' recognition and acceptance of these expertly selected flavor quality variables.
>
> The flavors of mint oils are related to their chemical constituents. Even the most sophisticated gas chromatograph, which can separate for identification over 100 chemical components in both peppermint and spearmint oils, is only now confirming what the flavor experts and consumers already recognize in quality variations. In the case of peppermint oil, recognition of the importance played in the flavor quality by menthofuran and its precursors ended the custom of judging quality solely on the basis of menthol content. Even the specifications of the *United States Pharmacopeia* depend heavily on the total menthol content. Yet the quantity of menthol may vary greatly without adversely affecting the taste quality. At the same time, menthofuran in excessive quantity and its precursors soon offset the fine flavor balance of high quality peppermint oil with a choking, oily, black strap molasses taste and a residual bitterness.
>
> It should be understood that this is only one of the flavor quality signals that distinguishes low quality peppermint oil. In use, the high quality oils retain a sparkling, floral bouquet or a taste excitation and unwavering constancy of pleasant flavor sensations that are not given by any other flavoring oils. Only in the United States has this quality been brought to a fine peak by careful quality control, suitable cultural practices, and the selection of production regions based on careful study.
>
> Spearmint, too, has its quality variations and high quality applies to both the Scotch and Native varieties. Where peppermint oil is fresh, exciting, cool, and refreshingly long lasting, spearmint oils are floral, edible, lively, and have a distinguishing bouquet unlike any other herbaceous oil. The Scotch variety of spearmint oil delights perfumers because of its diffusive, light floralcy, which may become very thin in years with high growing temperatures. It quickly shows the off-quality notes of weediness, immaturity, and second cutting, all three deficiencies occurring simultaneously in some second crop oils.
>
> The Native spearmint oil pleases the flavorist who recognizes high quality components as exemplified by the richness of body, deep warmth of flavor, and lasting qualities needed in chewing gum and dental creams. The very special balance of the chemicals created by nature in high quality spearmint oil is easily upset by neglect of wise cultural practices.

Both peppermint and spearmint oils require careful quality control from the farmer's field to his still, and from the blender to the laboratory. Only then can the flavorist create the fine harmonies of taste sensation which will continue to please the consumer with the same flavor beauty, and keep the American mint industry economically sound.[1]

There are still works that refer to the chief usage of the mint plants as a special dash of flavoring in the famed mint julep. Perhaps this is not unusual to lovers of the beverage, one can not be neutral about the mint julep, and a vigorous controversy once raged between adherents in Kentucky, Maryland, Louisiana, and Georgia, regarding the correct recipe. So concerned was Soule Smith of Lexington, Kentucky, the originator of this taste delight, that he was once caused to comment that "depraved New Yorkers gulp juleps concocted with such bizarre ingredients as Maraschino Cherries."[2] It is difficult to resist experimentation with a drink described in such a poetic manner as the following:[3]

then comes the zenith of man's pleasure. Then comes the julep—the mint julep. Who has not tasted one has lived in vain. The honey of Hymettus brought no such solace to the soul; the nectar of the Gods is tame beside it. It is the very dream of drinks, the vision of sweet quaffings.

For those who would find a history of the mint industry incomplete without it, the correct recipe, as given by Smith, consists of the following steps: mix spring water with sugar until like oil; crush mint leaves with a tablespoon within a glass, then crush the leaves around the borders of the glass; fill with cracked ice; pour in bourbon to suit; pour in the sugar water; let stand (do not stir); place sprigs of mint around the brim.[4]

The sentimentality toward the southern mint julep, however, bears little resemblance to the reality of the commercial peppermint and spearmint production in this country. The major plant and oil producing centers have always been in the northern states, and the major uses of mint oils, in such products as chewing gum, toothpaste, mouthwash, candy, and drugs, are certainly of the type that would be most agreeable to such a distinguished gentleman as Soule Smith.

And one need only to refer to the lines of the enigmatic poet, Edward E. Cummings, to discover how deeply the utilization of mint flavored products has become woven into the fabric of American life:[5]

take it from me kiddo
believe me
my country, 'tis of

you, land of the Cluett
Shirt Boston Garter and Spearmint
Girl With The Wrigley Eyes (of you
land of the Arrow Ide

and Earl &
Wilson
Collars) of you i
sing: land of Abraham Lincoln and
        Lydia E. Pinkham,
land above all of Just Add Hot Water
        And Serve—
from every B.V.D.

let freedom ring
amen.

As the American mint industry continues its way toward the completion of its second century the outlook is nothing but hopeful. The possibility of acceptance in the trade of new strains of mint plants, the development of new mint oil outlets, and the continuing increase of consumer demand for peppermint and spearmint flavored products, are all signs that indicate a strengthening industry in the years to come. There is no reason to believe that the future of the American mint industry will be any less interesting and productive than its past.

REFERENCES

[1]From George H. Fuller, Manager, Perfumery and Essential Oils, Colgate-Palmolive Company.

[2]*The Mint Julep: The Very Dream of Drinks; From the Old Receipt of Soule Smith, Down in Lexington, Kentucky,* p. 2, Gravesend Press, Lexington, Kentucky, 1949.

[3]*Ibid.*

[4]*Ibid.,* p. 5.

[5]*Poems, Or Beauty Hurts Mr. Vinal,* from *Familiar Quotations: John Bartlett,* p. 1030, 14th edition, revised, E. M. Beck (ed.), Little, Brown and Co., Boston, 1968.

Appendix I

Peppermint and Spearmint Acreage
In the U.S. in 1968

Region	Peppermint Acreage	Spearmint Acreage	
		Scotch	Native
Middle West	15,649	6,111	3,241
Indiana	5,224	4,171	710
Allen County	24	108	–
DeKalb	5	5	–
Jasper	1,270	2,000	–
Kosciusko	33	299	45
Lagrange	16	536	6
LaPorte	170	115	–
Marshall	113	28	165
Newton	245	10	45
Noble	–	26	5
Porter	315	13	–
Pulaski	1,165	330	97
Starke	727	275	290
St. Joseph	1,078	396	57
Whitley	63	30	–
Michigan	2,120	1,323	2,128
Arenac County	10	–	–
Branch	5	–	115
Clinton	145	119	1,196
Gennessee	5	10	–
Gratiot	–	8	145
Ingham	24	357	20
Isabella	2	–	25
Jackson	210	445	–
Livingston	50	–	30
Montcalm	40	–	–

215

Mason	150	–	–
Muskegon	197	39	–
Newaygo	589	50	5
Sanilac	42	166	15
Shiawassee	89	65	427
St. Joseph	60	25	–
Van Buren	286	39	150
Wisconsin	8,305	617	403
Columbia County	965	90	165
Dane	1,035	80	10
Dodge	220	65	–
Green Lake	450	–	–
Jefferson	1,187	160	118
Kenosha	250	–	–
Marquette	1,318	67	10
Monroe	140	–	–
Oconto	125	–	–
Portage	700	40	100
Sauk	650	115	–
Walworth	1,265	–	–
Far West	60,816	11,821	5,672
Oregon	30,944	–	–
Lower Columbia River	170	–	–
Willamette Valley	14,209	–	–
Grants Pass	850	–	–
Madras	13,876	–	–
Hermiston	475	–	–
Baker	30	–	–
Eastern Oregon	1,334	–	–
Washington	23,856	10,816	5,664
Lower Columbia River	1,226	–	–
Puget Sound Lowland	720	–	–
Kittitas County	45	–	–
Columbia Basin	8,332	1,642	411
Yakima Valley	13,483	9,174	5,253
Kennewick	50	–	–
Idaho	5,146	1,005	8
Montana	870	–	–
Total U.S.	76,465	17,932	8,913

Source: various reports from dealers and government publications.

Appendix II

County Reference Maps of the Major Mint Oil Producing States

Massachusetts
New York
Ohio
Michigan
Indiana
Oregon
Washington
California
Wisconsin
Idaho

State maps showing county boundaries and names from Rand McNally and Company, Chicago, Illinois.

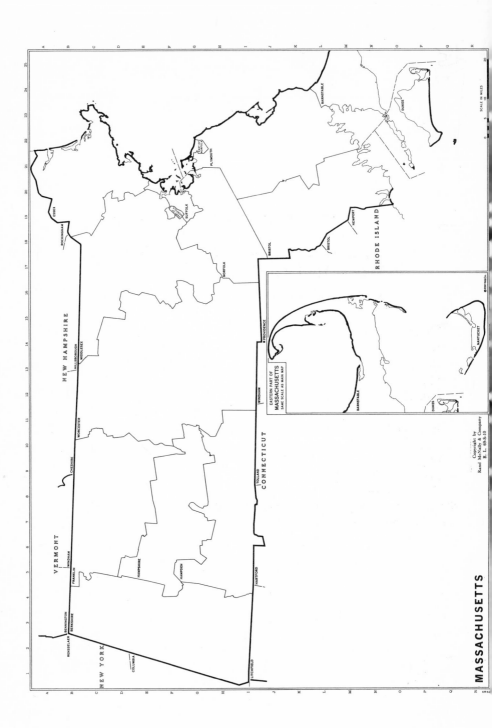

MASSACHUSETTS

Copyright by
Rand McNally & Company
R. L. 69-S-10

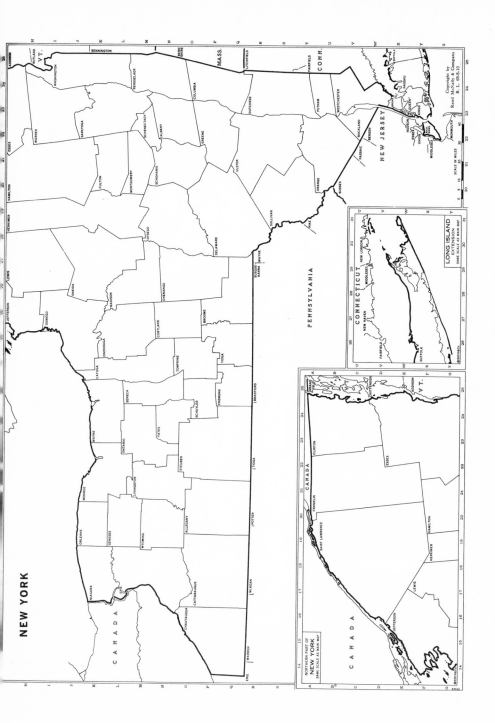

NEW YORK

LONG ISLAND
EXTENSION
SAME SCALE AS MAIN MAP

NORTHERN PART OF
NEW YORK
SAME SCALE AS MAIN MAP

219

OHIO

SCALE IN MILES

MICHIGAN

SCALE IN MILES

0 5 10   20   30   40   50   60

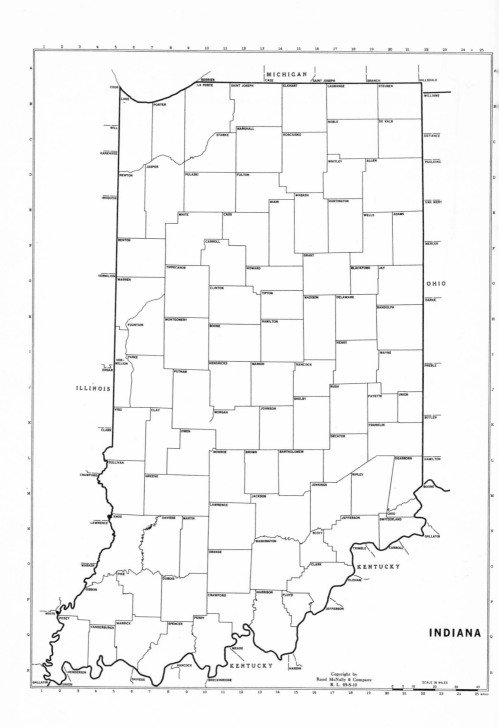

INDIANA

SCALE IN MILES

222

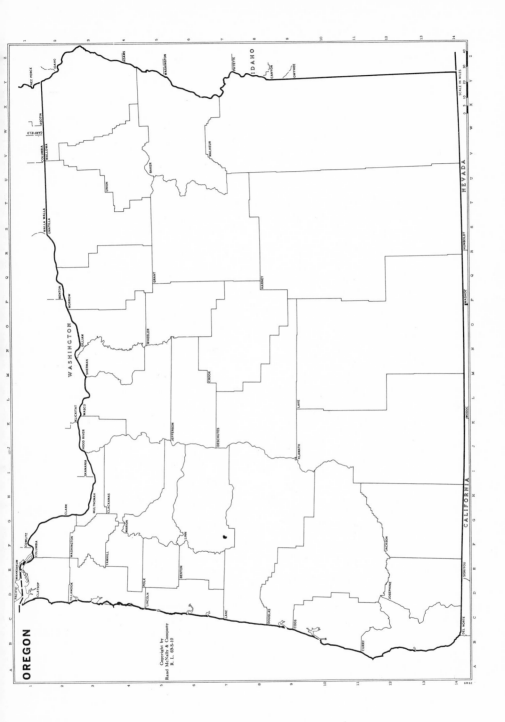

OREGON

Copyright by
Rand McNally & Company
R. L. 69-S-10

223

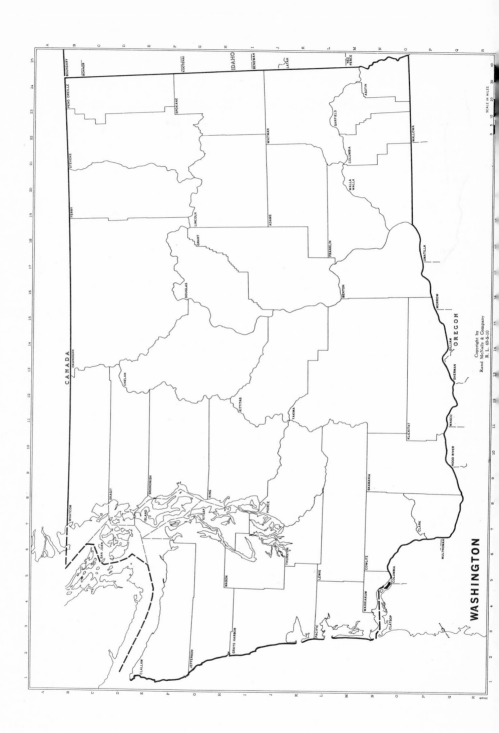

WASHINGTON

CALIFORNIA

OREGON

NEVADA

ARIZ.

MEXICO

SCALE IN MILES
0 10 20   40   60   80

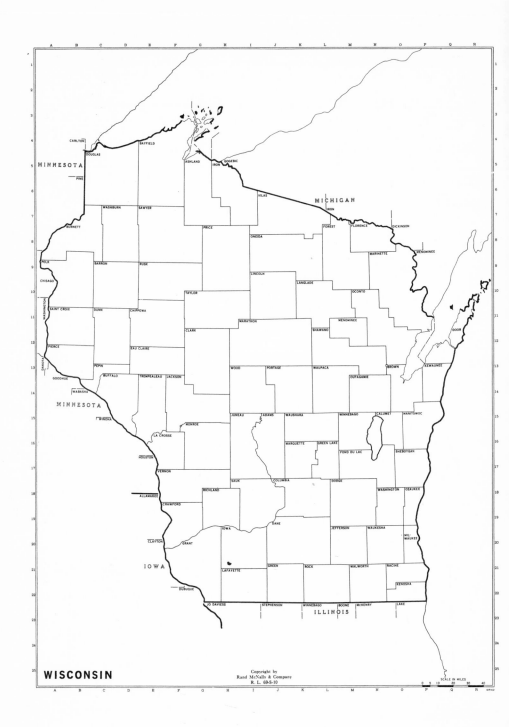

WISCONSIN

Copyright by
Rand McNally & Company
R. L. 69-S-10

SCALE IN MILES
0 5 10   20   30   40

226

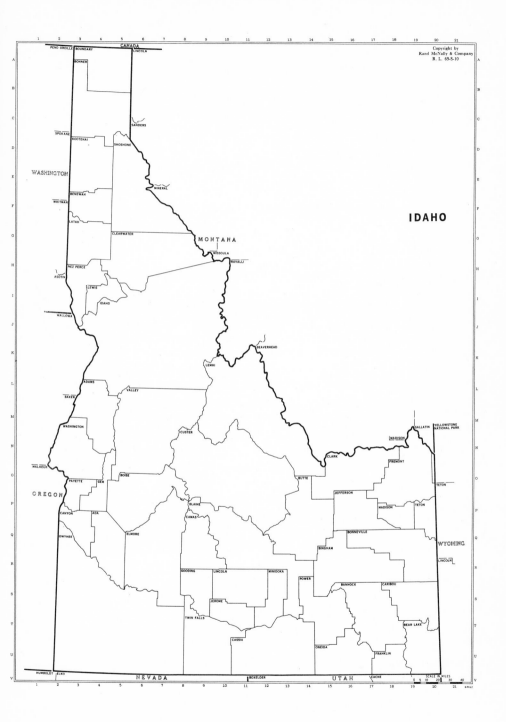

IDAHO

Copyright by
Rand McNally & Company
R. L. 69-S-10

227

Appendix III. Figure Credits

Frontispiece. W. A. Todd, Kalamazoo, Michigan.

Figure 1. Hunt Botanical Library, Pittsburgh, Pennsylvania.

Figure 2. New York Botanical Garden Library, Bronx, New York, New York.

Figure 3. New York Botanical Garden Library, Bronx, New York, New York.

Figure 4. New York Botanical Garden Library, Bronx, New York, New York.

Figure 5. U.S. Department of Agriculture, Washington, D.C.

Figure 6. U.S. Department of Agriculture, Washington, D.C.

Figure 7. Leslie Guilford and Ashfield Museum, Ashfield, Massachusetts.

Figure 8. Leslie Guilford and Ashfield Museum, Ashfield, Massachusetts.

Figure 9. Kalamazoo Public Museum, Kalamazoo, Michigan.

Figure 10. Berkshire Athenaeum, Pittsfield, Massachusetts.

Figure 11. U.S. Department of Agriculture, Washington, D.C.

Figure 12. H. G. Hotchkiss Essential Oil Company, Lyons, New York.

Figure 13. Hunt Botanical Library, Pittsburgh, Pennsylvania.

Figure 14. Leslie Guilford and Ashfield Museum, Ashfield, Massachusetts.

Figure 15. A. M. Todd Company, Kalamazoo, Michigan.

Figure 16. H. G. Hotchkiss Essential Oil Company, Lyons, New York.

Figure 17. H. G. Hotchkiss Essential Oil Company, Lyons, New York.

Figure 18. Linda Gaylord, Ontario, New York.

Figure 19. Linda Gaylord, Ontario, New York.

Figure 20. H. G. Hotchkiss Essential Oil Company, Lyons, New York.

Figure 21. H. G. Hotchkiss Essential Oil Company, Lyons, New York.

Figure 22. Library of Regional History, Cornell University, Ithaca, New York.

Figure 23. A. M. Todd Company, Kalamazoo, Michigan.

Figure 24. A. M. Todd Company, Kalamazoo, Michigan.

Figure 25. A. M. Todd Company, Kalamazoo, Michigan.

Figure 26. Waldo Library, Western Michigan University, Kalamazoo, Michigan.

Figure 27. A. M. Todd Company, Kalamazoo, Michigan.

Figure 28. A. M. Todd Company, Kalamazoo, Michigan.

Figure 29. New York State Library, Albany, New York.

Figure 30. Pattee Library, The Pennsylvania State University, University Park, Pennsylvania.

Figure 31. Pattee Library, The Pennsylvania State University, University Park, Pennsylvania.

Figure 32. Pattee Library, The Pennsylvania State University, University Park, Pennsylvania.

Figure 33. A. M. Todd Company, Kalamazoo, Michigan.

Figure 34. U.S. Patent Office, Arlington, Virginia.

Figure 35. *Decatur Republican,* Decatur, Michigan.

Figure 36. A. M. Todd Company, Kalamazoo, Michigan.

Figure 37. A. M. Todd Company, Kalamazoo, Michigan.

Figure 38. A. M. Todd Company, Kalmazoo, Michigan.

Figure 39. A. M. Todd Company, Kalamazoo, Michigan.

Figure 40. A. M. Todd Company, Kalamazoo, Michigan.

Figure 41. *Decatur Republican,* Decatur, Michigan.

Figure 42. A. M. Todd Company, Kalamazoo, Michigan.

Figure 43. H. G. Hotchkiss Essential Oil Company, Lyons, New York.

Figure 44. Walter Thomas, Quincy, Oregon.

Figure 45. A. M. Todd Company, Kalamazoo, Michigan.

Figure 46. A. M. Todd Company, Kalamazoo, Michigan.

Figure 47. U.S. Department of Agriculture, Washington, D.C.

Figure 48. A. M. Todd Company, Kalamazoo, Michigan.

Figure 49. U.S. Department of Agriculture, Washington, D.C.

Figure 50. Cobb Manufacturing Company, Jefferson, Oregon.

Figure 51. Walter Thomas, Quincy, Oregon.

Figure 52. William Gehring, North Judson, Indiana.

Figure 53. N. Kent Ellis, Purdue University, Lafayette, Indiana.

Figure 54. A. A. M. Todd Company, Kalamazoo, Michigan.

B. *South Bend Tribune,* South Bend, Indiana.

C. W. A. Todd, Kalamazoo, Michigan.

D. W. A. Todd, Kalamazoo, Michigan.

E. William Gehring, North Judson, Indiana.

Figures 55 through 57. W. A. Todd, Kalamazoo, Michigan.

Figure 58. A. W. A. Todd, Kalamazoo, Michigan.

B. Purdue University, Lafayette, Indiana.

C. *Detroit Free Press,* Detroit, Michigan.

D. A. M. Todd Company, Kalamazoo, Michigan.

E. William Gehring, North Judson, Indiana.

F. A. M. Todd Company, Kalamazoo, Michigan.

G. Ernest Guenther, Fritzsché Brothers, Inc., New York, New York.

H. Vera Todd McDonald, Eugene, Oregon.

Figure 59. A. M. Todd Company, Kalamazoo, Michigan.

Figure 60. A. Wm. Leman, Inc., Bremen, Indiana.

B. M. Brown and Sons, Inc., Bremen, Indiana.

C and D. I. P. Callison and Sons, Inc., Seattle, Washington.

E and F. A. M. Todd Company, Kalamazoo, Michigan.

Index

References are included in the Index in one of three ways. References to text are indicated by plain Arabic numerals; e.g.: 94. References to maps are given by text page preceded by the letter "m:" e.g.: m. 168. References to figures in the illustrative inserts are given in parentheses with the Roman numeral indicating the figure insert and the Arabic numeral indicating the figure number; e.g.: (II, 33).

Aberdeen (Mississippi), 44
Adams, 77
Ahtanum Ridge (Washington), 160
Alabama, 174, 176
Albany (New York), 14, 27
Albany (Oregon), 81, 83, m.82
Albion (Indiana), 130
Alden, C., 12, 16
Aldrin, 188
Alexander Brothers, 114
Allard, H., 181, 182
Alloway (New York), 19, 32, (I, 19)
Allegan County (Michigan), 57, 59, 61, 65, 119, 124, 125, (I,23), (II,42)
American Chicle Co., 77, 178, 203
American peppermint, 60, 65, 129, 184, 208, (I,3), (I,10)
American Society of Equity, 73, 74, 75, 83
American spearmint, (see Native spearmint)
Amish, 81, 107, 108, 109, 173
Anderson, C., 156
Angevine, S., 47
Antes, D. 44, 45
Appleby, A., 185
Arcadia (New York), 110
Arizona, 174, 176
Arkansas, 106, 107
Arlington Farm (Virginia), 80, 106, 191

Arlington Township (Michigan), 57
Ashfield (Massachusetts), 11, 12, 13, 14, 15, 16, 17, 18, 19, 21, 23, 24, 26, 46, (I,7), (I,8), (I,14)
Ashfield Museum, 16, 17, 18, (I,14)
Ashtabula County (Ohio), 21
associations, 46, 73, 74, 83, 87, 89, 95, 112, 114, 115, 116, 118, 120, 125, 126, 127, 129, 130, 131, 132, 136, 143, 145, 157, 163, 173, 190, 191, (II,30), (II,37), (II,46), (II,48)
Astoria (Oregon), 152
Atlantic Ocean, 8, 15

Bacon, F., 179
Baker County (Oregon), 156
Balch, W., 164
Baltimore County (Maryland), 174
Bancroft (Wisconsin), 167
Bangor (Michigan), 57
Bangor Township (Michigan), 57
Baraboo (Wisconsin), 168
Bastian, 48
Batt, 165
Beal, J., 34
Beardsley, B., 34
Bedoukian, P., 180
Beebe, A., 78
Beecham Products, 204
Beech-Nut, Inc., 77, 120, 126, 177, 178, 186, 203
Beemans, 77

231

Belding, Arthur, 16
Belding, Asher, 13
Belding, 19
Beltsville (Maryland), 191
Bement, A., 17
Bement, Jasper, 12, 13, 16, (I,14)
Bement, Joseph, 12
Bement ledger, 13, 17
Bement, S., 12
Bennington (Michigan), 125, 127
Benton City (Washington), 160
Benton County (Oregon), 118, 153
Benton County (Washington), 116
Berkshire County (Massachusetts), 9,
      16
Berkshires, 11, 14, 23
Berlin (Ohio), 107
Berlin Township (Ohio), 107
Berrien County (Michigan), 46, 53, 57,
      96, 119, 124
Berry Valley Farms, 159
Biggs, R., 182
Big Marsh (Michigan), 56, (I,28)
Bingham, J., 97
Bird Marsh (Wisconsin), 167, 168
Birmingham (Ohio), 30
Blackmer, 34
Black Mitcham peppermint, 60, 61,
      62, 65, 87, 101, 106, 112, 129,
      184, 187, 208, (I,6), (III,59)
Blake, S., 16
Blood Berry, 77
Bloom, 108
Blount, 46
Bolt, T., 76
Bonine, 112
Bonners Ferry (Idaho), 165
Boston (Massachusetts), 32
Bowling Green (Ohio), 43
Brady Township (Michigan), 57
Branch County (Michigan), 57, 119,
      124
Bremen (Indiana), 92, 97, 119, 199,
      206, (III, 60)
Brigham, L., 57, 65
Brigham shoe, 58
Brink, T., 34
British Museum, 4
Broadview Farming Co., 163, 164
Bronson, L., 17
Brooks, C., 97
Brown, B., 119, 200, (III,60)
Brown, D., 186
Brown, I., 200, (III,60)
Brown, J., 130
Brown, L., 126, 127

Brown, L.G., 130
Brown, M., 92, 119, 200
Brown, M. and Sons, Inc., 92, 119, 126,
      178, 198, 200, 206, (III,60)
Brown, S., 200
Brownsmead (Oregon), 152
Brownson, R., 16
Brunschweig, H., 4
Buck, C., 164
Buena·Vista (Oregon), 155
Buena Vista Marsh (Wisconsin), 167
Bullis, D., 180
Bully Creek (Oregon), 156
Burlington Township (Michigan), 57
Burlington (Vermont), 14
Burlington (Washington), 114, 115
Burnett, Andrew, 19
Burnett, Archibald, 18, 19, 23
Burnett, J., 34
Burnett, N., 18, 19, 23, 110
Burnett, 16, 21, 23
burr oak openings, 21, 25, (I,11)
Burton (Ohio), 80
Bushee, A.,
Byrd and Hudnall, 164

Calapooia River, 153
Caldwell (Idaho), 107, 165, (III,57)
Calhoun County (Michigan), 57
California, 43, 81, 106, 107, 111,
      m.111, 112, 113, 114, 145, 174,
      210, m.225, (II,46), (II,47)
Callison, C., 199
Callison, H., 163, 199
Callison, I.P., 144, 145, 199, (III,60)
Callison, I.P. and Sons, Inc., 145, 162,
      163, 178, 198, 199, 206, (III,60)
Camas Valley (Oregon), 117, 155
Cambridgeshire (England), 6
Campania (Michigan), 59, (I,23),
      (II,42)
Canada, 23, 203
Canajoharie (New York), 77, 178, 203
Canandaigua Outlet, 18-19, 208, (I,12)
candy, 84, 147
Canyon County (Idaho), 107
Capitulare, 4
Carland (Michigan), 125
Carson, R. 188
Carson City (Michigan), 85
Cascade Range, 152, 153, 155, 159,
      160, 196
Cass County (Michigan), 45, 53, 57,
      119
Cassopolis (Michigan), 83
Cathlamet (Washington), 115, 159

Cecil, J., 164
Centennial Exposition of 1876, 42, 46, 49
Central Oregon Mint Growers Association, 157
Centreville (Michigan), 43, 48
Chardon (Ohio), 30
Charlemagne, 4
Chatham Township, (Connecticut), 11, 13
Chehalis (Washington), 144, 159, 199, (III,60)
Chelatchie Prairie, 160
Cheshire (Massachusetts), 9, 10, 11, 12, 15-16, 23
chewing gum, 77-78, 87, 146, 149, 202-204, 206, 209
Chicago (Illinois), 77, 203
Chilcote, D., 185
Chillicothe (Ohio), 43
Cincinnati (Ohio), 15
Clackamas County (Oregon), 118, 153
Clark County (Washington), 116
Clark Gum, 203
Clark, M., 34
Clark, W., 57
Clatskanie (Oregon), 117, 143, 151, 152, 159
Clatskanie Mint Growers Association, 143
Clay County (Mississippi), 44-45
Clearspring Township (Indiana), 26
Clewiston (Florida), 121
Clinton County (Michigan), 85, 119, 124-125, 143, 170-171
Clyde (New York), 32
Clyde Township (Michigan), 57
Coast Range, 153, 155
Cobb, G., 18
Cobb Manufacturing Co., 153, 155, 184
Coburg (Oregon), 83, 117, 153, 155, 163, 190
Colborne, J., 34
Cold Creek Canyon (Washington), 164
Colgate-Palmolive Co., 77, 178, 204
Colon Township (Michigan), 48
Colorado, 43
Columbia River Basin, 115, 144, 164, 196, 198, 211
Columbia County (Oregon), 118, 151-152,
Columbia County (Wisconsin), 167, 169

Columbia River, m.82, 83-84, 114, 116-117, 143, 151-152, 159-160, 164, 180, 198
Columbus (Wisconsin), 67
Concord (Ohio), 30
Coney, 48
Connecticut, 11, 13-14, 16
Connecticut River, 14
Connecticut Western Reserve, 20
Constantine (Michigan), 21, 26, 47
convent gardens, 4
Cooley, W., 156
Cooper, 46
cooperative marketing (see associations)
copper kettle stills, 12, 26, 36, 67
Coquille (Oregon), 117, 155
Cornell University, 179, 182, 187
corn mint oil, 93, 147
Cortright, R., 125
Corunna (Michigan), 125
Corvallis (Oregon), 83, m.154, 155, 190
Corwin, I., 34
costs, 38-39, 40, 71, 146
Cottage Grove (Oregon), 155
County Surrey (England), 6
Couer d' Alene (Idaho), 81
Cowlitz County (Washington), 116
Crabtree (Oregon), 83, 155
Craig, 159
Cramer, F., 189
Crandall, 46
Crane, F., 182
Craw, M., 21
Craw, O., 21
Crawfish River, 167
Crawford County (Ohio), 108
Crawford, F., 125, 127
Crittenden, 46
Crosby, J., 85
Cross, J., 46
Crystal White oil, 42, 43, 67, (I,23), (I,25)
cultivating mint, 25-28, 46-47
Culver (Oregon), 156
Cummings, E., 213
Currituck County (North Carolina), 81
Curtis, 77
Cushman, H., 48
Cuyahoga County (Ohio), 21

Dallas (Oregon), 83
Dane County (Wisconsin), 168-169
Davis, 108

Davies, J., 112
Decatur (Michigan), 57, 59, 64-65, 96-97, 102, 130, (II,35), (II,41)
Delavan (Wisconsin), 167, 169, (III, 54)
Delevan (California), 114
Dellamater, D., 167, 176
demi-johns, 38, (II,31)
Deschutes River, 156, m.157
Detroit (Michigan), 23, 37
Dever (Oregon), 155
Diehl, D., 165
Dieldrin, 188
Dillard (Oregon), 117, 155
Dimock, 46
Dinkel, H., 156
Dioscorides, 4
Dismal Swamp (North Carolina), 81
distilleries, 71, 85, 103, 184, (I,8), (I, 15), (I,19), (I,26), (I,28), (II, 30), (II,31), (II,32), (II,33), (II, 43), (II,44), (II,45), (II,47), (III,50), (III,51), (III,52), (III, 55), (III,56), (III,57)
distilling, 6, 10, 12, 18, 21, 26, 36-38
Dodge County (Wisconsin), 168
Dodge and Olcott, Inc., 7
Dooley, H., 187
Dos Palos (California), 113, 114
Doublemint, 77
Dougherty, H., 30
Douglas County (Oregon), 118
Dow 2467, 187
Dowagiac River, 57
Dows and Cary Co., 28, 34
Driggs and Son, 164
Dunn, 77
Dunnington, J., 57
Du Pont, 186
Du Pont 1991, 190

Eagle (Idaho), 165
Eales, 4, (I,4)
Earl, 21
East Bristol (Wisconsin), 169
Eastman Brothers Manufacturing Co., 103, (II,44)
East Troy (Wisconsin), 169
Echo (Oregon), 156
Edon (Ohio), 109, 174
Edwards, L., 52
Egypt, 3
Eldred, 165
Elyria (Ohio), 30
Elkhart County (Indiana), 56, 71, 85, 95, 104, 107, 119

Elliott, J., 180
Elliott, S., 156
Ellis, N.K., 7, 133, 176, 178, 189, (III, 58)
Ellis, 16, 19, 21
Elsie (Michigan), 125
Eltopia (Washington), 164
Ely Glass Works, 32
Embast, H., 152
Emery, A., 48, (I,26)
Endeavor (Wisconsin), 168
Endecott, J., 8
England, 4, 6, 8, 9, 12, 23, 28, 39, 47, 54, 60, 93, 108, 137
Engle, G., 48
English mint (see Black Mitcham peppermint and White Mitcham peppermint)
Erickson, 160
Erie Canal, 27, 36, (I,21)
Essential Oil Products Co., 112-113
Essex (England), 4
Eugene (Oregon), 81, 117, 153
Europe, 4, 6, 12, 28, 41, 54, 61, 63, 66, 78, 123, 127, 136, 149
Everett (Washington), 115, 159
exhibitions, 32-33, 42, 50, 52
Exodus, 3
Exposition Universelle, 50

Fabius Township (Michigan), 48
Fairfax (Michigan), 81
Fairville (New York), 87, 110
Fargher Lake (Washington), 159-160
Farm Credit Association, 131
Farragut, Admiral, 11
Farragut castle, 11
Faulkner, L., 185
Federal Farm Board, 129
Federal Trade Commission, 125-126
Fenney, E., 34
Fenney, I., 34
Fennville (Michigan), 57, 97, (I,23)
Ferguson, D., 156
field mint oil, 93
Finger Lakes (New York), 18
fireweed, 35
Fleer Co., 77
Florence Township (Michigan), 21, 47-48, 56-57, (I,28)
Florida, 100, 121
Florida, University of, 101
Flower, W., 16
fog boiler, 103
Fond du Lac County (Wisconsin), 168
Food and Drug Administration, 140, 188

Force, I., 34
Foster, K., 158-159
Foster Manufacturing Co., 159
France, 135, 203
Francisco, D., 47
Freeland Co., 85
Freeborn County (Minnesota), 174
Frick, K., 185
Fry, D., 155, 159
Fry, D. Jr., 174
Funke, L., 153
Furtick, W., 185

Galesburg (Michigan), 23, (I,9)
Galveston (Texas), 145
Galveston County (Texas), 107
Ganargwa Creek, 27
Gardner, J., 43, 46
Gates, 46
Gaylord, L., 110, 121
Gearhart, H., 191
Gehring, W., 172, (III,58)
Gehring, W. Jr., (III,58)
Genesee County (New York), 14
Gentner, L., 185
Gerard, J., (I,1)
Gerber, L., 119
Germany, 4, 27, 54, 133, 135
Gervais (Oregon), 102
Getz, E., 95
Getz, J., 96
Gildemeister, E., 7
Gist Brothers, 112
Givens, L., 199
Glenn County (California), 113
Glenn Dale (Maryland), 80
Glenwood (Michigan), 102
Glover, 21
Godfrey, S., 34
Galen (New York), 110
Galushka, A., 34
Goshen (Indiana), 71
Gould, G., 185, 188
Grand Ronde (Oregon), 156
Grandview (Washington), 191
Grants Pass (Oregon), 155
Gratiot County (Michigan), 85
Gray, A., 93
Gray Mitcham peppermint, 183
Grayson County (Texas), 81
Green, R., 186-187, 192, (III,58)
Green Lake County (Wisconsin), 168
Greenleaf (Idaho), 165
Greens Bridge (Oregon), 155
Griffith, 46
Grovertown (Indiana), 89
Guenther, E., 64, 88, 175-176, 189

Guilford, 11
Gumz, E., 172
Gumz, R., 172
Gun Marsh (Michigan), 125
Gun River, 125

Hagerman, W., 48
Hale, A., 32, (I,19)
Hale and Parshall, 32, 43, (I,19)
Hale County (Texas), 174
Halfway (Oregon), 156
Hall, H., 48-49, 56, 109, (I,28)
Hamburg (Germany), 27, 50
Hancock County (Iowa), 80
Hanford (California), 112
Hanson, G., 28
Hardin County (Ohio), 108-109, 145, 174
Harding (Montana), 167
Harmer, P., 190
Harris, E., 23
Harrisburg (Oregon), 155
Harrisville (Wisconsin), 168
Hart, J., 71, (I,10)
Hartford (Connecticut), 14
Hartley, 159
Haviland, M., 167
Howes, F., 16, 23, 53
Harvey, 57
Hayes, E., 117
Hayes, J., 114, 117, 174
Hazleton (Iowa), 107
Heater, 46
Hebrews, 3
Hennigson-Ayers, 156
Henry, M., 174
Herman, 163
Hermiston (Oregon), 118, 144, 156
Hermo, C., 83
Hertfordshire (England), 4, 6
H.G.H. mint oil, 67, 84
Hickey, 94-95
Hildegard, 4
Hillsboro (Oregon), 83
Hillsdale County (Michigan), 28, 45, 53, 57
Hillyard, M., 44-45, 52
Hippocrates, 6
Hitchin (England), 6
Hocking, G., 52, 64, 88, 179
Hochstetler, C., 173
Hoffman, F., 7
Hogmire, M., 57
Holbrook, L., 23
Holmes County (Ohio), 107-109
Honeyville (Indiana), 108, 173
Honeyville Metal Works, 173

Hooper, R., 125
Hoosic River, 9, 11, 23
Hoover, H., 92
Hopkins (Michigan), 125
Horner, C., 175, 181, 186-187, 190, 192, (III,58)
Horse Heaven Hills (Washington), 160
Hotchkiss, A., 200
Hotchkiss, H. G., 26-28, 30-33, 35, 39, 43, 46-47, 50-51, 60-61, 63, 66-67, 73, 110, 183, 207-209, (I,17)
Hotchkiss Essential Oil Company, 27, 32, 34, 54, 76, 84, 87, 119, 200, (I,16), (I,18), (I,20), (I,21)
Hotchkiss, L., 26-27, 32, 43, 57
Hotchkiss Peppermint Planters Banking House, 27, (I,22)
Hotchkiss, W., 27
Housatonic River, 11
Howard, R., 108
Hughes, A., 184
Hull Farms, 164
Humboldt County (Nevada), 174
Huron (New York), 31, 110
Huron County (Ohio), 21, 108
Huston, F., 109
Huston, V., 174
Hutchby, J., 87
Hyde Park (England), 32

Idaho, 81, 106-107, m.117, 164-165, m. 166, 197-198, 211, 216, m.227, (III,55), (III,56), (III,57), (III, 58)
Idaho Falls (Idaho), 165
Illinois, 43
Imperial Packing Co., 77
Independence (Oregon), 155
Indiana, 21, 26, 28, 32-33, 43, 55, m.55, 56, 59, 61, 66, 71-73, 75, 78-79, 81, 84-87, 90-92, 94, 96, 100-101, 103-104, 106, 112-113, 118-119, 125, 128-130, 132-133, 135, 142, 145-147, 150-151, 155, 163, 167, 169, m.170, 172-173, m. 173, 175, 177-178, 185-187, 189, 191, 197-199, 208-211, 215, m.222, (II,48), (III,52), (III,54), (III, 58), (III,60)
Indianapolis (Indiana), 75
Indians, American, 8, 23-24, 164
Ingham County (Michigan), 170-171
.onia (Michigan), 45, 53
Iowa, 43, 80, 106-107
Iowa State Horticultural Society, 80, 100

Irmer, J., 111-112
Iroquois River, 128
Island district (California), 112

Jackson County (Michigan), 170-171
Jameson, 46
Japan, 3, 42, 91-92, 98, 133, 203
Japanese mint oil, 41-42, 52, 93-94, 112-113, 134-136, 142, 147, 149, 211
Jasper County (Indiana), 128, 172
Jefferson (Oregon), 143, 153, 155, 184, 190
Jefferson (Wisconsin), 167, 169
Jefferson County (Oregon), 156
Jefferson County (Wisconsin), 167, 169, 197
Jenison, G., 179
Jennings, J., 34
Jensen, H., 185
John Day Valley (Oregon), 156
Johnson, F., 116
Jones, C., 48
Jones, E., 47
Jones, R., 34
Jasa, P., 156, 158
Josselyn J., 9, 15, (I,13)
Junction City (Oregon), 155
Junius (New York), 19, 23, 31

Kalamazoo (Michigan), 23, 59, 61, 66, 72, 74, 75, 127, 198, 206-208, (I, 23), (I,25), (II,34), (III,60)
Kalamazoo County (Michigan), 46, 57, 60
Kalamazoo Public Museum, 23, (I,9)
Kolynos, 77
Kalish, A., 140
Kalona (Iowa), 107
Kandel, E., 107-108
Kandel, W., 108
Kansas, 43
Karmex, 158, 176
Keating (Oregon), 156
Keech, G., 43, 48-49
Kelly, C., 13
Kelly, T., 13
Kelso (Washington), 115, 159, 191
Kennedy Round, 146
Kennewick (Washington), 55, 114-116, 143, m.144, 145, 160-162, 180, 188-189
Kenosha County (Wisconsin), 168
Kentucky, 55, 174
Kerr, M., 164
Kern County (California), 174
Kieper, H., 156

Kings County (California), 112
Kings Patent peppermint oil, 23
Kirtland (Ohio), 30
kitchen gardens, 4
Kittitas (Washington), 164
Klamath Falls (Oregon), 155
Knippel and Held, 152
Knoblock, G., 95
Klostermeyer, E., 185
Knox Butte (Oregon), 83
Kootenai River, 165
Kosciusko County (Indiana), 85, 107, 172
Koyoma Farms, 167
Kremers, E., 80, 177, 179
Kunze, C., 156, 160
Kurtz, 81

Labbee, J., 164
Lafayette Center (Washington), 159
La Fourche Parish (Louisiana), 80
La Grande (Oregon), 156
Lagrange County (Indiana), 26, 56, 85, 107, 119, 172-173
Laingsburg (Michigan), 125, 127
Lake Company, 145
Lake County (Ohio), 21, 43, 52
Lake County (Oregon), 156
Lake Erie, 21
Lake Labish (Oregon), 83, 117, 143, 155
Lake Mills (Wisconsin), 167-168
Lake of the Woods (Indiana), 119
Lake Ontario, 18
Lake Stevens (Washington), 115, 159
Lakeview (Oregon), 156
Lakeville (Indiana), 95
Landing, J., 52, 88
Lane County (Oregon), 118, 153
Lanesborough (Massachusetts), 10-11, 71
Langston, R., 179, 182
Lapeer County (Michigan), 170
La Porte County (Indiana), 85, 94, 119, 129-130
Las Vegas (Nevada), 174
Laton (California), 112
Latin America, 142
Lee, E., 125
Legault, R., 188
Leman-Gerber Co., 97, 119, 126, 199
Leman, J., 199
Leman, S., 199
Leman, W. Jr., 199
Leman, W. Sr., 119, 199, (III,60)
Leman, Wm. Inc., 137, 178, 198-199, (III,60)

Lemli, J., 181
Lend-Lease, 137, 139
Lenox (Massachusetts), 11
leopard spot disease, 125, 129
Leopold, A., 182
Leusch, A., 34
Lewis County (New York), 28, 32
Liber de Arte Distillandi, 4, (I,15)
Liebel, L., 175, 189
Lincolnshire (England), 6
Lindskog, J., 116
Lingle and Sons, 109, 174
Linn County (Oregon), 118, 153, m. 154
Liverpool (England), 22, 28
Livingston, E., 85, 127
Lockport Township (Michigan), 47-48, 53, 57
Logan County (Ohio), 109
London (England), 6, 27, 49-50
Longview (Washington), 115, 152, 159, (III,51)
Loomis, W., 182
Lorain County (Ohio), 21, 43
Lotta, 77
Louisiana, 79
Louisville Bank for Cooperatives, 130-131
Lowder Brothers, 48
Lower Lake (California), 114
Luke, 3
Lyons (New York), 19, 23, 27-28, 30-31, 33-35, 47, 49, 66, 76, 87, 110, 200, 206-207, (I,12), (I,19), (I, 20), (I,21), (I,22), (I,29), (II, 43)
Lyons Township (Michigan), 53

Mabton (Washington), 162-163, 176, 197
Macedon (New York), 110
MacSwan, I., 190
Madras (Oregon), 156-157, m.157, 158-159, 163, 179, 181, 182-183, 190, 198, 211, (Frontispiece), (III, 54)
Malheur County (Oregon), 156
Mansfield Co., 77
Marcellus (New York), 41
Marcellus Township (Michigan), 53, 57
Marion (New York), 110
Marion (Oregon), 155
Marion County (Oregon), 118, 153
Market Deeping (England), 6
Marola Farms Inc., 158
Marquette County (Wisconsin), 168

Marshall, 83
Marshall County (Indiana), 85, 104, 119
Marshall Plan, 149
Martis, J., 85
Martin, J., 156
Martin (Michigan), 125
Maryland, 80, 174, 191
Mason County (Michigan), 171
Massachusetts, 8-9, m.10, 11, 15-16, 19, 21, 23, 46, 60, 66-67, 71, 207-209, m.218, (I,5), (I,7), (I,8), (I,14)
Massachusetts Bay Colony, 8
Maltby, J., 17
Matthew, 3
Matthews, O., 21
Matthews, R., 21
Mattison Township (Michigan), 57
Maxwell, J., 96-97
McDaniels, J., 156
McGhan, B., 116
McGuffey (Ohio), 108
McKenna (Washington), 115, 159
McKenzie River, 153
McNeil, D., 26
McPheeters, W., 156
medieval period, mint in, 3
Meriden (Connecticut), 14
Mendon (Michigan), 48, 57, (I,26)
Mendon Township (Michigan), 47-48, 57
Mennonites, 81, 107
Mentha arvensis L., see Japanese mint oil
Mentha cardiaca G., see Scotch spearmint
Mentha (Michigan), 59, 87, 104, 124, 130, 133, 183, (I,27), (II,45)
menthofuran, 180-183
menthol, 90, 92, 135-136, 141
Mentor (Ohio), 30
Mentz, W., 34
Merton (England), 6
Mexico, 203
Meyers, H., 109
Michigan, 21, m.22, 23-26, 28-29, 31-33, 35-37, 39-41, 43-47, m.48, 49-50, 53-57, m.58, 59-63, 66-67, 71-73, 75-76, 78-79, 81, 83-86, m. 86, 87, 90-92, 94, 96, 100-101, 103, 106, 112-113, 118-119, 124-126, 128, 132-133, 135-136, 138-139, 143, 146-147, 150-151, 153, 155, 167, 169-170, m.170, 171, m. 171, 172, m.172, 173, 175, 177-

178, 183, 185-186, 189, 191, 197-199, 208-210, 215-216, m.221, (I, 23), (I,24), (I,25), (I,26), (I,27), (I,28), (II,31), (II,33), (II,34), (II,35), (II,38), (II,39), (II,40), (II,41), (II,42), (II,48), (III,60)
Michigan Muck Farmers Association, 190
Michigan Peppermint Growers Association, 126-127, 172
Michigan State University, 124, 178, 181, 184, 186, 190, (III,58)
Middaugh, E., 34
Middlebury (Indiana), 85, 109
Midland (Oregon), 155
Miller, A., 108
Miller, E., 108
Miller, J., 108
Miller, S., 16
Miller's Basin (New York), 26
Minnesota, 43, 174
mint anthracnose, 125, 129
Mint Drops, 191
mint-flea beetle, 86, 184-185
Mint Growers Cooperative, 129-132,
Mint Industry Research Fund, 178, 202
mint julep, 213
Mint Research Conferences, 178
Mishawaka (Indiana), 71
Mississippi, 44-45, 51-52, 55
Missoula (Montana), 167
Missouri, 106-107
Mitcham (England), 6, 9, 39, 61
Mobile and Ohio Railroad, 44
modern period, mint in, 4
Modesto (California), 112, 174
Moisan, C., 102
monasteries, 3
monopoly, 28-33, 35, 43, 66, 72-73
Monroe (Oregon), 155
Monroe County (New York), 28
Monroe County (Wisconsin), 168
Montana, 166-167, 198, 216
Montello Marsh (Wisconsin), 169
Montezuma Marsh (New York), 87
Moore, A., 108
Moorland Township (Michigan), 57
Morris Company, 96
Morrison, H., 185
Morrow County (Oregon), 118, 156
Morton (Oregon), 152
Mosebar, 163
Moseby, 34
Moses, 3
Moses Lake (Washington), 160, 164

Mourer, K., 191
Moxee City (Washington), 164
mucklands, 56-58, m.58, 59-60, 62-63, 67, 85, 87, 124, 128, m.170, 187, 208-209, (I,23)
Mud Creek, 27
Mueller, N., 156
mulch paper, 105-106
Multnomah County (Oregon), 118, 153
Murray, M., 183-184, 187, 192, 199, (III, 58)
Muskegon County (Michigan), 57, 75, 171

Nampa (Idaho), 165
Nankin (Michigan), 53
National Research Council, 140
Native spearmint, 62, 78, 163, 165, 169, 197, 212, 215-216, (I,5), (III,59)
Nebraska, 174, 176
Nelson, E., 26
Nelson, R., 124, 133, 178, 181-184, 186, (III,58)
the Netherlands, 135
Nettrower, C., 95
Nevada, 174
Newaygo County (Michigan), 57, 170
Newark (New York), 26, 28, 31, 87
New Carlisle (Indiana), 130
New England, 9, 12, 18, 52
New Jersey, 15, 23, 43, 52, 55, 66
Newland (Indiana), 172, (III,58)
New Pre-emption Road, 23
New Testament, 3
New York City, 22, 27-29, 50, 72, 74-75
New York State, 15, 18-19, m.19, 21, 23, 25, 26, 28-31, m.31, 32-36, 38-39, 41, 43, 45-47, 49-50, 52, 54-56, 59-63, 66-67, 78, 84, 87, 109, 110, 120, 174, 183, 208-210, m.219, (I,12), (I,19), (I,20), (I, 21), (I,22), (I,29), (II,32)
Niagara County (New York), 14
Nichols, W., 156
Niles (Michigan), 78
Nisgally River, 115
Noble County (Indiana), 85, 119
North Carolina, 81
Northern Indiana Muck Crop Farmers Association, 145, 190
Northern Pacific Railroad, 55
North Judson (Indiana), 172
North Liberty (Indiana), 172
Northrup, B., 156

North Santiam River, 153
Northwestern University, 41
Nottawa (Michigan), 41-42, 48, 66, 198, 207
Nottawa Township (Michigan), 48
Nyssa (Oregon), 190

Oak Corners (New York), 46
Oaks, M., 23, 34, 53
Obendorf, 165
Oberholtzer, 108
Oconto County (Wisconsin), 167, 168
Ohio, 15, 17, m.20, 21, 24, 28-30, 32-33, 40, 43, 52, 60, 66, m.79, 80, 84, 106-109, 111, 145, 174, 209, m.220
Oil of Peppermint Advisory Committee, 140
Office of Price Administration (OPA), 136-139, 141-142
Okanogan County (Washington), 159
Olympic Mint Association, 159
Ontario (New York), 110
Ontario (Oregon), 156, 190
Ontario County (New York), 18-19, 23, 26, 28-29, 31, 46
Orange County, California, 174
Orchards (Washington), 160
Ord Landing (California), 113
Oregon, 81, m.82, 83-84, 87, 96, 100-103, 112-113, 115, 117, m.117, 118, 132-133, 142-143, m.144, 147, 150-151, 153, 155, 158, m.158, 161, 163, 167, 175, 178-180, 182, 185-187, 189-190, 191, 198, 209-211, 216, m.223, (Frontispiece), (III,50), (III,53), (III,54), (III, 58)
Oregon Essential Oil Growers League, 190
Oregon Mint Growers Cooperative Association, 89
Oregon State University, 178, 181-182, 184-185, 188, 190, (III,58)
O'Reilly, H., 190
Osborn, R., 76
Oswego County (New York), 109
Othello (Washington), 164, 191
Ottoville (Ohio), 174
Ovid (Michigan), 125
Owosso (Michigan), 125, 127

Pacific Coast Mint Company, 115, (II, 46)
Paine, J., 16
Painesville (Ohio), 30

Palmyra (New York), 31, 34, 110
Palmyra (Wisconsin), 169
Paris (France), 50
Parke, Davis and Co., 144
Parkinson, J., 47
Parry, E., 189
Parshall, 32
Pasco (Washington), 160, 164, 191
Patent Office, U.S., 49
Paterson (Washington), 164
Patterson (California), 174
Patterson, E., 28-31
Patterson, 73
Payette (Idaho), 165
Pearl Harbor (Hawaii), 136
Peck, H., 26
peddlers, 13, 14, 17, 18, 19, 23, (I,7), (I,9)
Penney Farms (Florida), 121
Peoria (Illinois), 119
Pepsodent, 77, 204
Perdita, 7
Peterson, N., 57
Petiver, J., (I,4)
Phelps (New York), 18, 23, 31, 51, 66
Philadelphia (Pennsylvania), 42, 46, 77
Phillips, W., 199
Phillips, 16, 19, 21
Phinney, A., 125
photoperiod, 135, 163, 181-182
Phygon, 187
Pierce County (Washington), 116, 159
Pure Food and Drug Act, 93-94, 134
Pioneer Company, 85
pip-menthol, 42
Pittsfield (Massachusetts), 9-11
Plains (Montana), 166
Plainwell (Michigan), 125
Pliny, 5-6
Plymouth Marsh (Ohio), 108
Polk County (Oregon), 153
Pomeroy, M., 49
Pompey, 5
Portage County (Wisconsin), 167
Porterville (California), 112, 114, (II, 47)
Portland (Oregon), 116-117, 152-153, 159
Pound (Wisconsin), 167
prices, 14, 17, 26, 28-29, 31, 40, 45-46, 65, 71-76, 79, 90, 92, 94, 97, 108, 113, 119, 123, 130-131, 135-139, 146, 149
Price, W., 81

Prince Albert, 32
Prineville (Oregon), 58
Procter and Gamble, 178, 204
prohibition, 104
propane flaming, 187, (III,54)
Prosser (Washington), 100, 163
Ptolemais, 3
Public Ownership League of America, 127
Pudding River, 153
Puget Island (Washington), 83-84, 159
Puget Sound, 114-115, m.115, 159
Pulaski County (Indiana), 172
Purdue University, 129, 178-179, 182, 187-189, (III,58)
Pusey, J., 152
Pusey Manufacturing Co., 152

Queen Victoria, 32
Quincy (Oregon), 83-84, 151-152, 164, (II, 44)

Rabak, Frank, 80, 181
Raceland (Louisiana), 80
Rainier (Oregon), 117, 151-152, 159, (III,53)
Ranney, G., 11-12
Ranney, J., 12, 16
Ranney, L., 21
Ranney, R., 13, 16, 19
Ranney, S., 12, 16, 18-19
Ranney, T., 11, 13
Ranney, W., 16
Ranney, 19, 21, 32
Rattlesnake Ridge (Washington), 160
Ravenna (Michigan), 76
Ray (Raii), J., 4, 7, (I,2)
Reasoner, S., 83
Redmond (Oregon), 158
Reed Gardner Tracts Co., 159
Reinhard, R., 34
Reitsema, R., 189
Reighenbach, E., 108
Reighenbach, J., 108
Reno (Nevada), 174
Revolution, American, 11
Reynen Brothers, 174
Richland County (New York), 174
Richland County (Ohio), 108-109, 145
Richland County (Washington), 114, 116, 143
Richmond, J., 16
Ringer, 46
Rio Grande, 145
Riston (Michigan), 53
Roberts (Idaho), 165

Roland, 108
Romulus Township (Michigan), 57
Rose (New York), 31, 110
Roseburg (Oregon), 117, 155
Rose Mitcham oil, 61
Roskamp, H., 164
Ross County (Ohio), 43
Rotterdam (the Netherlands), 27
Roy, C., 26
Royalton Township (Michigan), 57
Roys, F., 48
Roys, G., 48
Roys, W., 48
Roza Canal, 160
Rumbaugh, J., 109
Rumbolz, S., 164
rust of mint, 143, 152-153, 160, 186-187
Ruttle, M., 179, 183

Saginaw (Michigan), 125
Salem (Oregon), 81, 117, 155, 190
Salmon River, 164
Sanderson, C., 17
Sanilac County (Michigan), 170
San Joaquin Valley, 111
Sauk County (Wisconsin), 167
Satus (Washington), 162-163
Sauvie Island (Oregon), 152
Sawyer, C., 21
Scapoose (Oregon), 152
Schenectady (New York), 14
Schermerhorn, R., 48
Scio (Oregon), 155
Scioto Land Co., 109, 174
Scioto Marsh (Ohio), 109
Scotch spearmint, 78-79, 101, 106, 162, 165, 169, 172, 197, 212, 215-216, (I,5), (III,55), (III,58), (III,59)
Scotland, 78
Scott., L., 156
Seattle (Washington), 199, 206
Seely, S., 164
Seely, 160
Seneca County (New York), 23, 26, 28-29, 31, 109
Seneca Falls (New York), 27
Sen Sen, 77
Sequim (Washington), 159
Sethi, S., 5
Severance, 46
Severens, H., 57, 65
Severens Marsh (Michigan), 57, 59
Shakespeare, 7
Shell Corporation, 188
Sherman (Texas), 81

Sherman Township (Michigan), 47-48
Sherwood (Michigan), 73, 76
Shiawassee County (Michigan), 125, 143, 170
Shiloh (Ohio), 108
Shirley, J., (II,34)
Sidwell, C., 83
Sievers, A., 89, 100, 102, 109, 114, 117, 120, 122, 155, 175
Silverton (Oregon), 103, (II,44)
Sinbar, 161, 186
Skagit County (Washington), 116, 159
Skagit River, 115
Skamakowa (Washington), 115, 159
Slabaugh, J., 81
Smith, B., 85
Smith, H., 129, 130, 132
Smith, S., 213
Snake River, 107, 114, 160, 165, 211
Sodus (New York), 31, 110
South Ashfield (Massachusetts), 11
South Bend (Indiana), 23, 95-98, 129-130
South Dakota, 80
South Santiam River, 153
Spearmint, 77, 146
Sprague, C., 85
Springdale (Washington), 164
Springfield (Oregon), 155, 190
Stambaugh, J., 109
Stark County (Ohio), 107
Starke County (Indiana), 85, 119, 172
Star Tank Co., 85, 173
St. Clair County (Michigan), 170
Stearns, F., 24, 37, 51, 183
Stearns, S., 16
Steenland, A., 186, 190
Steuben County (Indiana), 56
Stevens, 57
Stevens, A., 156
Stevens County (Washington), 164
Stevenson, E., 7, 178
Steward, F., 179
Stewart County (Tennessee), 55
St. Johns (Michigan), 85, (m.86), 124, 126-127, 130, 167
St. Joseph County (Indiana), 56, 71, 85, 104, 118-119, 172
St. Joseph County (Michigan), 21, 24, 28, 39, 41, 43-47, m.48, 49, 52-53, 56-57, 59, 61, 208, (I,11), (I, 26), (I,28)
St. Joseph Valley Mint Growers Co-operative Association, 95-98, (II, 36), (II,37)
St. Maries (Idaho), 81

Stockton (California), 114, 145, 174
Stonebrook, R., 166
Stroud, R., 104
Stuart, S., 95
Sturgis (Michigan), 41, 85
Subtilitatum, 4
Sun, The, 10, 16
Sunnyside Canal, 160
Sunnyside (Washington), 116, 162-164, 191
Sutherlin (Oregon), 117, 155
Sutton, R., 34,
Synesius of Alexandria, 3
synthetics, 94

Tacoma (Washington), 114
Talbot (Oregon), 155-156
tariff, 54, 94, 146
Taylor, I., 17
Teller, G., 48
Tennessee, 55
terbacil (see Sinbar)
Terriere, L., 188
Texas, 43, 81, 106-107, 145, 174
Texas, University of, 107, 145
Theophrastus, 6
Thomas, W., 152
Thomson, J., 127
Three Rivers (Michigan), 47-48
Tinkertown (Massachusetts), 11
Todd, A.A., 76
Todd, A.A. Jr., 199
Todd, A.J., 76, 199, (III,60)
Todd, A.J. Jr., 199
Todd, Alfred, 41
Todd, A.M., 41-42, 46, 48, 50-51, 53-55, 59-61, 63-67, 72-73, 76, 78-79, 81, 83, 88, 127, 199, 207-209, (I, 24), (III,60)
Todd, O.H., 41, 81, 83-84, (III,58)
Todd, P.H., 76
Todd, W.A., 199
Todd Co., A.M., 64, 76, 79-80, 87, 97, 104, 108, 119-120, 125-126, 137, 156, 176-179, 184, 187, 189, 198-199, 206, (I,23), (I,24), (I,25), (III,58), (III,60)
Tombigbee Valley, 44
Tompsett-Shortline Manufacturing Co., 159
toothpaste, 77-78, 87, 146, 149-150, 202, 204, 206, 209
Toppenish (Washington), 163-164
Toppenish Ridge (Washington), 160
Tornow, P., 178
Towery, W., 158

Trombley, E., 125
Trout Lake (Washington), 164
Tulare (California), 111-112
Turlington, R., 23
Turnidge, G., 155
Turnidge, W.J., 83, 115-116
Tuscola County (Michigan), 170
Tuttle, 109
Twin Falls (Idaho), 164
Tipton (California), 112

Ulrath, R., 80
Umatilla County (Oregon), 156
Union Gap (Washington), 160
Union of Soviet Socialist Republics, 134-135, 145-146
United Kingdom, 135, 203
United Mint Growers, 172
Upper Lake (California), 113-114
United States Department of Agriculture, 80, 93-94, 100, 106, 137, 181, 188, 191
United States Sugar Corporation, 121
Utica (New York), 14
Utrecht (the Netherlands), 6

Vale (Oregon), 156
VanAuken, D., 34
vanAuken, T., 46
Van Buren County (Michigan), 57, 59, 61, 97, 119, 124, 171, (I,27), (II, 45)
Vancouver (Washington), 159-160
Vandemark, B., 34
VanDemark, E., 18
VanDemark, H., 18
VanMarter, B., 49, 110
VanMarter, J., 49
Van Wert County (Ohio), 109
Vassar, 77
Veith, M., 125
Vermont, 14
Vernita (Washington), 164
Verticillium wilt, 124-125, 133, 143, 150, 153, 157, 160, 162, 168-169, 177-178, 183, 186-187, 190, 192, 211, (III,54)
Vick Chemical Co., 136
Vienna (Austria), 50
Vienna (New York), (also see Phelps), 18-19, 21, 23, 26-27, 32
Vincent, R., 112
Virginia, 80, 106, 191
Vorlex, 187

Wagner, 48

Wagner, H., 191
Wahkiakum County (Washington), 116
Walker, A., 189
Wallace, E., 83
Walulla (Washington), 116
Walworth County (Wisconsin), 167, 169
Wapato (Washington), m.162
War Food Administration (WFA), 138-142, (II,49)
War Manpower Commission (WMC), 137
Warner, 46
Warner Lambert Pharmaceutical Co., 203
War Production Board (WPB), 136, 140
Washington, 55, m.82, 84, 100-101, 113, 114-115, 116, 118, 132-133, 142-143, m.144, 145, 147, 151, 158-159, 161, m.162, 163-164, m. 165, 167, 173, 175, 178, 180, 183, 185-187, 189, 192, 196-198, 209, 211, 216, m.224, (III,51), (III, 54), (III,55), (III,58), (III,59), (III,60)
Washington County (Oregon), 118, 153
Washington, D.C., 60, 136, 140
Washington Mint Commission, 191
Washington Mint Growers Association, 191
Washington Mint Research, 191
Washington State Mint Growers, Inc., 143, 190
Washington State Mint Growers League, 191
Washington State University, 178, 188
Washington, University of, 84, 178
Waterloo (Wisconsin), 169
Wattles, G., 73, 76
Waukesha County (Wisconsin), 168
Waverly (Mississippi), 44
Wayne County (Michigan), 45, 53, 57
Wayne County (New York), 23, 26, 27-31, m.31, 33-34, 43, 46, 50, 53, 62, 75, 84, 109-111, 208
Wayne County (Ohio), 107-109, 145
Wayne County Historical Museum, 34
Weaver, G., 97
Webster (South Dakota), 80
Welch and Kandra, 164
Went, F., 182
Western Mint Company, 114
Western Reserve University, 179
West Germany, 203

Westport (Oregon), 152
Weston (Oregon), 156
Whatcom County (Washington), 159
Whately (Massachusetts), 15
Wheatland Township (Michigan), 53
Whitbeck, 46
White, 21, 77
White Mitcham peppermint, 61, 64, 121
White Pigeon Prairie (Michigan), 21, m.48
White Pigeon Township (Michigan), 21
Wilcox, R., 174
Wilder (Idaho), 165
Wiley City (Washington), 164
Willamette River, 152-153
Willamette Valley, 81, m.82, 83, 117, 143, 153, m.154, 155-156, 159, 175, 181, 198, (III,54), (III,58)
Willamette Valley Mint Growers Association, 83, 89, 118
Williams, I., 16
Williams, 163
Williams County (Ohio), 109, 174
Williamson (New York), 110
Willshire (Ohio), 109
Winters Tale, The, 7
Winthrop, J., 8
Wisconsin, 78, 80, 145, 155, 167, 168, m.168, 169, m.169, 176, 197-198, 211, 216, m.226, (III,54)
Wisconsin, University of, 80, 177, 179
Wolcott (New York), 110
Wolf Brothers, 43, 49
Wolf D., 48
Wolf, J., 48
Wood, N., 10
Wood County (Ohio), 43
Woodhams, E., 76
Woodland (Washington), 114, 117
Woodland Mint Growers Inc., 116
Woodson (Oregon), 152
Woodward Brothers, 89
Wooster (Ohio), 108
Wren, C., 11
Wrigley, Wm. Jr., 77, 113
Wrigley, Wm. Jr. Company, 126, 178, 203, 213
Wyatt (Indiana), 119

Yakima County (Washington), 116, 186
Yakima Indians, 164
Yakima Ridge (Washington), 160
Yakima River, 114, 160, m.162
Yakima Valley, 114-115, 143, m.144, 145, 156, 158, 160, m.162, 163-

164, 167, 173, 175, 181-183, 185,
188-189, 196-198, 211, (III,55),
(III,59)
Yamhill County (Oregon), 118, 153
Yamhill River, 153
Yankee notions, 12-14
Yoncalla (Oregon), 117, 155
York, H., 143, 190

Yoshino, V., 164
Young, W., 44
Young, G., 44
Yungun, A., 156

Zeno, 77
Zillah (Washington), 164